MECHANICS' INSTITUTE
❧ MECHANICS' *❧*
MERCANTILE LIBRARY

❖　❖　❖

Western Trails

WESTERN LITERATURE SERIES

Mary Austin, ca. 1905

Western Trails

A COLLECTION OF
SHORT STORIES BY
MARY AUSTIN

❖   ❖   ❖   ❖   ❖

SELECTED AND EDITED BY
MELODY GRAULICH

UNIVERSITY OF NEVADA PRESS
RENO & LAS VEGAS

"The Portrait," "Kate Bixby's Queerness," and "Blue Roses" are reproduced by permission of the Huntington Library. "How the Corn Came" and "The Secret of the Holy Places" are reprinted by permission of Houghton Mifflin Co. from the *Trail Book* by Mary Austin, copyright © 1918 by Mary Austin, copyright © renewed 1946 by the School of American Research. "The Man Who Lied About a Woman," "The Medicine of Bow-Returning," "Stewed Beans," "White Wisdom," "The Man Who Was Loved by Women," "Papago Wedding," and "The Last Antelope" are reprinted by permission of Houghton Mifflin Co. from *One-Smoke Stories* by Mary Austin, copyright © 1934 by Mary Austin, copyright © renewed 1962 by the School of American Research. Houghton Mifflin Co. has granted permission to quote from *Earth Horizon* by Mary Austin, copyright © 1932 by Mary Austin, copyright © renewed 1960 by the School of American Research. "Western Magic" is quoted by permission of Houghton Mifflin Co. from *The Children Sing in the Far West* by Mary Austin, copyright © 1928 by Mary Austin, copyright © renewed 1956 by the School of American Research. The frontispiece is reprinted from the *Critic* (1905).

Western Literature Series Editor: John H. Irsfeld

Library of Congress Cataloging-in-Publication Data

Austin, Mary Hunter, 1868–1934.
    Western trails : a collection of short stories /
by Mary Austin : selected and edited by Melody Graulich
    p.   cm.—(Western literature series)
    Includes index.
    ISBN 0-87417-127-X (alk. paper)
    1. Western stories.   2. West (U.S.)—Fiction.
I. Graulich, Melody, 1951–   .   II. Title.   III. Series.
PS3501.U8A6   1987b
813'.52—dc19   87-16501

University of Nevada Press
Reno, Nevada 89557 USA

The paper used in this book meets the requirements of American National Standard for Information Sciences—Permanence of Paper for Printed Library Materials, ANSI Z39.48–1984. Binding materials were chosen for strength and durability.   ∞

Design by Richard Hendel

Contents

❖ ❖ ❖

Western Trails

Not to know their own prophets is
rather a serious predicament for women.

Mary Austin, "Greatness in Women"

INTRODUCTION

In *Earth Horizon,* an autobiography written in the third person, Mary Austin said of her childhood that she "was never much taken with the wish of many girls of her acquaintance that they had been boys. She thought there might be a great deal to be got out of being a woman; but she definitely meant neither to chirrup nor twitter. She meant not to remit a single flash of wit, anger, or imagination. She had no idea of what, in her time, such a determination would entail. She was but dimly aware of something within herself, competent, self-directive; she meant to trust it."[1] Unwilling to appropriate a male point of view or to accept the chirrups and twitters expected of the woman writer, Austin sought a tradition and a language that would liberate a woman's "wit, anger, [and] imagination." Claiming in 1918 that "what women have to stand on squarely [is] not their ability to see the world in the way men see it, but the importance and validity of their seeing it in some other way," Austin spent her life developing and trusting her own way of seeing, trying to understand what was "to be got out of being a woman."[2]

Yet the sixty-four-year-old author's defiant tone obscures the difficulties she experienced as she learned to trust that competent and self-directive inner self. When she went west to homestead in southern California in 1888, Austin was an unhappy young woman, her frequent illnesses the result of the conflicts she experienced between her needs and aspirations and those her society assigned to young women of the period. In the arid Southwest she would call "the land of little rain," Austin found a voice and a subject matter, developed her confidence, and learned to be herself. An early story, "The Walking Woman," serves as a parable to reveal what the desert taught her. The narrator, herself a seeker, meets the Walking Woman, a desert wanderer who had "begun by walking off an illness" and was "healed at last by the large soundness of nature." Although her story has its ambiguities and costs, she inspires the narrator, who concludes, "She was the Walking Woman. That was it. She had walked off all sense of society-made values, and, knowing the best when the best came to her, was able to take it." Such women became Austin's prophets, for, independent as she was, she looked for footsteps to follow, for a path to share—as is demonstrated by one of the most frequently recurring images in her work, the trail, which she uses as a metaphor for pioneering and for communication. She stresses the Walking Woman's role as spiritual leader in the story's final image: remembering the rumors that the Walking Woman is "twisted," the narrator looks at her footsteps and discovers that "the track of her two feet bore evenly and white."

Austin's biography is a classic in the pathfinder tradition: rejecting the capitulations and conformity of small-town life, the solitary and rebellious hero heads west in search of a richer spiritual vision, a union with the American landscape, a deeper understanding of native cultures, the freedom of self-definition promised by the wilderness. But this western wanderer was a woman. Describing herself as "committed to the idea that she was to write of the West," she explored familiar themes in the western landscape, but she did so from a self-consciously female point of view (*Earth Horizon,* 228). Austin filled her work with women "guides," many Native American, but, ultimately, she had to find her own trail, to discover—and create—her own tradition as she explored what was to be got out of being an unconventional white woman artist and a feminist in the turn-of-the-century Southwest, a literary landscape usually associated with men.

From the landscape and the Native American cultures of the Southwest, Austin learned her art. Although she would later join artist communities in Carmel, Greenwich Village, and London, she devoted most of her life and her art to the Southwest. The people of the arid region, their traditions, the land and its effect on human character were her major subjects, and she explored them from many angles. "I would write imaginatively, not only of people," she said, "but of the scene, the totality which is called Nature, and . . . I would give myself intransigently to the quality of experience called Folk, and to the frame of behavior known as Mystical" (*Earth Horizon,* vii).

Yet Austin was no naive mystic. She was a sharp social critic with a developed sense of irony, and she was always self-conscious about her relations to literary traditions. Interested in the ways in which culture reflects and shapes the human spirit, she wrote a variety of essays on art, culture, and politics. Like her friends Willa Cather and Sinclair Lewis, she criticized the conventionality of small-town life, but she believed that America possessed great riches in its regional cultures. In "Regionalism in American Fiction" (1932), she argued that art is generated through the writer's relationship to a region and its history; and because she tried to put her beliefs into action, she became a leader in the movement to preserve southwestern art, raising the money to prevent the dispersion of the Spanish Sanctuario de Chimayo and leaving most of her estate and her Santa Fe house to the Indian Arts Fund.[3] Like many of her contemporaries, she experimented with form in search of a uniquely American life. Austin was in the forefront of many cultural movements of her time.

She was also an influential woman. The author of over 30 books in a number of genres and some 250 periodical publications, she was highly regarded by her contemporaries but nearly forgotten by subsequent generations. Critics like Van Wyck Brooks and Carl Van Doren praised her work, and Willa Cather wrote of her, "She will be my sternest critic—and she has the right to be. I will always take a calling-down from my betters."[4] In an obituary in the *Saturday Review of Literature,* Elizabeth Shepley Sergeant placed Austin among the most important American women writers. Although Austin's best-known book, *The Land of Little Rain,* has remained in print throughout the years, acknowledged as a classic in the tradition of American nature writing, her varied and original work received little attention from her death in 1934 until the feminist resurgence of the 1970s.

Recent reprints of Austin's nature works and her fine feminist novel, *A Woman of Genius* (1912), have gained her new readers and attention. Still out-of-print, however, are the five collections of short stories she published over a period of nearly forty years, stories in which she effectively merged her interests in culture, art, nature, and women. Often based on local legends, blending history and myth, her stories are imagistic, often brief and ambiguous, sometimes lyrical and sometimes satiric. Experimental in form, the stories self-consciously explore the imagination and the art of storytelling. In *Western Trails,* we offer to a new audience a selection of stories from each of Austin's collections, some uncollected stories, and a few previously unpublished stories from the Henry E. Huntington Library's Austin holdings. The occasional variations in spelling and punctuation found in the previously published stories reflect the original publishers' practices. Editorial work on the unpublished stories was limited to minor changes in spelling and punctuation; several of the longer paragraphs were subdivided for ease of reading.

BIOGRAPHY

In her life and her art, Mary Austin (1868–1934) attempted to create a set of traditions that would reflect the American experience of casting off inherited ways of thinking and establishing a new life on the frontier, whether it be literal or metaphorical. She rejected the patterns of her personal past—the conformity of the midwestern small town with its repressive religions, its anti-intellectualism, and its rigid gender roles—but she sought new patterns to organize her own life and the culture of what she would have called her "tribe." Austin's many "trails" reflect that constant search for pattern in her life. Describing one of the stories she tells in *The Flock* (1906), she said, "One finds tales like this at every point of contact with the Tejon [region], raying out fanwise like thin, white runways of rabbits from any waterhole in a rainless land."[5] For Austin, art was a spiritual activity, a trail originating from a fertile source, the individual creative self, inevitably a wanderer in quest of spiritual meaning. The trails she traveled—as writer, ecologist, feminist, philosopher, poet, folklorist—rayed out fanwise, yet her trail metaphors always stress connections between places, people, cultures. The trails her work and life reveal in the American landscape represent her efforts to create a new American mythology.

Austin's trail began in Carlinville, Illinois, in a childhood she described as pinched and starved, despite mystical moments when she realized the "pulsing light of consciousness" (*Earth Horizon*, 371 n. 13). At ten, she lost her father, who had encouraged her interest in stories, and her beloved sister Jennie, whose death led her mother to ask, "Why couldn't it have been Mary?" Memories like this characterized Austin's intense relationship with her strong-willed Methodist mother, which she explored in the autobiographical *A Woman of Genius* and in *Earth Horizon*, stressing that she felt throughout her life the "need of mothering."[6] Alternately trying to get her mother's approval and affection and defying her strictures on "young ladihood," Mary developed a sense of inadequacy *and* a stubborn independence.

Austin responded to these conflicting feelings by splitting herself in two. The poignant name she gave to her rejected self, "Mary-by-herself," expressed the feelings of being unacceptable, lonely, and estranged she would never wholly escape. Because she expected lack of response and rejection so long as she persisted in being herself, Austin created another self, one that would allow her to reshape the isolation of Mary-by-herself into independence, the transcendent "I-Mary" she would later associate with her creative self. "With I-Mary there was always a sense of something assured and comforting that you had expected and never found elsewhere. . . . I-Mary suffered no need of being taken up and comforted; to be I-Mary was more solid and satisfying than to be Mary-by-herself" (*Earth Horizon,* 47). Throughout her life, Austin saw her relationships as recapitulating the one she had shared with her mother; she came to believe that the price for being I-Mary was the loneliness of Mary-by-herself.

Of course, we know Susanna Savilla Hunter—a widow with three young children to support—only through her daughter's voice. Although Austin struggled for years to understand her mother's point of view and the forces acting upon her, her portrayal of Susanna inevitably focused on her own pain, on her efforts to draw closer to her mother and her desires for her understanding. Although Susanna supported temperance and women's rights, sharing rare moments of communion with her daughter as they listened together to such speakers as Frances Willard, she pressured Mary away from what Austin called the "natural motions" of her being into "traditional attitudes," as did the mother from *A Woman of Genius,* who wondered "why in the world [her daughter Olivia] couldn't be like other people" (73). Susanna discouraged the child from imagining, making her feel that "storying was wicked," telling her she would have to punish her or Mary "would grow up a story-teller"; in later years, she was never very interested in Austin's writing (*Earth Horizon,* 42, 43). She favored Mary's brother James, encouraging him to make the family decisions and to control the family finances. Although she allowed Mary to attend Blackburn College, she expected her daughter to conform to the passivity and selflessness of what Austin called "true womanliness" and Barbara Welter later described as "The Cult of True Womanhood."[7] Suffering throughout her adolescence for her assertiveness, her curiosity, and her physical "unattractiveness," Austin came to think of herself as "falling short . . . as a young lady" (*Earth Horizon,* 169). In many of her stories she explored social expectations that located a woman's value in her beauty and her willingness to give to men her "exclusive attention" (*Earth Horizon,* 144).

Despite their conflicts, or perhaps because of them, Austin remained greatly attached to Susanna, describing herself years after her mother's death as wanting to avoid writing about the "incalculable ravening in the loss of your mother" (*Earth Horizon,* 273). Her failure "to make a vital connection" with Susanna created and fed a strong need to discover connections with other women, to be understood (*Earth Horizon,* 255). Yet, in a contradictory way, Susanna provided Mary with some of her major themes by simultaneously urging her daughter to marry and revealing to her the costs of marriage. From the women's rights meetings she attended with her mother and from analyzing the constrictions of Susanna's life, Austin learned her feminism. She realized that much of Susanna's anger stemmed from having "always wanted another sort of life for herself. . . . It was what most women wanted; time and adventure of their own" (*Earth Horizon,* 177). Her work presents a feminist analysis of marriage—looked at from many angles, in different races and classes—and of relations between men and women. While she was interested in the effects of marriage on all women, Austin focused on the independent and aspiring woman who struggled to merge marriage with her unconventional needs for self-expression, success, and power, a major theme in nineteenth-century women's literature—she read Harriet Beecher Stowe, Louisa May Alcott, and Sarah Orne Jewett, among others—and in works by her friends Charlotte Perkins Gilman, Willa Cather, and others.

At twenty, just graduated from college, Austin went west to homestead with her mother and brothers in the Owens Valley in southern California. She continued to feel outcast, her shyness perceived as arrogance, her intensity as humorlessness. She was mocked for innocent efforts to listen and respond to the West's meaning: sitting alone in the desert moonlight; letting down her heavy hair; talking to such disreputable characters as Paiutes, Chinese, half-breeds, "greasers." She could not entirely escape the pressures to be refined, but she moved relatively freely through her fledgling frontier society made up of a varied cast of classes and races, which broadened her experience and provided her with diverse points of view. And the landscape intrigued her. Convinced that she would be a writer, Austin was ready to seek the "lurking, evasive" presence of the desert Southwest that "fled from pursuit" but finally "fastened on your vitals" (*Earth Horizon,* 187). Like many before her, she associated the West with feelings of liberation. "Its treeless spaces," she wrote, "uncramp the soul" and reveal the "bare core of things."[8] She found herself "spellbound" with "wanting to know" (*Earth Horizon,* 195).

The change the Southwest brought to Austin's life can be seen in an autobiographical anecdote, which, as usual, she rendered symbolic. Initially malnourished from eating only game, she went into the wilderness and gorged on wild grapes.

> But there was more to the incident than that; there was the beginning of a notion in Mary's mind of a poor appetite of any sort being cured by its proper food; that there was something you could do about unsatisfactory conditions besides being heroic or a martyr to them, something more satisfactory than enduring or complaining, and that was getting out to hunt for the remedy. This, for young ladies in the eighteen-eighties, was a revolutionary discovery to have made (*Earth Horizon,* 195).

In the Southwest, Austin began to "hunt for the remedy" and there she found her "proper food." She had always loved botany, and she brought to her desert wanderings curiosity and patient observation as she attempted to understand the ecology—the interrelationships—of the region. "The sagebrush and other things that grow all of one kind together are called social shrubs," she wrote in her Tejon notebook. "Each one of them has its own kind of herbs growing up in its shade."[9] By the time she wrote *The Land of Little Rain,* she had begun to follow the "trails" in the desert and to understand the patterns of life in the region. Despite her feeling of being a loner and her interest in isolated wanderers, her ecological perspective extended to her study of local cultures as she attempted to understand the interrelations between humans, nature, and culture. She was always interested in the tension her characters felt between their responsibilities to and need for others and their obligations to themselves.

Austin entered an exotic culture of conflicting elements. In solitary desert wanderings she encountered not only buzzards and coyotes but also the sheepherders, prospectors, and wanderers like the Walking Woman who eventually peopled her stories. In the stagecoach and mining towns, she could observe faro games at the local saloon, Chinese New Year's celebrations, Spanish fiestas, and church socials, while listening to boardinghouse tales of lost mines, unsolved murders, and illicit affairs. She was delighted with "all the engaging incidents in other people's lives to which Mary became a party through her incurable want of a proper sense of social distinction" (*Earth Horizon,* 238). At the huge Tejon Ranch of her friend General Beale, she heard firsthand historical accounts of early California and its clash of cultures and the fireside legends of the sheepherders; there she also entered into the elaborate hospitality of the Spanish adobe and observed roundups and sheepshearings, which she would later chronicle in *The*

Flock. Travels on the Mojave Stage introduced her to "'oldtimers,' liquor salesmen, mining experts, an occasional stray 'girl' from the local bawdy-house, or . . . those pitiable 'lungers' of whom you had the grace only to hope that he wouldn't die on your shoulder" (*Earth Horizon*, 257–58). But Austin preferred to ride outside, swapping stories with the stagecoach drivers, whom she claimed to be the best "purveyors of story material" and whose stories she retold in *Lost Borders* (1909) and *One-Smoke Stories* (1934). The stage provided her with her own adventures: one dark night her coach was stopped by a group of mysterious men who wanted someone to pray over a shot comrade, which Austin volunteered to do; another time her driver was taken ill and Mary strapped herself into the harness and drove the stage in.

Meanwhile she visited the campoodies, intrigued by the art, myths, and cosmology of the Paiutes and outraged at their treatment at the hands of the local whites. In *Earth Horizon* she described the source of her lifelong political activism on behalf of Native Americans:

> What set me off on that trail was dreadful enough, a flagrant instance of a local pastime, known as *mahala* chasing. Many of the younger Indian women were employed in the town as household help, and it was no uncommon experience for them, on their way home unattended, to be waylaid by white men—in this instance two young girls, who had lingered behind to sweep the schoolhouse, and were afterward captured and detained for the greater part of the night by a gang of youths. . . . The Indian girls closed their part of the episode by eating wild parsnip root—the convulsions induced by that bane being mercifully shorter than the sufferings already endured—and though the community did actually take measures to prevent the recurrence of such incidents, nothing was done to the offenders, who were sons, some of them, of the "best families" (267).

Austin eventually described herself as a "fierce and untiring opponent of the colossal stupidities, the mean and cruel injustices, of our Indian Bureau" (*Earth Horizon*, 266). But her interest in the Paiutes was not only political. Their belief in a creative principle in the universe from which the individual artist receives energy gave her a feeling of new confidence. She felt the Paiutes showed her how to envision patterns in art, to realize rhythm. Her feeling of connection and gratitude to the Paiutes was conveyed in her creation of several characters who were Native American women artists, women with farseeing powers—she called them "chiseras"—who served as Austin's guides or prophets, and through whom she explored her artistic concerns. They were especially important to Austin because they integrated traditional women's domestic concerns with the individual quest of the artist.

Austin also came to know the West through another group of western settlers: the children. For two years she worked as a traveling teacher, telling children stories to illustrate natural history lessons and making up many of the rhymes she would later publish in *Children Sing in the Far West* (1928). The title suggests Austin's feeling that children respond imaginatively to the West and her desire to give voice to them. Her interest in education was connected to her belief that American literature and art should be founded in relation to the American landscape and rhythm; she argued that school curriculum, like American high culture, was dominated by the influence of Europe and New England, and that children should read stories based on Native American and pioneer experiences. Her own children's collections, *The Basket Woman* and *The Trail Book,* are efforts to give expression to a mythology of the continent, of the West.

While teaching school, eager to have her own children and badly in need of *"somebody* who would talk—[who was] interested in the same things that interested her, in the same way," Austin met her future husband, Wallace Stafford Austin, a well-educated man who shared her love of the desert (*Earth Horizon,* 228–29). Although marriage had been presented to her as a "shining destiny" prescribed for all women, Austin had resisted, obsessed with her desire to be a writer. Her mind was changed when she found her mother crying: "I've brought you out here where there is nobody of your sort to marry" (*Earth Horizon,* 202). Yet when Mary tried to talk to her mother about what to expect from marriage, Susanna refused to discuss it. Mary's ignorance about her sexuality contributed to her fears—and eventually to her disappointment with her marriage. Women's sexual needs, so often repressed, would become a major theme in her work.

The young woman with a desperate need for communication married in 1891 a slow, "inarticulate" man who felt she talked too much about her writing. Wallace Austin's character reveals why Mary wrote so often about western drifters who evade responsibility to women. Like Austin's Mr. Wills, Wallace was a desert dreamer who would not keep a job; he once left his six-months-pregnant wife in a boardinghouse, knowing she would be evicted because he had failed to pay the bills. (Mary put on an apron and convinced another landlady to let her earn her keep by working as a cook.) Her husband's irresponsibility hurt and unnerved her, but money was not the deepest problem in her marriage. Wallace, she said, "never looked with me at any single thing. He never, any more than he could help, afforded me a clue as to where he himself might be looking" (*Earth Horizon,* 243). Austin's feelings about her marriage, explored fully in *A Woman of Genius,* were summed up neatly in the odd title to an autobiographical story: "Frustrate."

A year after her marriage and only four years after moving to California, Austin published her first story, the result of having summoned her nerve and taken her work to Ina Coolbrith, who gave her "friendly direction" on how to submit it to the *Overland Monthly.* Austin's Tejon notebooks show that she had been collecting stories and experimenting with form and style since arriving in California, which she saw as largely an unstoried land. Although she had read dozens of Beadle's dime novels as a youngster, she rejected what she called their "'Wild' Westerness" (*Earth Horizon,* 228). Always more interested in character and landscape than in plot, she was dissatisfied with the romance and melodrama of Bret Harte's tales and Helen Hunt Jackson's popular *Ramona* (1884). She felt that western writers had not yet captured the region's spirit: "the courage to sheer off what is not worthwhile" (*The Land of Little Rain,* 77–78).

But it would take almost ten years for her stylistic experiments to pay off and for her understanding of her subject matter to mature. Austin's earliest stories are local color, capitalizing on the strange, unfamiliar landscape of the Southwest and its exotic cultures, manipulating racial stereotypes. Their subject matter symbolically reflects Austin's feelings about her journey toward becoming an artist: several stories deal with characters who seek a trail to some fabled treasure or lost mine.

After her first success in the early 1890s, Austin was distracted for several years by painful personal problems. She was emotionally wrenched by her gradual realization that her daughter Ruth was retarded. Ruth's birth in 1892 was long and difficult, leaving Austin weak for months afterwards. Feeling unprepared for and incompetent at taking care of her baby, she found medical information insufficient in her frontier environment and health care inadequate, though her Indian women friends helped her. She found no one with whom she could communicate her awareness that something was wrong with her daughter and her fear that somehow she was responsible. Feeling "the need of having [her mother] know that [she] was not to blame," and hoping that she and Susanna "would weep and console one another," Austin sent her little girl to visit Susanna, who returned Ruth with this response: "'I don't know what you've done, daughter, to have such a judgment upon you'" (*Earth Horizon,* 256–57). These were the last words to pass between Mary and Susanna, who was taken ill a few months later and died before her daughter could reach her. Her mother's death was a great shock, and Austin was left with feelings of loss and frustrated communication, feelings she would attempt to work out in her fiction.

As Ruth grew older and Wallace more and more refused to accept his responsibility for providing adequate support for his family, Austin took several teaching positions and tried to write at night. Criticized as "un-womanly" for "abandoning" her daughter and husband, she had one strong supporter in a young woman doctor, Helen McKnight Doyle, who returned to the region to practice. Finally Austin had a source of accurate medical information for herself and Ruth. Doyle assured her that the emotional and financial instability of her life had not caused Ruth's problems. She supported Mary in her feeling that the child was better off without her, encouraging her to board Ruth with older, childless couples and eventually to institutionalize her. Doyle's support helped the distraught mother immeasurably, and she would remain a loyal friend, writing a biography of Austin in 1939 in which she focused on how her community had misunderstood Austin.[10]

Austin also found a sympathetic friend in Charlotte Perkins Stetson (later Gilman), who had been criticized for sending her daughter to live with her former husband. Stetson was one of a number of congenial writers Austin met at the elegant adobe of Charles Lummis in Pasadena, writers, such as Edwin Markham, Margaret Collier Graham, Sharlott Hall, and David Starr Jordan, who were interested in developing an experimental regional literature. Lummis encouraged Austin to write for his journal, the *Land of Sunshine,* and she became close friends with his wife, Eve. The dedication in her first book, *The Land of Little Rain,* reads: "To Eve: 'The Comfortress of Unsuccess.'"

But after the years of apprenticeship, success came relatively quickly. From about 1900, Austin published regularly in national periodicals like *Harper's, Atlantic, Century,* and *St. Nicholas. The Land of Little Rain,* published in 1903, received fine reviews, and a few years later her first novel, *Isidro,* was serialized in the *Atlantic Monthly.* Her public success brought only further dissatisfaction with her personal life. Trips to Oakland, where she met William James, and San Francisco, where she met the poet George Sterling and other members of the Bohemian Club, made Austin all the more aware that she needed intellectual stimulation. If Wallace would not leave the stultifying small desert towns, she would go alone. Her resolve was no doubt spurred by an invitation from Sterling in 1904 to visit Carmel, then undeveloped and a properly sylvan setting for the affair the two probably began. In 1906, after years of trying to work out her marriage, Austin left Wallace and moved to Carmel. Wallace did not divorce Mary until 1914.

For a year, Sterling may have provided the "passionate encounter" Doyle claimed her friend yearned for throughout her life and Carmel the community of artists she sought. At Carmel, Austin met Jack London, Lincoln Steffens, Charles Warren Stoddard, and a number of other writers. She worked well, finishing *Isidro,* a romance of colonial California; *The Flock* (1906), a legendary history of sheep ranching in California; *Santa Lucia* (1908), a novel about unhappy marriages and the need for divorce in the contemporary West; *Lost Borders* (1909), a short-story collection; and *The Arrow-maker,* (1911) a play about a prophetic Paiute medicine woman, the Chisera, betrayed by love. Her allegorical fantasy *Outland* (1910), about the cultural conflicts between two tribes, the House Folk and the Outliers, is set in a beautiful seaside village like Carmel and its ideas about society based on debates among the Carmel literati.

Yet while I-Mary wrote productively in Carmel, she often lived as Mary-by-herself. Eager for emotional and sexual fulfillment, Austin found herself mocked and rejected by the hard-drinking male "bohemians," as she shows in "Frustrate" (1912), one of her best stories.[11] The narrator, an unhappy middle-aged woman frustrated with her marriage, seeks self-expression in an artist colony, where the male artists ignore the "plain-looking" women in favor of "the pretty women, young and kind of empty-headed." Like many of Austin's stories, "Frustrate" turns on a moment when two women come together to share their perceptions; the narrator meets a woman writer, also overlooked, who tells her: "It is the whole art of putting yourself into your appearance. I have too much waist for that sort of thing. I have my own game." Both the insecure narrator and the confident writer are reflections of Austin and her experience in Carmel; they parallel Mary-by-herself and I-Mary. Once more feeling hurt and outcast, depressed, and ill with what she feared was breast cancer, she left Carmel in 1908 for a trip to Europe, but her success with her writing had given her the confidence to know that having her "own game" more than made up for a thick waist.

Her success in Europe increased her confidence. Her interest in mysticism and religion led her to Florence and Rome, where the symptoms of her illness vanished and she did research on art and Christianity. In London, her friend Lou Hoover introduced her to a variety of intellectuals and to Anne Martin, with whom Austin marched in her first suffrage parade. Two admirers of her work, H. G. Wells and Joseph Conrad, asked to meet her, and she and May Sinclair became close friends. When Austin returned to New York in 1911 for a production of her play *The Arrow-maker,* she was far more certain of herself and her talent, ready to risk the rejection she had always feared. Although she continued to think of Carmel as home, she was ready to take on New York, knowing that personal contact with her publishers and the editors of the leading periodicals would advance her career.

Austin claimed to feel out of place in New York, but she responded with enthusiasm to the intellectual stimulation it offered. She became friends with Willa Cather, Sinclair Lewis, and Mabel Dodge, whose salon she often visited. Cather's *Song of the Lark* (1915) and Lewis's *Main Street* (1920) both owe much to *A Woman of Genius,* the story of the growth of the woman artist who rebels against the conformity and lack of culture in small-town America. She knew a host of New York writers and intellectuals, including Vachel Lindsay, Amy Lowell, and Carl Van Doren. She became involved with radical politics, the subject of much of her writing of the period. A painful affair with Lincoln Steffens, which he abruptly ended, caused Austin to become obsessed with a variation of her repeated theme about male betrayal of women. In *Love and the Soul Maker* (1914), *No. 26 Jayne Street* (1920), and her unpublished novella, "Cactus Thorn," she created "progressive" male leaders who maintain traditional attitudes about male/female relations. Although *No. 26 Jayne Street* was conceived as "a war novel from the American woman's point of view," [12] it also "aimed to uncover," Austin said, "the sleazy quality of current radicalism, the ways in which the personal expression of radicals contradicted and reversed the political expression" (*Earth Horizon,* 337). For Austin, the personal was political.

Life in New York gave Austin opportunities for political activism. With her friends Charlotte Perkins Gilman, Anne Martin, Emma Goldman, Margaret Sanger, Ida Tarbell, and Elizabeth Gurley Flynn, Austin worked for various feminist causes: for suffrage, for birth control, for social programs like communal kitchens to help conserve food and free women workers during World War I, for increased awareness of violence against women. She even wrote a chapter of a composite novel, *The Sturdy Oak* (1917), a comic treatment of small-town politics and public morals, whose profits went to the suffrage movement. [13] The influence of the feminist movement can be seen in *A Woman of Genius,* written during her first year in New York, in *The Young Woman Citizen* (1918), an exploration of how women can take political power, and in a series of columns and essays for such periodicals as *Harper's* and the *Nation,* where she put forth a feminist agenda for social change that she called "Woman Thought."

During her years in New York, Austin became a prominent feminist theorist, articulating what would become major concerns of the feminist movement some sixty years later. She wrote about women's culture, literature, politics, and history, developing a theoretical language, describing nineteenth-century American women's literary traditions as "homecentric," and commenting on how "androcentric" models influenced culture: [14]

> Civilization as we now have it is one-eyed and one-handed. It is kept going by man's way of seeing things, and man's way of dealing with the things he sees (*Young Woman Citizen,* 17).

Austin never objected to "man's way of seeing"; she only wanted society to have the benefit of two hands. Claiming that she could not find her own needs, character, or experience reflected in her culture's assessment of womanhood, she questioned how attitudes about women's capacities are shaped, wondered what "obligates us most to impeach the validity of a woman's opinion at the points where it is most supported by experience." Trusting her own experience, she found herself "suspicious of the social estimate of women [because of] the general social conspiracy against her telling the truth about herself" (*Woman of Genius,* 4). Feeling that women had been silenced—by a "wall of men, a filtered, almost sound-proof wall of male intelligence, male reporters, critics, managers, advertisers . . . men editors, men publishers, men reviewers"—Austin was determined to tell the truth about her life and feelings.[15]

The truths Austin revealed have lately been identified as recurring themes in women's literature. She analyzed the restrictions in her mother's life with sympathy and showed its centrality to her understanding of her own womanhood. Exposing the narrowness of her culture's idea of "true womanliness," she did not follow male patterns, but instead explored the power of women's culture and the value of women's traditional domestic role. "Women, in their hundred thousand years of managing the family," she said, "have developed a genius for personal relations," a genius for cooperation and affiliation that should be put to use for the public good.[16] At the same time, she argued that the "traditional . . . structure of married life [is based on] the pattern of male dominance and feminine subser-

vience," that women must have the opportunity for meaningful work outside the home and the "courage to live lives of their own" (*Earth Horizon*,
271; *Woman of Genius*, 451). She wrote women's history, defining the special
concerns of different generations of women and their contributions to society. She challenged the portrayal of women in many works by male writers. She revealed how gender roles handicap both women and men and
pointed out that women are not passive receptors of culture but its creators. She encouraged young women to see their unique contributions to
politics. As Carol Gilligan has recently done, Austin showed that women
see the world "in some other way." "I have always believed," she said, "that
there is a distinctly feminine approach to intellectual problems and its recognition is indispensible to intellectual wholeness. All that I have ever, as a
feminist, protected against, is the prevailing notion that the feminine is
necessarily an inferior approach." [17]

"Woman Thought" belonged to women of all classes and races, to "new
women" and to traditional women. In *A Woman of Genius*, the story of
Olivia Lattimore's growth as a woman and an actress, Austin turned to the
exceptional woman, the trailblazer. Like her creator, Olivia wants to tell
the truth about her life to make it "easier for women who must tread [her]
path of work and loneliness," to "help other women to speak out what they
think, unashamed" (*Woman of Genius*, 503). "Hemmed and pinned in" by
the book's villain, the "social ideal" of small-town America, Olivia has no
models to help her become an artist, no models to suggest how a woman
might combine work and love. Yet unlike her predecessors—Avis Os-
trander from Elizabeth Stuart Phelps's *Story of Avis*, Edna Pontellier from
Kate Chopin's *Awakening*, Lily Bart from Edith Wharton's *House of Mirth*,
and the unnamed narrator of Gilman's "Yellow Wallpaper"—Olivia successfully overcomes the restrictions in her life. Although her success has its
emotional costs, destroying her marriage and denying her her one great
love, she is a satisfied woman at the novel's end. Strong and creative, she
anticipates Cather's Alexandra Bergson of *O Pioneers* (1913) and Thea
Kronberg of *The Song of the Lark* (1915).

Olivia's faith in herself as a "woman of genius" reflects Austin's maturing
confidence in herself and her vision. Having explored how women were
expected to give up their work for marriage, Austin ended the novel with a
possibility she still hoped for in her life: like Alexandra, Olivia plans to
marry an old friend, Jerry McDermott, a playwright with whom she can
share her work. In *A Woman of Genius*, as in *The Ford* (1917) and *Starry
Adventure* (1931), Austin tried to imagine the foundations for an egalitarian

marriage, something earlier writers such as Alcott, Phelps, Jewett, and Mary Hallock Foote had been unable to do. She saw this theme as belonging particularly to women of her generation:

> Miss [Frances] Willard had had, everybody knew she had had, a perfectly good opportunity to marry, and had put it by as incompatible with the thing she had in her heart to do. But to Mary's generation and the next one after her, it was to appear that marriage should not be a hindrance to the choice of the soul, or, if it proved so, then the item to be remedied was marriage. . . . And, of course, Mary's generation discovered that reshaping marriage, so that the woman shouldn't be torn continually between the man's demand for exclusive attention and the woman's natural social aptitudes, was by no means as easy as it promised. Miss Willard had made, it turned out, if not the most courageous, the most practicable, choice (*Earth Horizon,* 143–44).

Throughout her life Austin vacillated about whether "Miss" Willard was right. In 1912, the same year as *A Woman of Genius,* she published "Frustrate" with its conclusion that the artistic or independent woman will inevitably find herself without male love, a theme she developed in several early stories: "The Basket Maker," "The Coyote-Spirit and the Weaving Woman," and *The Arrow-maker.* Some of her heroines are controlled, even destroyed, by sexuality and passion; others decide, as Austin wrote in the title to her final unpublished novel, that "Love is Not Enough." She devoted a good deal of attention to love, marriage, and divorce, but she found no remedy. Although she said she felt modern feminists paid too much attention to the battles between the sexes, sexual relationships in her fiction are often transitory and painful.

During the busy New York years, Austin tried to spend part of every year in the West, first in Carmel and later in the Southwest. She visited friends in New Mexico, including Mabel Dodge Luhan, who had moved her salon to Taos. In Taos, Austin met Georgia O'Keeffe, D. H. Lawrence, and others, and she had what was for a time a satisfying affair with Daniel T. MacDougal, a prominent botanist from Tucson, touring Arizona and New Mexico with him and other friends. It was inevitable that the woman who wrote so often about westward trails would return to the West. In the city, as one of her characters said, "Man . . . don't have no chance to stretch his vision."[18] Often ill, depressed, worried about money, in need of re-establishing her mystical relation to her creative sources, she heard "the call of the West, which is never quite silenced in the soul of anyone who had heard it."[19] She felt a renewed fascination with the Southwest's cultural heritage; she wanted to feel the earth in her hands, to set down roots.

Drawn to Santa Fe by the School of American Research, which named her an Associate in Native American Literature, and by friends there, she made a permanent move west in 1925. Long interested in how houses reflected cultural values and aesthetics, she built a "beloved house," Casa Querida, which she filled with a collection of southwestern native art; there she could indulge her passion for cooking and gardening. Already a leader in the active artistic community in Santa Fe, she immediately made a number of new friends, among them art patron Albert Bender and writer Frank Applegate. The move west gave her new energy: she continued to write fiction, but turned much of her attention to nonfiction, exploring the connections between landscape and culture in *The Land of Journey's Ending* (1924), an account of her trip with MacDougal, and in *The American Rhythm* (1923).

She remained politically active, "connected," as Henry Smith wrote in 1931, "with almost every enterprise which shows any tendency to enrich and deepen the life of the West."[20] Her novel *The Ford* (1917) had explored land and water use in the Owens Valley in California, and Austin was named New Mexico representative to the Second Colorado River Conference in 1927, where she argued against California's rights to Colorado water. She testified before Congress against legislation that threatened Pueblo land and water rights; the bill was defeated. She became involved in curriculum choices in elementary schools, where she supported bilingual education for Hispanic and Indian children and study of regional cultural traditions. She devoted much of her energy to preserving the cultures of New Mexico, organizing the Indian Arts Fund in 1925, to which she bequeathed her house, and the Spanish Colonial Arts Society. Her interests became increasingly anthropological; late works like *The Land of Journey's Ending* (1924) and her novel *Starry Adventure* (1931) self-consciously explore all the factors—landscape, natural history, history, legend, art, archaeology—that make up southwestern cultural traditions.

Having circled the United States, living in and writing about midwestern towns, desert wildernesses, and New York City, Austin returned to the West. She sought what she called the "earth horizon," an expression from a Zia rain song meaning the "blue ring of sky meeting earth, which is the source of experience" (*Earth Horizon,* 33). Looking back on the patterns of her life in her autobiography, *Earth Horizon,* she associated the search for the horizon with the West, where she learned from the landscape the courage to shear off what was not worthwhile, to seek her own trail, to daydream about the hidden treasure, and from western dwellers that art is a process, a way of living, an expression of the spiritual search. In associating the movement west, literal and metaphorical, with imaginative vision, spiritual wholeness, psychological liberation, and creative power, Austin identified the central pattern in her life with the best spirit of the American dream. Always aware of where the United States had failed to pay off on its promises, always offering solutions to the problems she perceived, Austin kept her faith in the vision and the possibility, and her autobiography is in the American grain, a story of a true pioneer with a gift for prophecy.

Earth Horizon can be seen as Austin's final chisera story. In Santa Fe she achieved the eminence she had always sought. Critics began to write about her work; she organized a national lecture tour that was a great success, earning her reviews that referred to her as "a woman of tremendous power, wisdom, and charm"; Yale invited her to give a series of lectures on drama.[21] Those who knew her during these years described her as a "sage," "sibyl," "prophetess," like so many of her desert heroines. Ansel Adams, who did a book with her called *Taos Pueblo* (1930), offered a final tribute:

> Seldom have I met and known anyone of such intellectual and spiritual power and discipline. . . . She is a "future" person—one who will, a century from now, appear as a writer of major stature in the complex matrix of our American culture.[22]

A few days after giving a mesmerizing poetry reading, still working on a book on Spanish colonial arts, Austin died in her sleep in 1934. At her memorial, a poem was read that expressed her feelings about death. It is entitled "Going West."

> Some day I shall go West,
> Having won all time to live it in, at last
> Too still to boast.
> But when I smell the sage,
> When the long, marching landscape line
> Melts into wreathing mountains,
> And the dust cones dance
> Something in me that is of them shall stir.[23]

As she had requested, her ashes were interred on the peak of one of the Sangre de Cristo mountains, which she had viewed from her Santa Fe house. She is buried on Mount Picacho, "summit top" in Spanish.[24]

THE SHORT STORIES

In 1920, Mary Austin wrote a short essay that began:

> There are some American writers who simply write about the West, and there are others so intrinsically western in their point of view that any book by them becomes a western book. Foremost in this latter class is Willa Sibert Cather.
>
> Of that West which is bounded on the East by the popular magazines and on the other three sides by the Movies, Miss Cather knows nothing. Nor does she infringe on the territory of Bret Harte, Owen Wister, Harry Leon Wilson, nor of any other writer whose name we associate with the country west of the Mississippi. The West Miss Cather tells of is all her own so far as love and knowledge of it will take her, and all our own to the extent that it is utterly trustworthy and American.[25]

Austin's subject was her friend Willa Cather, but she might have been writing about her own work. It is intrinsically western, and the territory she loved and knew so well is all her own. Almost all of her short stories are set in the West. Their form and style were inspired by what she would have called the "landscape line," the perception of the lived-in land that she believed shaped art and culture. She succeeded in doing what she believed art should do: express an individual vision within shared cultural patterns. Like Cather's, her art is both unique and "utterly . . . American."

Austin published short stories for about forty years in a variety of periodicals. Four collections contain most of her stories: *Lost Borders* (1909); *The Basket Woman* (1910); *The Trail Book* (1918); and *One-Smoke Stories* (1934). After her death, Franklin Walker collected some of her first fiction in *Mother of Felipe and Other Early Stories* (1950). A few of her best stories remain uncollected, and Austin's papers at the Henry E. Huntington Library contain some excellent unpublished stories. *Western Trails* also includes some "sketches," short personal essays that use fictional techniques, from her books about California.

In her stories Austin often blurred the line between fiction and non-fiction. The narrative voice in *The Land of Little Rain,* a collection of mystical nature sketches in the Emersonian tradition, is similar to the narrator's voice in *Lost Borders,* a collection of stories about the same region; in fact, the two works could easily be read as companion pieces. Both works are autobiographical: both are in many ways tales about the teller, about perception, storytelling, and the search for meaning. Writing as she did in so many genres, Austin thought carefully about form, and she was willing to take risks.

In her first years as a writer, Austin sought to express her feeling about the desert West, a feeling she had never seen described. "There was something else there," she said, "besides what you find in the books; a lurking, evasive Something" (*Earth Horizon,* 187). Austin could find few models for the kind of western writing she wanted to do. Many California writers were busy producing publicity literature, and she would not be part of what she called the "sentimental aftermath" to *Ramona.* She could tell stories, but she couldn't figure out how to write them.

> It had never been any part of my intention to write short stories. If you have access to the popular examples of them in the early nineties, you will not need to be told how little appeal the sentimental personalities of that form would have had for a mind always reaching wider and more deeply into the movement of American society (*Earth Horizon,* 230).

Austin's comment is unjust to many of her contemporaries, perhaps most particularly Hamlin Garland, whose vision of the West and feminism resembled her own but whose work she never mentioned. Yet her comment underscores her feeling that to write as she wanted about the westward "movement of American society," she would have to set out on her own trail.

As a western writer, Austin was also entering male territory. Although recent scholarship has uncovered a number of women who wrote about the frontier, the classic western tale of the nineteenth century belonged to the lone male who headed west in search of his own identity and moral values. Like most women writers, Austin was ambivalent about this rebellious male: as a rebellious wanderer herself, she was attracted to his freedom, but as a woman interested in marriage, she saw the costs to his family, as stories like "The Return of Mr. Wills" demonstrate. The western loner appears often in Austin's stories, usually in relation to a woman, but because she was "not much interested" in being a boy, Austin could not use this story "pattern," as she would call it, to help her write about what "was to be got out of being a woman" in the West.

Nor could Austin use the story pattern she associated with nineteenth-century women writers, a pattern she called "homecentric." While she admired writers like Stowe, Alcott, and Jewett, and while she was interested in women's domestic lives, her experiences in the lost border region were not of the homecentric sort, though they often concerned relations between women and men. From these writers she may have learned to consider the connections between region and character; she also took west with her their thematic interest in the question of how women can combine career, particularly an artistic career, and marriage. Austin did know the work of Mary Hallock Foote, who began to publish stories about California, Colorado, and Idaho in the 1870s. Foote's struggles to write about women's lives in the West may have pointed out the difficulties of adapting a homecentric vision to the West, and her beautiful descriptive passages may have influenced Austin's style.

Austin's breakthrough as a writer came when she began to think about the implications of Native American art.

> She had begun the study of Indian verse, strange and meaningful; of Indian wisdom, of Indian art. The Paiutes were basket-makers; the finest of their sort. What Mary drew from them was their naked craft, the subtle sympathies of twig and root and bark. . . . She learned what it meant; how to prevail; how to measure her strength against it. Learning that, she learned to write (*Earth Horizon*, 289).

In the Paiute concept of prayer Austin found what other poets might call their muse. "Prayer," she said, was "an outgoing act of the inner self toward something, not a god, toward a responsive activity in the world about you, designated as The-Friend-of-the-Soul-of-Man" (*Earth Horizon*, 276). Like the Indians, Austin learned to express communion with this Friend-of-the-Soul rhythmically, in patterns, and she gradually "perceived that these patterns made writing" (*Earth Horizon*, 289). Indian artists taught her to be "sensitive to the spirit of existence," to see art as a "logical necessity" in life, a natural act (*Earth Horizon*, 362).

This description of Austin's relation to Native American culture stresses her mystical side. She also learned practical lessons from the Indians. She listened to their stories and attended to their way of telling them. They taught her to prune: their stories gave her "literary style its best thing, a selective economy of phrase."[26] They taught her "the art of occupying space without filling it" (*American Rhythm,* 56). They taught her to be ambiguous and suggestive, to leave much unsaid: "No Indian ever says all his thought. Always there is some petal left unfurled" (*American Rhythm,* 60). From the Indians she learned "to interpret the significance of common things" (*Earth Horizon,* 362). Ultimately, they taught her to recognize how the trails converged, to see the connections between land, people, culture, and language. She learned about the Indians through knowing "the land they lived in": "It is only by such familiarity with the conditions under which a land permits itself to be lived with that I was able to overcome the difficulty of language" (*American Rhythm,* 38–39).

The Native American oral tradition also led Austin to think about narrative voice and to experiment with how to tell a story. Austin's first stories were those she heard from Indians or from the various characters she met in the West, characters with idiosyncratic voices and points of view: stagecoach drivers, shepherds, ordinary people who had imaginations, used colorful language, and connected themselves to the legends of the regions through the stories they told. Like Twain, Austin learned to imitate oral storytelling, to let stories wander, to tie them together by letting the narrator draw the conclusion about the story told. In early collections like *The Land of Little Rain* and *Lost Borders,* she developed her voice as a writer by acknowledging her role as storyteller, by *not* trying to disappear, by emphasizing her relationship to her material. Her later collections often use dramatized narrators: the basket woman, the talking animals of *The Trail Book,* the Indian storytellers of *One-Smoke Stories.*

Austin's interest in folk culture and folk art also grew out of the oral tradition. Like Emerson, who influenced her work in a variety of ways, she believed America had "listened too long to the courtly muses of Europe," and she experimented with form partially to develop a native tradition. In *The American Rhythm,* she explored how rhythm results from "a perception of movement arising out of experiences in an environment" and challenged American poets to develop indigenous rhythms based on the American landscape and experience. Her comments about the new verse form she envisioned in America could also describe her goals in the short-story form:

> It would be a form as lacking in tradition as the American experience itself. It would be democratic in the sense that it would be within the capacity of the democractically bred. Anybody could use it, as any-

body has been able to use native verse form freely. Finally it would be a statement of life as for the first two or three hundred years, life presented itself on the western continent in terms of things lived through rather than observed or studied (*American Rhythm*, 10).

Claiming that there are "so few books that are genuinely representative of American culture," Austin tried to write books expressing "that intuitive access to the collective consciousness, which it is the dream and probably the mission of democracy to achieve."[27]

Coherent in outlook but varied in styles, Austin's short stories take many forms. She always focused more on character than on plot; sometimes nothing much happens in her stories, but a character, often the narrator, comes to some realization, points out some meaning. Yet the meaning is not a moral; it is almost always ambiguous or undercut in an ironic manner. Often a story turns on a moment of communication, of mutual realization, between two women. She felt her stories took the shape of the landscape: "The palpable sense of mystery in the desert air breeds fables" (*The Land of Little Rain*, 12). Many of her stories, which were often based on folk tales, myths, and legends, are not realistic but seek to express an inner truth.

In her experiments with form and her interest in telling uniquely American stories, Austin resembled a number of her better-known contemporaries: poets like Edgar Lee Masters, Vachel Lindsay, Robert Frost, Langston Hughes, Hart Crane, and William Carlos Williams, fiction writers like Cather, Sinclair Lewis, Jean Toomer, Zora Neale Hurston, and Sherwood Anderson. Like Cather, she read Sarah Orne Jewett, and she may well have been influenced by *The Country of the Pointed Firs,* from which she may have learned to create short-story collections with thematic and formal coherence and dramatized narrators. *Lost Borders* is such a collection, and it anticipates later influential collections like Anderson's *Winesburg, Ohio* (1919) and Hemingway's *In Our Time* (1924).[28]

Austin also experimented with style. She later claimed that "the only writer out of those days who affected her style was Emerson"; certainly he helped her to develop her tendency to see natural facts as symbols of spiritual facts and to search for the right word (*Earth Horizon,* 165). She once told her friend Helen McKnight Doyle, "I worked four hours today . . . trying to get the right word to describe the hills to the east. But I got the word—puckery—and it is right!"[29] In *Earth Horizon,* she described her obsession with language, with collections of colloquial phrases, Spanish folklore, intensively pondered adjectives for the color and form of natural things, the exact word for a mule's cry—'maimed noises'—the difference between the sound of ripe figs dropping and the patter of olives shaken down by the wind; single lines of verse imprisoning these things, all the sort of thing that her mother, when she found it about the house, thrust into the waste-basket impatiently (*Earth Horizon,* 228).

The use of colloquial phrases and language from Indian and Spanish characterizes Austin's nativist style. She also attended to the rhythm of her prose; she was able to finish *The Land of Little Rain* only when she finally found the key "in the rhythm of the twenty-mule teams that creaked in and out of the borax works, the rhythm of the lonely lives blown across the trails" (*Earth Horizon,* 296).

Austin's style varied over the forty years she wrote short stories. She wrote Jamesian convoluted sentences to mirror the workings of consciousness, lyrical descriptions of nature, brief proverbial comments about human experience, but her ironic tone most characterizes and distinguishes her writing. Understated, humorous, and very appealing, her voice is uniquely her own, as one example from *The Return of Mr. Wills* will suggest: after abandoning his family, Mr. Wills returns to settle on them "like a blight," announcing: "'There's no place like home' . . . or something to that effect."

Finally, Austin's portrayal of western experience emphasizes the woman's point of view. Although many of her themes—ecological awareness, love of nature, storytelling and its relation to tradition—are not inherently linked to gender, she always stressed that as a woman, she saw the world "in some other way" from men. As a woman, self-consciously concerned with and shaped by women's culture, she tried to find a way to merge the stereotypical masculine and feminine Wests, to allow individualism to cohabit with community, to encourage free self-expression and full possibilities for personal growth while showing the importance of cultural traditions and social obligations. As a woman she discovered new western patterns and presented a revisionist interpretation of the classic western themes in stories like "The Return of Mr. Wills" and "The Man Who was Loved by Women." In many of her short stories, she focused on what she called "the unexplored treasure of women's experience" in the West.[30] Peopled with a variety of women—basket weavers, schoolteachers, mothers, solitaries, common-law wives, Spanish matrons, Indian girls, middle-class ladies, artists—Austin's stories explore what was "to be got out of being a woman" in the various races, cultures, and classes that made up the West.

As an early western writer, Austin identified a set of themes associated with women's lives in the West, themes based on what she said women liked to "gossip" about: children, marriage, and relations between women and men. Several stories explore a woman's desire for a child; and she frequently explored the differences in how men and women respond to the call of the West, sometimes stressing the isolation and unhappiness of women's lives there, sometimes the feeling of liberation they find in the desert. In her stories, Austin presents an ironic critique of assumptions—men's and women's—about marriage and of sexual politics, and she is not sanguine about the possibilities for love or deep communication between women and men.

Although many stories—"The Bitterness of Women," "Frustrate," "Kate Bixby's Queerness"—suggest how women are entrapped in various ways by social expectations, Austin's heroines are generally successful in taking some control over their lives. Feeling hedged in by femininity when she went west, Austin associated the West with a feeling of liberation, with the chance to walk off "society-made values." She found in Indian women a model for the woman artist. In a number of stories—"The Basket Maker," "The Coyote-Spirit and the Weaving Woman," "The Walking Woman," and her play, *The Arrow-Maker,* are the best examples—she created the strong, prophetic women artists she sometimes called chiseras. Some are medicine women, influential women in their tribes; others are outcasts. Some live happily in their independent solitude; others long for human ties. All reflect Austin's interest in women who are "different from other people" because their vision is larger, women who are "not afraid of anything," who "wander . . . far into the desert" to see where "all the trails converged," as she says of the Weaving Woman. "Weaving patterns in her baskets of all that she saw or thought," the Weaving Woman creates out of her own experience and her connections to nature. Thinking and writing about such women helped Austin to break away from what she experienced as the limitations of her womanhood, from "young ladihood," to accept herself. They showed her a new trail.

In writing about these women and others, Austin reclaimed the domestic women's tradition as culture. Her western women weave baskets, cook, garden, make artificial roses, tell stories, seek spiritual meaning—and Austin saw all of these activities as art. Creators of civilization, these women are not cut off from nature.

Because Austin was so interested in private moments of communication between women, it seems fitting that one of the best assessments of her work is contained in a personal letter she received in 1903 from Mary Hallock Foote, then well known as an important western writer. Foote praised Austin's stories about the arid West, particularly admiring in them "something . . . that is pure woman." Perhaps speaking out of her own experience of trying to write about the effect of the West on a woman's sensibility, she encouraged Austin not to doubt her work, saying, "For I know no one who has done or is likely to do what you are doing, dear young lady. . . . Only one of our great prose poets could write as you do of the un-writable, tell as you can the untellable." [31]

Foote was right about Austin's originality and her ability to write the "un-writable." Mary Austin was a pioneer—and a prophet.

NOTES

1. Mary Austin, *Earth Horizon* (New York: Literary Guild, 1932), 157–58. Page numbers follow subsequent quotations in the text of the Introduction and the headnotes.

2. Mary Austin, *The Young Woman Citizen* (New York: Woman's Press, 1918), 19. Page numbers follow subsequent quotations in the text.

3. Mary Austin, "Regionalism in American Fiction," *English Journal* 21 (February 1932): 97–107. Austin makes a similar argument about form in "The Folk Story in America," *South Atlantic Quarterly* 33 (January 1934): 10–19.

4. Cather made this comment in a personal note to Austin in a copy of *Death Comes for the Archbishop*, which she had written in Austin's house in Santa Fe. Austin's copy of the novel is in the Huntington Library's Austin Collection. Austin was upset by Cather's sympathetic treatment of the influence of French Catholicism on New Mexican culture in *Death Comes for the Archbishop*, feeling Cather overlooked the more important Spanish influence.

5. Mary Austin, *The Flock* (Boston: Houghton Mifflin Co., 1906), 221.

6. Mary Austin, *A Woman of Genius* (Garden City, N.J.: Doubleday, Page and Co., 1912). Page numbers follow subsequent quotations in the text. Since I did the research for this introduction, the Feminist Press has issued a reprint of the novel, with an excellent afterword by Nancy Porter (Old Westbury, N.Y: Feminist Press, 1985).

7. Barbara Welter, "The Cult of True Womanhood," in *Dimity Convictions: The American Woman in the Nineteenth Century* (Athens: University of Ohio Press, 1976).

8. Mary Austin, *The Land of Little Rain* (Albuquerque: University of New Mexico Press, 1974). Page numbers follow subsequent quotations in the text.

9. Austin's Tejon notebooks are in the Huntington Library's Austin Collection, box 24c.

10. Helen McKnight Doyle, *Mary Austin, Woman of Genius* (New York: Gotham House, 1939).

11. For sneering comments about Austin by Carmel friends, see Augusta Fink, *I-Mary: A Biography of Mary Austin* (Tucson: University of Arizona Press, 1983) and Franklin Walker, *The Seacoast of Bohemia* (Santa Barbara: Peregrine Smith, 1973). Accepting the comments of George Sterling, Jack London, and Jimmy Hopper, Walker variously describes Austin as "dumpy" (27), "flat-chested" (26), "too homely and assertive," and "almost purring at being included in the inner circle" (26).

12. Quoted in Fink, *I-Mary*, 181.

13. *The Sturdy Oak: A Composite Novel of American Politics by Fourteen American Authors*, ed. Elizabeth Jordan (New York: Henry Holt and Co., 1917). Among Austin's fellow authors were Dorothy Canfield, Fannie Hurst, and Harry Leon Wilson.

14. Austin discussed the "homecentric" novel in a speech to the National Arts Club in 1922 at a dinner honoring her. The talk was entitled "Understanding America Through Her Literature." I read the copy contained in the Huntington Library's Austin Collection. A character in Mary Austin's *The Ford* discusses "Androcentric Culture" (Boston: Houghton Mifflin Co., 1917), 233.

15. Mary Austin, *No. 26 Jayne Street* (Boston: Houghton Mifflin Co., 1920), 6.

16. "Woman Looks at Her World," *Pictoral Review*, November 1924, 69.

17. Austin made this comment in a letter to the *New Republic* about a review by Lewis Mumford of *American Rhythm*. Clipping contained in the Huntington Library's Austin Collection, box 25.

18. Mary Austin, *Lost Borders* (New York: Harper and Bros., 1909), 133.

19. Mary Austin, "Willa Sibert Cather," *El Palacio* 7 (March/April 1920): 90.

20. Henry Smith, "The Feel of the Purposeful Earth: Mary Austin's Prophesy," *New Mexico Quarterly* 1 (February 1931): 33.

21. Quoted in Fink, *I-Mary*, 237.

22. Ansel Adams, "Notes on Mary Austin," in *Mary Hunter Austin, a Centennial booklet published by The Mary Austin Home* (Independence, Calif., 1968), 7.

23. Mary Austin, "Going West," *Bookman* 56 (September 1922): 8.

24. Austin's last days, memorial, and burial are described by T. M. Pearce in *Mary Hunter Austin* (New York: Twayne Publishers, 1965), 66–69. Pearce has been one of Austin's most devoted scholars.

25. Austin, "Willa Sibert Cather," 89.

26. Mary Austin, *The American Rhythm: Studies and Re-expressions of American Songs* (New York: Harcourt, Brace and Co., 1923), 39. Page numbers follow subsequent quotations in the text.

27. "Understanding America Through Her Literature" and "The American Form of the Novel," *New Republic,* April 12, 1922, 4.

28. In 1923, Sherwood Anderson wrote Austin a letter from California about discovering her books. "They have been such a relief to me after all the other books of the western country I have read. What Twain and Harte missed you have found and set down with such fine understanding. The books have been a real joy to me." Quoted in *Literary America: The Mary Austin Letters,* ed. T. M. Pearce (Westport, Conn.: Greenwood Press, 1979), 177.

29. Quoted in Doyle, *Mary Austin,* 211.

30. Quoted in T. M. Pearce, *The Beloved House* (Caldwell, Idaho: Caxton Printers, 1940), 211.

31. This letter is contained in the Huntington Library's Austin Collection, box 9.

❖ ❖ ❖

The Land of Little Rain

THE BASKET MAKER

The Land of Little Rain (1903) is Austin's best-known work, a series of sketches or essays describing the interrelationships among land, plants, animals, and human inhabitants of the desert regions of southern California. The collection reveals the years Austin spent trying to understand the "language" of the land—and her own efforts to record that language, to find the right word. As her preface makes clear, the book is partially about naming, about the search for a personal style in relation to a landscape. As many critics have pointed out, it is a fine example of the Emersonian tradition in American literature.

Like all of Austin's best works, *The Land of Little Rain* has a strong narrative voice, a voice that invites the reader to join her on what she calls the "trails" of her region, on "Water Trails of the Ceriso," "The Mesa Trail," and "The Streets of the Mountains." It is the voice of a patient, precise, and insightful observer, but the voice is not retiring or unobtrusive. It is very personal, almost conversational, establishing a relationship to the reader by the use of "we" or "you." Yet the casual feeling of the style is hard won, for the writing is tight and evocative. The narrator, though undramatized, is a real presence because her tone and characteristic way of looking are unique. Through her style as well as her subject matter, Austin conveys that her narrator is a wanderer on a search to understand the meaning in her experience. She is an appealing guide into the region and the spirit.

Because *The Land of Little Rain* has long been in print, we include only one story from the collection, "The Basket Maker," which Austin first published in the *Atlantic Monthly* in 1903. The story is an important one, reflecting her feeling of affinity for American Indian women, from whom she felt she learned both how to live and how to be an artist. She recalls the formation of her bond with the Paiute women in a passage from *Earth Horizon:*

That winter, when she lay sick in bed [after childbirth] day after day with no help but the uncertain visits of Indian women, she grew gradually aware by the way the child throve, that the *mahala* was nursing it along with her own beady-eyed brown dumpling. Mary roused herself sufficiently to have the Doctor see the Paiute woman to make sure they ran no danger, and for the rest, since the *mahala* was shy about her service, accepted it gratefully in silence. Two or three years later, because Mary's child was not talking as early as it should, that *mahala* came all the way to Lone Pine to bring her dried meadowlarks' tongues, which make the speech nimble and quick. It was in experiences such as this that Mary began genuinely to know Indians. There was a small campody up George's Creek, brown wickiups in the chaparral like wasps' nests. Mary would see the women moving across the mesa on pleasant days, digging wild hyacinth roots, seed-gathering, and, as her strength permitted, would often join them, absorbing women's lore, plants good to be eaten or for medicine, learning to make snares of long, strong hair for the quail, how with one hand to flip trout . . . how and when to gather willows and cedar roots for basket-making. It was in this fashion that she began to learn that to get at the meaning of work you must make all its motions, both of body and mind (*Earth Horizon,* 246–47).

The meadowlarks' tongues could not help Mary's daughter Ruth, but the mahala who brought them inspired Austin to discover her own way to speak. The Basket Maker, who feeds her own precious child meadowlarks' tongues, is the first of Austin's chisera figures: independent and farseeing American Indian women artists whose lives are intimately tied to the natural world. Although Austin's reference to the "beady-eyed" child might suggest that she never wholly escaped racist stereotypes, Indian women became her literary and spiritual models.

The Basket Maker

"A man," says Seyavi of the campoodie, "must have a woman, but a woman who has a child will do very well."

That was perhaps why, when she lost her mate in the dying struggle of his race, she never took another, but set her wit to fend for herself and her young son. No doubt she was often put to it in the beginning to find food for them both. The Paiutes had made their last stand at the border of the Bitter Lake; battle-driven they died in its waters, and the land filled with cattlemen and adventurers for gold: this while Seyavi and the boy lay up in the caverns of the Black Rock and ate tule roots and fresh-water clams that they dug out of the slough bottoms with their toes. In the interim, while the tribes swallowed their defeat, and before the rumor of war died out, they must have come very near to the bare core of things. That was the time Seyavi learned the sufficiency of mother wit, and how much more easily one can do without a man than might at first be supposed.

To understand the fashion of any life, one must know the land it is lived in and the procession of the year. This valley is a narrow one, a mere trough between hills, a draught for storms, hardly a crow's flight from the sharp Sierras of the Snows to the curled, red and ochre, uncomforted, bare ribs of Waban. Midway of the grove runs a burrowing, dull river, nearly a hundred miles from where it cuts the lava flats of the north to its widening in a thick, tideless pool of a lake. Hereabouts the ranges have no foothills, but rise up steeply from the bench lands above the river. Down from the Sierras, for the east ranges have almost no rain, pour glancing white floods toward the lowest land, and all beside them lie the campoodies, brown wattled brush heaps, looking east.

In the river are mussels, and reeds that have edible white roots, and in the soddy meadows tubers of joint grass; all these at their best in the spring. On the slope the summer growth affords seeds; up the steep the one-leaved pines, an oily nut. That was really all they could depend upon, and that only at the mercy of the little gods of frost and rain. For the rest it was cunning against cunning, caution against skill, against quacking hordes of wild fowl in the tulares, against pronghorn and bighorn and deer. You can guess, however, that all this warring of rifles and bowstrings, this influx of overlording whites, had made game wilder and hunters fearful of being hunted. You can surmise also, for it was a crude time and the land was raw, that the women became in turn the game of the conquerors.

There used to be in the Little Antelope a she dog, stray or outcast, that had a litter in some forsaken lair, and ranged and foraged for them slinking savage and afraid, remembering and mistrusting humankind, wistful, lean and sufficient for her young. I have thought Seyavi might have had days like that, and have had perfect leave to think, since she will not talk of it. Paiutes have the art of reducing life to its lowest ebb and yet saving it alive on grasshoppers, lizards, and strange herbs, and that time must have left no shift untried. It lasted long enough for Seyavi to have evolved the philosophy of life which I have set down at the beginning. She had gone beyond learning to do for her son, and learned to believe it worth while.

In our kind of society, when a woman ceases to alter the fashion of her hair, you guess that she has passed the crisis of her experience. If she goes on crimping and uncrimping with the changing mode, it is safe to suppose she has never come up against anything too big for her. The Indian woman gets nearly the same personal note in the pattern of her baskets. Not that she does not make all kinds, carriers, water-bottles, and cradles,—these are kitchen ware,—but her works of art are all of the same piece. Seyavi made flaring, flat-bottomed bowls, cooking pots really when cooking was done by dropping hot stones into water-tight food baskets, and for decoration a design in colored bark of the procession of plumed crests of the valley quail. In this pattern she had made cooking pots in the golden spring of her wedding year, when the quail went up two and two to their resting places about the foot of Oppapago. In this fashion she made them when, after pillage, it was possible to reinstate the housewifely crafts. Quail ran then in the Black Rock by hundreds,—so you will still find them in fortunate years,—and in the famine time the women cut their long hair to make snares when the flocks came morning and evening to the springs.

Seyavi made baskets for love and sold them for money, in a generation that preferred iron pots for utility. Every Indian woman is an artist,—sees, feels, creates, but does not philosophize about her processes. Seyavi's bowls are wonders of technical precision, inside and out the palm finds no fault with them, but the subtlest appeal is in the sense that warns us of humanness in the way the design spreads into the flare of the bowl. There used to be an Indian woman at Olancha who made bottle-neck trinket baskets in the rattlesnake pattern, and could accommodate the design to the swelling bowl and flat shoulder of the basket without sensible disproportion, and so cleverly that you might own one a year without thinking how it was done; but Seyavi's baskets had a touch beyond cleverness. The weaver and the warp lived next to the earth and were saturated with the same elements. Twice a year, in the time of white butterflies and again when young quail ran neck and neck in the chaparral, Seyavi cut willows for basketry by the creek where it wound toward the river against the sun and sucking winds. It never quite reached the river except in far between times of summer flood, but it always tried, and the willows encouraged it as much as they could. You nearly always found them a little farther down than the trickle of eager water. The Paiute fashion of counting time appeals to me more than any other calendar. They have no stamp of heathen gods nor great ones, nor any succession of moons as have red men of the East and North, but count forward and back by the progress of the season; the time of *taboose*, before the trout begin to leap, the end of the piñon harvest, about the beginning of deep snows. So they get nearer the sense of the season, which runs early or late according as the rains are forward or delayed. But whenever Seyavi cut willows for baskets was always a golden time, and the soul of the weather went into the wood. If you had ever owned one of Seyavi's golden russet cooking bowls with the pattern of plumed quail, you would understand all this without saying anything.

Before Seyavi made baskets for the satisfaction of desire, for that is a house-bred theory of art that makes anything more of it, she danced and dressed her hair. In those days, when the spring was at flood and the blood pricked to the mating fever, the maids chose their flowers, wreathed themselves, and danced in the twilights, young desire crying out to young desire. They sang what the heart prompted, what the flower expressed, what boded in the mating weather.

"And what flower did you wear, Seyavi?"

"I, ah,—the white flower of twining (clematis), on my body and my hair, and so I sang:—

> "I am the white flower of twining,
> Little white flower by the river,
> Oh, flower that twines close by the river;
> Oh, trembling flower!
> So trembles the maiden heart."

So sang Seyavi of the campoodie before she made baskets, and in her later days laid her arms upon her knees and laughed in them at the recollection.

But it was not often she would say so much, never understanding the keen hunger I had for bits of lore and the "fool talk" of her people. She had fed her young son with meadowlarks' tongues, to make him quick of speech; but in late years was loath to admit it, though she had come through the period of unfaith in the lore of the clan with a fine appreciation of its beauty and significance.

"What good will your dead get, Seyavi, of the baskets you burn?" said I, coveting them for my own collection.

Thus Seyavi, "As much good as yours of the flowers you strew."

Oppapago looks on Waban, and Waban on Coso and the Bitter Lake, and the campoodie looks on these three; and more, it sees the beginning of winds along the foot of Coso, the gathering of clouds behind the high ridges, the spring flush, the soft spread of wild almond bloom on the mesa. These first you understand are the Paiute's walls, the other his furnishings. Not the wattled hut is his home, but the land, the winds, the hill front, the stream. These he cannot duplicate at any furbisher's shop as you who live within doors, who if your purse allows may have the same home at Sitka and Samarcand. So you see how it is that the homesickness of an Indian is often unto death, since he gets no relief from it; neither wind nor weed nor skyline, nor any aspect of the hills of a strange land sufficiently like his own. So it was when the government reached out for the Paiutes, they gathered into the Northern Reservation only such poor tribes as could devise no other end of their affairs. Here, all along the river, and south to Shoshone land, live the clans who owned the earth, fallen into the deplorable condition of hangers-on. Yet you hear them laughing at the hour when they draw in to the campoodie after labor, when there is a smell of meat and the steam of the cooking pots goes up against the sun. Then the children lie with their toes in the ashes to hear tales; then they are merry, and have the joys of repletion and the nearness of their kind. They have their hills, and though jostled, are sufficiently free to get some fortitude for what will come. For now you shall hear of the end of the basket maker.

In her best days Seyavi was most like Deborah, deep bosomed, broad in the hips, quick in counsel, slow of speech, esteemed of her people. This was that Seyavi who reared a man by her own hand, her own wit, and none other. When the townspeople began to take note of her—and it was some years after the war before there began to be any towns—she was then in the quick maturity of primitive women; but when I knew her she seemed already old. Indian women do not often live to great age, though they look

incredibly steeped in years. They have the wit to win sustenance from the
raw material of life without intervention, but they have not the sleek look
of the women whom the social organization conspires to nourish. Seyavi
had somehow squeezed out of her daily round a spiritual ichor that kept
the skill in her knotted fingers long after the accustomed time, but that also
failed. By all counts she would have been about sixty years old when it
came her turn to sit in the dust on the sunny side of the wickiup, with little
strength left for anything but looking. And in time she paid the toll of the
smoky huts and became blind. This is a thing so long expected by the
Paiutes that when it comes they find it neither bitter nor sweet, but tolerable because common. There were three other blind women in the campoodie, withered fruit on a bough, but they had memory and speech. By
noon of the sun there were never any left in the campoodie but these or
some mother of weanlings, and they sat to keep the ashes warm upon the
hearth. If it were cold, they burrowed in the blankets of the hut; if it were
warm, they followed the shadow of the wickiup around. Stir much out of
their places they hardly dared, since one might not help another; but they
called, in high, old cracked voices, gossip and reminder across the ash
heaps.

Then, if they have your speech or you theirs, and have an hour to spare,
there are things to be learned of life not set down in any books, folk tales,
famine tales, love and longsuffering and desire, but no whimpering. Now
and then one or another of the blind keepers of the camp will come across
to where you sit gossiping, tapping her way among the kitchen middens,
guided by your voice that carries far in the clearness and stillness of mesa
afternoons. But suppose you find Seyavi retired into the privacy of her
blanket, you will get nothing for that day. There is no other privacy possible in a campoodie. All the processes of life are carried on out of doors or
behind the thin, twig-woven walls of the wickiup, and laughter is the only
corrective for behavior. Very early the Indian learns to possess his countenance in impassivity, to cover his head with his blanket. Something to
wrap around him is as necessary to the Paiute as to you your closet to
pray in.

So in her blanket Seyavi, sometime basket maker, sits by the unlit
hearths of her tribe and digests her life, nourishing her spirit against the
time of the spirit's need, for she knows in fact quite as much of these
matters as you who have a larger hope, though she has none but the certainty that having borne herself courageously to this end she will not be
reborn a coyote.

Lost Borders

Although *Lost Borders* (1909) has never been reprinted, it ranks among Austin's best work.[1] In it she explores those souls who have the "mark of the land" upon them: frontier wives, prospectors, stagecoach drivers, Indian women, con men, "lungers," and a host of storytellers. The collection's major strength is the unnamed storyteller who narrates every story, a woman who is always on the trail of some story. She tells stories she has heard or invented of passion, desperation, and love, but most are singularly unmelodramatic, taking their tone from her ironic voice. Their subjects are those the narrator says Indian women inevitably talk about "in the course of an afternoon—children, marriage, and the ways of the whites," whose behavior in the desert seems so inexplicable (*Lost Borders*, 39). "And," she adds, "what in the conduct of men most interests women of the campody, or women anywhere for that matter, is their relation to women" (*Lost Borders*, 40). The "gossip" between these women suggests a further theme of the collection: communication and mutual support among women of divergent backgrounds.

It is often the narrator who comes to understand, in the course of her storytelling, the life of another woman. She believes "it is the men who go mostly into the desert, who love it past all reasonableness, slack their ambitions, cast off old usages, neglect their families because of the pulse and beat of a life laid bare to its thews and sinews." She claims that women hate the isolation, the barren emptiness, and she shows how women deprived of community and work depend on love to give their lives meaning, love of men who cannot be relied upon. Yet the narrator loves the desert and its stories; in *The Land* she likens the desert to a woman like herself, suggesting her identification with the region. She also creates other women marked by the desert, most notably the Walking Woman, whose story closes the

---

1. After *Western Trails* went to press I learned that Rutgers University Press had recently reprinted *Lost Borders* and *Land of Little Rain* in one volume entitled *Stories From the Country of Lost Borders*, ed. Marjorie Pryse.

collection. Although each has her own needs and values, the narrator and the Walking Woman are both independent, strong women whose footsteps into the desert provide a trail for other unconventional women.

Ultimately *Lost Borders* is a series of tales about the teller, a woman whose perceptions about human character and relationships—and about herself—convey the state of mind Austin thought of as western. Her voice is well developed and unique: spare, ironic, humorous, self-revealing, compassionate. The collection resembles another regional work, Sarah Orne Jewett's *The Country of the Pointed Firs,* in its thematic coherence, its careful development of metaphors and symbols from nature, its interest in regional characters and stories, its use of a narrator, and its exploration of human relationships. *Lost Borders* is an unknown American masterpiece.

❖ ❖ ❖

The Land

"The Land" introduces the narrative voice of Lost Borders *and the metaphor of story trails throughout the region. The narrator offers her stories as trails into the desert, as ways to explore the land; she tracks a friend by the trail of a story they share; and she begins the story that follows "The Land" by saying, "All the trails in this book begin at Lone Pine, winding east by south and east again" (12). The land marks the form of the stories as it marks its inhabitants: "Every story of that country is colored by the fashion of the life there," says the narrator. Like the country, "the best part" of her stories "remains locked, inviolate," the trail petering out. She is less concerned with what happened than with what the "Borderers" thought or felt. Her stories are ambiguous, suggestive, questioning laws, conscience, and convention. Aptly, they break convention themselves: "Out there where the boundary of soul and sense is as faint as a trail in a sand-storm" anything might happen.*

When the Paiute nations broke westward through the Sierra wall they cut off a remnant of the Shoshones, and forced them south as far as Death Valley and the borders of the Mojaves, they penned the Washoes in and around Tahoe, and passing between these two, established themselves along the snow-fed Sierra creeks. And this it was proper they should do, for the root of their name-word is Pah, meaning water, to distinguish them from their brothers the Utes of the Great Basin.

In time they passed quite through the saw-cut cañons by Kern and Kings rivers and possessed all the east slope of the San Joaquin, but chiefly they settled by small clans and family groups where the pines leave off and the sage begins and the desert abuts on the great Sierra fault. On the northeast they touched the extreme flanks of the Utes, and with them and the southerly tribes swept a wide arc about that region of mysterious desertness of which you shall presently hear more particularly.

The boundaries between the tribes and between the clans within the tribe were plainly established by natural landmarks—peaks, hillcrests, creeks, and chains of water-holes—beginning at the foot of the Sierra and continuing eastward past the limit of endurable existence. Out there, a week's journey from everywhere, the land was not worth parcelling off, and the boundaries which should logically have been continued until they met the cañon of the Colorado ran out in foolish wastes of sand and inextricable disordered ranges. Here you have the significance of the Indian name for that country—Lost Borders. And you can always trust Indian names to express to you the largest truth about any district in the shortest phrases.

But there is more in the name than that. For law runs with the boundary, not beyond it; it is as fast to the given landmarks as a limpet to its scar on the rock. I am convinced most men make law for the comfortable feel of it, defining them to themselves; they shoulder along like blindworms, rearing against restrictions, turning thereward for security as climbing plants to the warmth of a nearing wall. They pinch themselves with regulations to make sure of being sentient, and organize within organizations.

Out there, then, where the law and the landmarks fail together, the souls of little men fade out at the edges, leak from them as water from wooden pails warped asunder.

Out there where the borders of conscience break down, where there is no convention, and behavior is of little account except as it gets you your desire, almost anything might happen; does happen, in fact, though I shall have trouble making you believe it. Out there where the boundary of soul and sense is as faint as a trail in a sand-storm, I have seen things happen that I do not believe myself. That is what you are to expect in a country where the names mean something. Ubehebe, Pharanagat, Resting Springs, Dead Man's Gulch, Funeral Mountains—these beckon and allure. There is always a tang of reality about them like the smart of wood smoke to the eyes, that warns of neighboring fires.

Riding through by the known trails, the senses are obsessed by the coil of a huge and senseless monotony; straight, white, blinding alkali flats, forsaken mesas; skimpy shrubs growing little and less, starved knees of hills sticking out above them; black clots of pines high upon rubbishy mountain-heads—days and days of this, as if Nature herself had obscured the medium to escape you in her secret operations.

One might travel weeks on end and not come on any place or occasion whereby men may live, and drop suddenly into close hives of them digging, jostling, drinking, lusting, and rejoicing. Every story of that country is colored by the fashion of the life there, breaking up in swift, passionate intervals between long, dun stretches, like the land that out of hot sinks of desolation heaves up great bulks of granite ranges with opal shadows playing in their shining, snow-piled curves. Out there beyond the borders are the Shivering Dunes, heaps upon heaps of blinding sand all acrawl in the wind, drifting and reforming with a faint, stridulent rustle, and black, wall-sided box cañons that give the stars at midday, scored over with picture-writings of a forgotten race. There are lakes there of a pellucid clearness like ice, closed over with man-deep crystals of pure salt. Long Tom Bassit told me a story of one of these which he had from a man who saw it. It was of an emigrant train all out of its reckoning, laboring in a long, hollow trough of desolation between waterless high ranges, arriving at such a closed salt-pit, too much spent to go around it and trusting the salt crust to hold under their racked wagons and starveling teams. But when they had come near the middle of the lake, the salt thinned out abruptly, and, the forward rank of the party breaking through, the bodies were caught under the saline slabs and not all of them recovered. There was a woman among them, and the Man-who-saw had cared—cared enough to go back years afterward, when, after successive oven-blast summers, the salt held solidly over all the lake, and he told Tom Bassit how, long before he reached the point, he saw the gleam of red in the woman's dress, and found her at last, lying on her side, sealed in the crystal, rising as ice rises to the surface of choked streams. Long Tom wished me to make a story of it. I did once at a dinner, but I never got through with it. There, about the time the candles began to burn their shades and the red track of the light on the wine-glasses barred the cloth, with the white, disdainful shoulders and politely incredulous faces leaning through the smoke of cigarettes, it had a garish sound. Afterward I came across the proof of the affair in the records of the emigrant party, but I never tried telling it again.

That is why in all that follows I have set down what the Borderers thought and felt; for that you have a touchstone in your *own* heart, but I should get no credit with you if I were to tell what really became of Loring, and what happened to the man who went down into the moaning pit of Sand Mountain.

Curiously, in that country, you can get anybody to believe any sort of a tale that has gold in it, like the Lost Mine of Fisherman's Peak and the Duke o' Wild Rose. Young Woodin brought me a potsherd once from a kitchen-midden in Shoshone land. It might have been, for antiquity, one of those Job scraped himself withal, but it was dotted all over with colors and specks of pure gold from the riverbed from which the sand and clay were scooped. Said he:

"You ought to find a story about this somewhere."

I was sore then about not getting myself believed in some elementary matters, such as that horned toads are not poisonous, and that Indians really have the bowels of compassion. Said I:

"I will do better than that, I will *make* a story."

We sat out a whole afternoon under the mulberry-tree, with the landscape disappearing in shimmering heat-waves around us, testing our story for likelihood and proving it. There was an Indian woman in the tale, not pretty, for they are mostly not that in life, and the earthenware pot, of course, and a lost river bedded with precious sand. Afterward my friend went to hold down some claims in the Coso country, and I north to the lake region where the red firs are, and we told the pot-of-gold story as often as we were permitted. One night when I had done with it, a stranger by our camp-fire said the thing was well known in his country. I said, "Where was that?"

"Coso," said he, and that was the first I had heard of my friend.

Next winter, at Lone Pine, a prospector from Panamint-way wanted to know if I had ever heard of the Indian-pot Mine which was lost out toward Pharump. I said I had a piece of the pot, which I showed him. Then I wrote the tale for a magazine of the sort that gets taken in camps and at miners' boarding-houses, and several men were at great pains to explain to me where my version varied from the accepted one of the hills. By this time, you understand, I had begun to believe the story myself. I had a spasm of conscience, though, when Tennessee told me that he thought he knew the very squaw of the story, and when the back of the winter was broken he meant to make a little "pasear" in search of the lost river. But Tennessee died before spring, and spared my confessing. Now it only needs that some one should find another sherd of the gold-besprinkled pot to fix the tale in the body of desert myths. Well—it had as much fact behind it as the Gunsight, and is more interesting than the Bryfogle, which began with the finding of a dead man, clothless as the desert dead mostly are, with a bag of nuggets clutched in his mummied hands.

First and last, accept no man's statement that he knows this Country of Lost Borders well. A great number having lost their lives in the process of proving where it is not safe to go, it is now possible to pass through much of the district by guide-posts and well-known water-holes, but the best part of it remains locked, inviolate, or at best known only to some far-straying Indian, sheepherder, or pocket hunter, whose account of it does not get into the reports of the Geological Survey. But a boast of knowledge is likely to prove as hollow as the little yellow gourds called apples of Death Valley.

Pure desertness clings along the pits of the long valleys and the formless beds of vanished lakes. Every hill that lifts as high as the cloud-line has some trees upon it, and deer and bighorn to feed on the tall, tufted, bunch grass between the boulders. In the year when Tonopah, turning upon itself like a swarm, trickled prospectors all over that country from Hot Creek to the Armagosa, Indians brought me word that the men had camped so close about the water-holes that the bighorn died of thirst on the head-lands, turned always in the last agony toward the man-infested springs.

That is as good a pointer as any if you go waterless in the Country of Lost Borders: where you find cattle dropped, skeleton or skin dried, the heads almost invariably will be turned toward the places where water-holes should be. But no such reminders will fend men from its trails. This is chiefly, I am persuaded, because there is something incomprehensible to the man-mind in the concurrence of death and beauty. Shall the tender opal mist betray you? the airy depth of mountain blueness, the blazonry of painted wind-scoured buttes, the far peaks molten with the alpen glow, cooled by the rising of the velvet violet twilight tide, and the leagues and leagues of stars? As easy for a man to believe that a beautiful woman can be cruel. Mind you, it is men who go mostly into the desert, who love it past all reasonableness, slack their ambitions, cast off old usages, neglect their families because of the pulse and beat of a life laid bare to its thews and sinews. Their women hate with implicitness the life like the land, stretch-ing interminably whity-brown, dim and shadowy blue hills that hem it, glimmering pale waters of mirage that creep and crawl about its edges. There was a woman once at Agua Hedionda—but you wouldn't believe that either.

If the desert were a woman, I know well what she would be like: deep-breasted, broad in the hips, tawny, with tawny hair, great masses of it lying smooth along her perfect curves, full lipped like a sphinx, but not heavy-lidded like one, eyes sane and steady as the polished jewel of her skies, such a countenance as should make men serve without desiring her, such a largeness to her mind as should make their sins of no account, passionate, but not necessitous, patient—and you could not move her, no, not if you had all the earth to give, so much as one tawny hair's-breadth beyond her own desires. If you cut very deeply into any soul that has the mark of the land upon it, you find such qualities as these—as I shall presently prove to you.

❖ ❖ ❖

A Case of Conscience

When Austin submitted Lost Borders, *her publishers asked her to emphasize the thematic coherence of the collection by writing brief transitions between stories. Although annoyed, she complied, and sometimes in the introductory material the narrator does provide one of her trails into the story. The lead to "A Case of Conscience" suggests that "conscience, in so far as it is a hereditary prejudice in favor of a given line of behavior, is no sort of baggage to take into the wilderness" (25). The definition of "conscience" as "prejudice" prepares the reader for the narrator's ironic view of Saunders's sense of duty.*

Although the story presents some unfortunate stereotypes about "all Indian women," the narrator supports the Indian mother's challenge to the man she considers her husband that the child is "mine,

not yours!" The narrator's reference to the "Anglo-Saxon prejudice that makes a man responsible for his offspring" is an ironic one. Saunders is one of many irresponsible men in Lost Borders *who "formed relations such as this and left them off with the land, as they left off the clothes they wore there and its tricks of speech"; native women are commonly the victims of such men, but white women like Mrs. Wills, whose story follows, also find their lives blighted. Yet Austin's irony is two-fold for she believed, like Turwhasé, that mothers were responsible for their children, that only prejudice gave a man, in marriage, possession of his wife and children. Later, she would explore the theme even more ironically in one of her most famous stories, "Papago Wedding."*

Saunders was an average Englishman with a lung complaint. He tried Ashfork, Arizona, and Indio, and Catalina. Then he drifted north through the San Jacinta mountains and found what he was looking for. Back in England he had left so many of the things a man wishes to go on with, that he bent himself with great seriousness to his cure. He bought a couple of pack-burros, a pair of cayaques, and a camp kit. With these, a Shakespeare, a prayer-book, and a copy of *Ingoldsby Legends,* he set out on foot to explore the coast of Lost Borders. The prayer-book he had from his mother; I believe he read it regularly night and morning, and the copy of *Ingoldsby Legends* he gave me in the second year of his exile. It happened about that time I was wanting the *Ingoldsby Legends,* three hundred miles from a library, and book money hard to come by. Now there is nearly always a copy of *Ingoldsby Legends* in the vicinity of an Englishman. Englishmen think them amusing, though I do not know why. So I asked my friend, the barkeeper at the Last Chance, to inquire for it of the next Englishman who hit the town. I had to write the name out plainly so the barkeeper could remember it. The first who came was an agent for a London mining syndicate, and he left an address of a book-shop where it could be bought. The next was a remittance man, and of course he hadn't anything. If he had he would have put it in soak. That means he would have put the book up for its value in bad drink, and I write it as a part of our legitimate speech, because it says so exactly what had occurred: that particular Englishman had put everything, including his honor and his immortal soul, in soak. And the third was Saunders. He was so delighted to find an appreciator of the *Ingoldsby Legends* in the wilderness, that he offered to come to the house and render the obscure passages, and that was the beginning of my knowing about what went on later at Ubehebe.

Saunders had drifted about from water-hole to water-hole, living hardily, breathing the driest, cleanest air, sleeping and waking with the ebb and flow of light that sets in a mighty current around the world. He went up in summer to the mountain-heads under the foxtail pines, and back in winter to watch the wild almond bloom by Resting Springs. He saw the Medicine dance of the Shoshones, and hunted the bighorn on Funeral Mountains, and dropped a great many things out of his life without making himself unhappy. But he kept the conscience he had brought with him. Of course it was a man's conscience that allowed him to do a great many things that by the code and the commandments are as wrong as any others, but in the end the wilderness was too big for him, and forced him to a violation of what he called his sense of duty.

In the course of time, Saunders came to a range of purplish hills lying west from Lost Valley, because of its rounded, swelling, fair twin peaks called Ubehebe (Maiden's Breast). It is a good name. Saunders came there in the spring, when the land is lovely and alluring, soft with promise and austerely virgin. He lingered in and about its pleasant places until the month of the Deer-Star, and it was then, when he would come up a week's journey to Lone Pine, for supplies, he began to tell me about Turwhasé, the gray-eyed Shoshone. He thought I would be interested, and I was, though for more reasons than Saunders at first supposed. There is a story current and confirmed, I believe, by proper evidence, that a man of one of the emigrant trains that suffered so much, and went so far astray in the hell trap of Death Valley, wandering from his party in search of water, for want of which he was partly crazed, returned to them no more and was accounted dead. But wandering in the witless condition of great thirst, he was found by the Shoshones, and by them carried to their campody in the secret places of the hills. There, though he never rightly knew himself, he showed some skill and excellences of the white men, and for that, and for his loose wit, which was fearful to them, he was kept and reverenced as a Coyote-man and a Medicine-maker of strange and fitful powers. And at the end of fifteen years his friends found him and took him away. As witness of his sojourning, there is now and then born to the descendants of that campody a Shoshone with gray eyes.

When Saunders began to tell me about Turwhasé, I knew to what it must come, though it was not until his mother wrote me that I could take any notice of it. Some too solicitous person had written her that Saunders had become a squaw-man. She thought he had married Turwhasé, and would bring home a handful of little half-breeds to inherit the estate.

She never knew how near Saunders came to doing that very thing, nor to say truth did I when I wrote her that her son was not married, and that she had nothing to fear; but with the letter I was able to get out of Saunders as much as I did not already know of the story.

I suppose at bottom the things a man loves a woman for are pretty much the same, though it is only when he talks to you of a woman not of his own class that he is willing to tell you what those things are. Saunders loved Turwhasé: first, because he was lonely and had to love somebody; then because of the way the oval of her cheek melted into the chin, and for the lovely line that runs from the waist to the knee, and for her soft, bubbling laughter; and kept on loving her because she made him comfortable.

I suppose the white strain that persisted in her quickened her aptitude for white ways. Saunders taught her to cook. She was never weary nor afraid. She was never out of temper, except when she was jealous, and that was rather amusing. Saunders told me himself how she glowed and blossomed under his caress, and wept when he neglected her. He told me everything I had the courage to know. When a man has gone about the big wilderness with slow death and sure camping on his trail, there is not much worth talking about except the things that are. Turwhasé had the art to provoke tenderness and the wish to protect, and the primitive woman's capacity for making no demands upon it. And this, in fine, is how these women take our men from us, and why, at the last, they lose them.

If you ask whether we discussed the ethics of Saunders' situation—at first there didn't appear to be any. Turwhasé was as much married as if Church and State had witnessed it; as for Saunders, society, life itself, had cast him off. He was unfit for work or marrying; being right-minded in regard to his lung complaint, he drank from no man's cup nor slept in any bed but his own. And if society had no use for him, how had it a right to say what he should do out there in the bloomy violet spaces at Maiden's Breast? Yet, at the last, the Englishman found, or thought he found, a moral issue.

Maiden's Breast—virgin land, clear sun, unsullied airs, Turwhasé. Isn't there a hint all through of the myth of the renewal of life in a virgin embrace? A great many myths come true in the big wilderness. Saunders went down to Los Angeles once in the year to a consulting physician to please his mother, not because he hoped for anything. He came back from one such journey looking like a sleepwalker newly awakened. He had been told that the diseased portion of his lung was all sloughed away, and if nothing happened to him in six months more of Ubehebe, he might go home! It was then Saunders' conscience began to trouble him, for by this time, you understand, Turwhasé had a child—a daughter, small and gold-colored and gray-eyed. By a trick of inheritance the eyes were like Saunders' mother's, and in the long idle summer she had become a plaything of which he was extremely fond. The mother, of course, was hopeless. She had never left off her blanket, and like all Indian women when they mature, had begun to grow fat. Oh, I *said* he had a man's conscience! Turwhasé must be left behind, but what to do about the daughter lay heavily on Saunders' mind.

It made an obstinate ripple in his complacency like a snag in the current of his thought, which set toward England. Out there by the water-holes, where he had expected to leave his bones, life had been of a simplicity that did not concern itself beyond the happy day. Now the old needs and desires awoke and cried in him, and along with them the old, obstinate Anglo-Saxon prejudice that makes a man responsible for his offspring. Saunders must have had a bad time of it with himself before he came to a decision that he must take the child to England. It would be hard on Turwhasé; if it came to that, it would be hard on him—there would be explanations. As matters stood he looked to make a very good marriage at home, and the half-breed child would be against him. All his life she would be against him. But then it was a question of duty. Duty is a potent fetish of Englishmen, but the wilderness has a word bigger than that. Just how

Turwhasé took his decision about the child I never heard, but as I know Indian women, I suppose she must have taken it quietly at first, said no, and considered it done with; then, as she saw his purpose clear, sat wordless in her blanket, all its folds drawn forward as a sign of sullenness, her thick hair falling on either side to screen her grief; neither moved to attend him, nor ate nor slept; and at last broke under it and seemed to accept, put the child from her as though it was already not hers, and made no more of it.

If there was in this acquiescence a gleam in her gray eye that witnessed she had found the word, Saunders was not aware of it.

As to what he felt himself in regard to Turwhasé I am equally uninformed. I've a notion, though, that men do not give themselves time to feel in such instances; they just get it over with. All I was told was, that when at last he felt himself strong for it, Saunders put the child before him on the horse—she was then about two years old—and set out from Ubehebe. He went all of one day down a long box cañon, where at times his knees scraped the walls on either side, and over the tortuous roots of the mountain blown bare of the sand. The evening of the next day saw the contour of the Maiden's Breast purpling in the east, fading at last in the blurred horizon. He rode all day on glittering pale sands and down steep and utterly barren barrancas. All through that riding something pricked between his shoulders, troubled his sleep with expectancy, haunted him with a suggestion of impossible espionage. The child babbled at first, or slept in his arm; he hugged it to him and forgot that its mother was a Shoshone. It cried in the night and began to refuse its food. Great tears of fatigue stood upon its cheeks; it shook with long, quivering sobs, crying silently as Indian children do when they are frightened. Saunders' arm ached with the weight of it; his heart with the perplexity. The little face looked up at him, hard with inscrutable savagery. When he came to the Inyo range and the beaten trail, he distrusted his judgment; his notion of rearing the child in England began to look ridiculous. By the time he had cleared the crest and saw the fields and orchards far below him, it appeared preposterous. And the hint of following hung like some pestiferous insect about his trail.

In all the wide, uninterrupted glare no speck as of a moving body swam within his gaze. By what locked and secret ways the presence kept pace with him, only the vultures hung high under the flaring heaven could have known.

At the hotel at Keeler that night he began to taste the bitterness he had chosen. Men, white men, mining men, mill superintendents, well-dressed, competent, looked at the brat which had Shoshone written plainly all over it, and looked away unsmiling; being gentlemen, they did not so much as look at one another. Saunders gave money to the women at the hotel to keep his daughter all night out of his sight. Riding next day toward Lone Pine between the fenced lands, farms and farmhouses, schools, a church, he began to understand that there was something more than mere irresponsibility in the way of desert-faring men who formed relations such as this and left them off with the land, as they left the clothes they wore there and its tricks of speech.

He was now four days from Ubehebe. The child slept little that night; sat up in bed, listened; would whisper its mother's name over and over, questioning, expectant; left off, still as a young quail, if Saunders moved or noticed it. It occurred to him that the child might die, which would be the best thing for it.

Coming out of his room in the early morning he stumbled over something soft in a blanket. It unrolled of itself and stood up—Turwhasé! The child gave a little leap in his arms and was still, pitifully, breathlessly still. The woman stretched out her own arms, her eyes were red and devouring.

"My baby!" she said. "Give it to me!" Without a word Saunders held it out to her. The little dark arms went around her neck, prehensile and clinging; the whole little body clung, the lines of the small face softened with a sigh of unutterable content. Turwhasé drew up her blanket and held it close.

"Mine!" she said, fiercely. "Mine, not yours!"

Saunders did not gainsay her; he drew out all the money he had and poured it in her bosom. Turwhasé laughed. With a flirt of her blanket she scattered the coins on the ground; she turned with dignity and began to walk desertward. You could see by the slope of the shoulders under the blanket and the swing of her hips, as she went, that she was all Indian.

Saunders reached down to me from the platform of the train that morning for a last good-bye. He was looking very English, smug and freshly shaven.

"I am convinced," he said, "that it really wouldn't have done, you know." I believe he thought he had come to that conclusion by himself.

The Return of Mr. Wills

Austin admired and was close friends with many male writers. Though she praised writers like Sinclair Lewis and H. G. Wells for "thinking of woman in terms of her worth to society as against her individual value in terms of her emotional relation to one man," she often challenged men (and women) to create richer women characters (Earth Horizon, 98). When she met William Dean Howells in New York, she "asked him about the women in his books; how it happened that they were shallow and slight, that they did not bite down on life," and was dissatisfied with his answer that "'one has to write what one knows'" (Earth Horizon, 330). And she felt that her friend George Sterling's "chief incapacity" as a poet was his "failure of ability as a man to enter participatingly into the psychic life of women" (Earth Horizon, 321).

Believing that men and women look at the world differently, Austin never objected to the male point of view but only to its presumed universality; she sought throughout her career to balance it with the female viewpoint. This she did effectively in "The Return of Mr. Wills," a story that retells that classic American tale of the opposing values of the sexes, "Rip Van Winkle," by presenting it from the female point of view.

Mrs. Wills had lived seventeen years with Mr. Wills, and when he left her for three, those three were so much the best of her married life that she wished he had never come back. And the only real trouble with Mr. Wills was that he should never have moved West. Back East I suppose they breed such men because they need them, but they ought really to keep them there.

I am quite certain that when Mr. Wills was courting Mrs. Wills he parted his hair in the middle, and the breast-pocket of his best suit had a bright silk lining which Mr. Wills pulled up to simulate a silk handkerchief. Mrs. Wills had a certain draggled prettiness, and a way of tossing her head which came back to her after Mr. Wills left, which made you think she might have been the prettiest girl of her town. They were happy enough at first, when Mr. Wills was a grocery clerk, assistant Sunday-school superintendent, and they owned a cabinet organ and four little Willses. It might have been that Mr. Wills thought he could go right on being the same sort of a man in the West—he was clerk at the Bed Rock Emporium, and had brought the organ and the children; or it might have been at bottom he thought himself a very different sort of man, and meant to be it if he got a chance.

There is a sort of man bred up in close communities, like a cask, to whom the church, public opinion, the social note, are a sort of hoop to hold him in serviceable shape. Without these there are a good many ways of going to pieces. Mr. Wills' way was Lost Mines.

Being clerk at the Emporium, where miners and prospectors bought their supplies, he heard a lot of talk about mines, and was too new to it to understand that the man who has the most time to stop and talk about it has the least to do with mining. And of all he heard, the most fascinating to Mr. Wills, who was troubled with an imagination, was of the lost mines: incredibly rich ledges, touched and not found again. To go out into the unmapped hills on the mere chance of coming across something was, on the face of it, a risky business; but to look for a mine once located, sampled and proved, definitely situated in a particular mountain range or a certain cañon, had a smack of plausibility. Besides that, an ordinary prospect might or might not prove workable, but the lost mines were always amazingly rich. Of all the ways in the West for a man to go to pieces this is the most insidious. Out there beyond the towns the long Wilderness lies brooding, imperturbable; she puts out to adventurous minds glittering fragments of fortune or romance, like the lures men use to catch antelopes—clip! then she has them. If Mr. Wills had gambled or drank, his wife could have gone to the minister about it, his friends could have done something. There was a church in Maverick of twenty-seven members, and the Willses had brought letters to it, but except for the effect it had on Mrs. Wills, it would not be worth mentioning. Though he might never have found it out in the East, Mr. Wills belonged to the church, not because of what it meant to himself, but for what it meant to other people. Back East it had meant social standing, repute, moral impeccability. To other people in Maverick it meant a weakness which was excused in you so long as you did not talk about it. Mr. Wills did not, because there was so much else to talk about in connection with lost mines.

He began by grub-staking Pedro Ruiz to look for the Lost Ledge of Fisherman's Peak, and that was not so bad, for it had not been lost more than thirty years, the peak was not a hundred miles from Maverick, and, besides, I have a piece of the ore myself. Then he was bitten by the myth of the Gunsight, of which there was never anything more tangible than a dime's worth of virgin silver, picked up by a Jayhawker, hammered into a sight for a gun; and you had to take the gun on faith at that, for it and the man who owned it had quite disappeared; and afterward it was the Duke o' Wild Rose, which was never a mine at all, merely an arrow-mark on a map left by a penniless lodger found dead in a San Francisco hotel. Grub-staking is expensive, even to a clerk at the Bed Rock Emporium getting discounts on the grub, and grub-staked prospectors are about as depend-able as the dreams they chase, often pure fakes, lying up at seldom-visited waterholes while the stake lasts, returning with wilder tales and clews more alluring. It was a late conviction that led Mr. Wills, when he put the last remnant of his means into the search for the White Cement mines, to resign his clerkship and go in charge of the expedition himself. There is no doubt whatever that there is a deposit of cement on Bald Mountain, with lumps of gold sticking out of it like plums in a pudding. It lies at the bottom of a small gulch near the middle fork of Owens River, and is over-laid by pumice. There is a camp kit buried somewhere near, and two skele-tons. There is also an Indian in that vicinity who is thought to be able to point out the exact location—if he would. It is quite the sort of thing to appeal to the imagination of Mr. Wills, and he spent two years proving that he could not find it. After that he drifted out toward the Lee district to look for Lost Cabin mine, because a man who had immediate need of twenty dollars, had, for that amount, offered Wills some exact and unpub-lished information as to its location. By that time Wills' movements had ceased to interest anybody in Maverick. He could be got to believe any-thing about any sort of a prospect, providing it was lost.

The only visible mark left by all this was on Mrs. Wills. Everybody in a mining-town, except the minister and professional gamblers who wear frockcoats, dresses pretty much alike, and Wills very soon got to wear in his face the guileless, trustful fixity of the confirmed prospector. It seemed as if the desert had overshot him and struck at Mrs. Wills, and Richard Wills, Esther Wills, Benjy Wills, and the youngest Wills, who was called Mugsey. Desertness attacked the door-yard and the house; even the cabi-net organ had a weathered look. During the time of the White Cement obsession the Wills family appeared to be in need of a grub-stake them-selves. Mrs. Wills' eyes were like the eyes of trail-weary cattle; her hands grew to have that pitiful way of catching the front of her dress of the woman not so much a slattern as hopeless. It was when her husband went out after Lost Cabin she fell into the habit of sitting down to a cheap novel with the dishes unwashed, a sort of drugging of despair common among women of the camps. All this time Mr. Wills was drifting about from camp to camp of the desert borders, working when it could not be avoided, but mostly on long, fruitless trudges among the unmindful ranges. I do not know if the man was honest with himself; if he knew by this time that the clew of a lost mine was the baldest of excuses merely to be out and away from everything that savored of definiteness and responsibility. The fact was, the desert had got him. All the hoops were off the cask. The mind of Mr. Wills faded out at the edges like the desert horizon that melts in mists and mirages, and finally he went on an expedition from which he did not come back.

He had been gone nearly a year when Mrs. Wills gave up expecting him. She had grown so used to the bedraggled crawl of life that she might never have taken any notice of the disappearance of Mr. Wills had not the Emporium refused to make any more charges in his name. There had been a great many dry water-holes on the desert that year, and more than the usual complement of sun-dried corpses. In a general way this accounted for Mr. Wills, though nothing transpired of sufficient definiteness to justify Mrs. Wills in putting on a widow's dress, and, anyway, she could not have afforded it.

Mrs. Wills and the children went to work, and work was about the only thing in Maverick of which there was more than enough. It was a matter of a very few months when Mrs. Wills made the remarkable discovery that after the family bills were paid at the end of the month, there was a little over. A very little. Mrs. Wills had lived so long with the tradition that a husband is a natural provider that it took some months longer to realize that she not only did not need Mr. Wills, but got on better without him. This was about the time she was able to have the sitting-room repapered and put up lace curtains. And the next spring the children planted roses in the front yard. All up and down the wash of Salt Creek there were lean coyote mothers, and wild folk of every sort could have taught her that nature never makes the mistake of neglecting to make the child-bearer competent to provide. But Mrs. Wills had not been studying life in the lairs. She had most of her notions of it from the church and her parents, and all under the new sense of independence and power she had an ache of forlornness and neglect. As a matter of fact she filled out, grew stronger, had a spring in her walk. She was not pining for Mr. Wills; the desert had him—for whatever conceivable use, it was more than Mrs. Wills could put him to—let the desert keep what it had got.

It was in the third summer that she regained a certain air that made me think she must have been pretty when Mr. Wills married her. And no woman in a mining-town can so much as hint at prettiness without its being found out. Mrs. Wills had a good many prejudices left over from the time when Mr. Wills had been superintendent of the Sunday-school, and would not hear of divorce. Yet, as the slovenliness of despair fell away from her, as she held up her head and began to have company to tea, it is certain somebody would have broached it to her before the summer was over; but by that time Mr. Wills had come back.

It happened that Benjy Wills, who was fourteen and driving the Bed Rock delivery wagon, had a runaway accident in which he had behaved very handsomely and gotten a fractured skull. News of it went by way of the local paper to Tonopah, and from there drifted south to the Funeral Mountains and the particular prospect that Mr. Wills was working on a grub-stake. He had come to that. Perhaps as much because he had found there was nothing to it, as from paternal anxiety, he came home the evening of the day the doctor had declared the boy out of danger.

It was my turn to sit up that night, I remember, and Mrs. Meyer, who had the turn before, was telling me about the medicines. There was a neighbor woman who had come in by the back door with a bowl of custard, and the doctor standing in the sitting-room with Mrs. Wills, when Mr. Wills came in through the black block of the doorway with his hand before his face to ward off the light—and perhaps some shamefacedness— who knows?

I saw Mrs. Wills quiver, and her hand went up to her bosom as if some one had struck her. I have seen horses start and check like that as they came over the Pass and the hot blast of the desert took them fairly. It was the stroke of desolation. I remember turning quickly at the doctor's curt signal to shut the door between the sitting-room and Benjy.

"Don't let the boy see you to-night, Wills," said the doctor, with no hint of a greeting; "he's not to be excited." With that he got himself off as quickly as possible, and the neighbor woman and I went out and sat on the back steps a long time, and tried to talk about everything but Mr. Wills. When I went in, at last, he was sitting in the Morris chair, which had come with soap-wrappers, explaining to Mrs. Meyer about the rich prospect he had left to come to his darling boy. But he did not get so much as a glimpse of his darling boy while I was in charge.

Mr. Wills settled on his family like a blight. For a man who has prospected lost mines to that extent is positively not good for anything else. It was not only as if the desert had sucked the life out of him and cast him back, but as if it would have Mrs. Wills in his room. As the weeks went on you could see a sort of dinginess creeping up from her dress to her hair and her face, and it spread to the house and the doorway. Mr. Wills had enjoyed the improved condition of his home, though he missed the point of it; his wife's cooking tasted good to him after miner's fare, and he was proud of his boys. He didn't want any more of the desert. Not he. "There's no place like home," said Mr. Wills, or something to that effect.

But he had brought the desert with him on his back. If it had been at any other time than when her mind was torn with anxiety for Benjy, Mrs. Wills might have made a fight against it. But the only practical way to separate the family from the blight was to divorce Mr. Wills, and the church to which Mrs. Wills belonged admitted divorce only in the event of there being another woman.

Mrs. Wills rose to the pitch of threatening, I believe, about the time Mr. Wills insisted on his right to control the earnings of his sons. But the minister called; the church put out its hand upon her poor, staggered soul that sunk aback. The minister himself was newly from the East, and did not understand that the desert is to be dealt with as a woman and a wanton; he was thinking of it as a place on the map. Therefore, he was not of the slightest use to Mrs. Wills, which did not prevent him from commanding her behavior. And the power of the wilderness lay like a wasting sickness on the home.

About that time Mrs. Wills took to novel-reading again; the eldest son drifted off up Tonopah way; and Benjy began to keep back a part of the wages he brought home. And Mr. Wills is beginning to collect misinformation about the exact locality where Peg-leg Smith is supposed to have found the sunburnt nuggets. He does not mention the matter often, being, as he says, done with mines; but whenever the Peg-leg comes up in talk, I can see Mrs. Wills chirk up a little, her gaze wandering to the inscrutable grim spaces, not with the hate you might suppose, but with something like hope in her eye, as if she had guessed what I am certain of—that in time its insatiable spirit will reach out and take Mr. Wills again.

And this time, if I know Mrs. Wills, he will not come back.

❖ ❖ ❖

The Woman at the Eighteen-Mile

The subject of "The Woman at the Eighteen-Mile" is a story the narrator is tracking, "the biggest story of the desert ever" and one sure to make her reputation. Like so many desert stories, this one is about men and male territory, but its main characters and details remain elusive and vague, for it is not the story the narrator tells. She meets a woman who "had no more pertinence to the plot than most women have to desert affairs," a woman who takes over her story.

In "The Woman at the Eighteen-Mile," Austin develops her repeating theme about how two women come to understand and empathize with each other through sharing stories: the narrator, understanding how important a story can be to a woman, keeps her promise not to tell the woman's story. But the story has a deeper message to offer. Austin suggests how within the male western story—with "a mine in it, a murder and a mystery, great sacrifice, Shoshones, . . . and the magnetic will of a man . . . lonely water-holes, deserted camps where coyotes hunted"—there is a hidden story about a woman, a woman "with the mark of the desert." Her story may not be the one that sells, that makes a reputation; in fact, it often remains untold, this story of "that which the world knows so little what to do with that it mostly throws away—a good woman with great power and possibilities of passion."

I had long wished to write a story of Death Valley that should be its final word. It was to be so chosen from the limited sort of incidents that could occur there, so charged with the still ferocity of its moods that I should at length be quit of its obsession, free to concern myself about other affairs. And from the moment of hearing of the finding of Lang's body at Dead Man's Spring I knew I had struck upon the trail of that story.

It was a teamster who told it, stopping over the night at McGee's, a big, slow man, face and features all of a bluntness, as if he had been dropped before the clay was set. He had a big, blunt voice through which his words rolled, dulled along the edges. The same accident that had flattened the outlines of his nose and chin must have happened to his mind, for he was never able to deliver more than the middle of an idea, without any definiteness as to where it began or ended and what it stood next to. He called the dead man Long, and failed to remember who was supposed to have killed him, and what about.

We had fallen a-talking round the fire of Convict Lake, and the teamster had handed up the incident of Dead Man's Spring as the only thing in his experience that matched with the rooted horror of its name. He had been of the party that recovered the body, and what had stayed with him was the sheer torment of the journey across Death Valley, the aching heat, the steady, sickening glare, the uncertainty as to whether there was a body in the obliterated grave, whether it was Lang's body, and whether they would be able to prove it; and then the exhuming of the dead, like the one real incident in a fever dream. He was very sure of the body, done up in an Indian blanket striped red and black, with a rope around it like a handle, convenient for carrying. But he had forgotten what set the incident in motion, or what became of Lang after that, if it really were Lang in the blanket.

Then I heard of the story again between Red Rock and Coyote Holes, about moon-set, when the stage labored up the long gorge, waking to hear the voices of the passengers run on steadily with the girding of the sand and the rattle of harness-chains, run on and break and eddy around Dead Man's Springs, and back up in turgid pools of comment and speculation, falling in shallows of miner's talk, lost at last in a waste of ledges and contracts and forgotten strikes. Waking and falling asleep again, the story shaped itself of the largeness of the night; and then the two men got down at Coyote Holes an hour before dawn, and I knew no more of them, neither face nor name. But what I had heard of the story confirmed it exactly, the story I had so long sought.

Those who have not lived in a mining country cannot understand how it is possible for whole communities to be so disrupted by the failure of a lode or a fall in the price of silver, that I could live seven years within a day's journey of Dead Man's Spring and not come upon anybody who could give me the whole of that story. I went about asking for it, and got sticks and straws. There was a man who had kept bar in Tio Juan at the time, and had been the first to notice Whitmark's dealing with the Shoshone who was supposed to have stolen the body after it was dug up. There was a Mexican who had been the last to see Lang alive and might have told somewhat, but death got him before I did. Once, at a great dinner in San Francisco, a large, positive man with a square forehead and a face below it that somehow implied he had shaped it so butting his way through life, across the table two places down, caught at some word of mine, leaning forward above the bank of carnations that divided the cloth.

"Queer thing happened up in that country to a friend of mine, Whitmark—" But the toast-master cut *him* off. All this time the story glimmered like a summer island in a mist, through every man's talk about it, grew and allured, caressing the soul. It had warmth and amplitude, like a thing palpable to be stroked. There was a mine in it, a murder and a mystery, great sacrifice, Shoshones, dark and incredibly discreet, and the magnetic will of a man making manifest through all these; there were lonely water-holes, deserted camps where coyotes hunted in the streets, fatigues and dreams and voices of the night. And at the last it appeared there was a woman in it.

Curiously, long before I learned of her connection with the story, I had known and liked her for a certain effect she had of being warmed and nourished from within. There was about her a spark, a nuance that men mistook—never more than once, as the stage-driver told me confidently— a vitality that had nothing, absolutely nothing, but the blank occasionless life of the desert to sustain it. She was one of the very few people I had known able to keep a soul alive and glowing in the wilderness, and I was to find out that she kept it so against the heart of my story. Mine! I called it so by that time; but hers was the right, though she had no more pertinence to the plot than most women have to desert affairs.

She was the Woman of the Eighteen-Mile House. She had the desert mark upon her—lean figure, wasted bosom, the sharp, upright furrow between the eyes, the burned, tawny skin, with the pallid streak of the dropped eyelids, and of course I suppose she knew her husband from among the lean, sidling, vacuous-looking Borderers; but I couldn't have identified him, so like he was to the other feckless men whom the desert sucks dry and keeps dangling like gourds on a string. Twenty-five years they had drifted from up Bodie way, around Panamint, toward Mojave, worse housed and fed than they might have been in the ploughed lands, and without having hit upon the fortune which is primarily the object of every desert adventure. And when people have been as long as that among the Lost Borders there is not the slightest possibility of their coming to anything else. And still the Woman's soul was palpitant and enkindled. At the last, Mayer—that was the husband's name—had settled at the Eighteen-Mile House to care for the stage relays, and I had met the Woman, halting there with the stage or camping nights on some slower passage.

At the time I learned of her connection with the Whitmark affair, the story still wanted some items of motive and understanding, a knowledge of the man himself, some account of his three months' *pasear* into the hills beyond Mesquite, which certainly had to do with the affair of the mine, but of which he would never be persuaded to speak. And I made perfectly sure of getting the rest of it from the Woman at the Eighteen-Mile.

It was full nine o'clock before the Woman's household was all settled and she had come out upon the stoop of the Eighteen-Mile House to talk, the moon coming up out of Shoshone land, all the hollow of the desert falling away before us, filled with the glitter of that surpassing wonder, the moon-mirage. Never mind what went before to draw her to the point of talking; it could have come about as simply as my saying, "I mean to print this story as I find it," and she would have had to talk to save it. Consider how still it was. Off to the right the figures of my men under their blankets stretched along the ground. Not a leaf to rustle, not a bough to creak. No grass to whisper in the wind, only stiff, scant shrubs and the sandy hills like shoals at the bottom of a lake of light. I could see the Woman's profile, thin and fine against the moon, and when she put up her hand to drag down the thick, careless coil of her hair, I guessed we were close upon the heart of the story. And for her the heart of the story was the man, Whitmark.

She had been, at the time he came into the country seventeen years before, that which the world knows so little what to do with that it mostly throws away—a good woman with great power and possibilities of passion. Whitmark stood for the best she had known, I should have said from all I learned, just a clean-minded, acute, tolerably cultivated American business man with an obsession for accomplishing results.

He had been sent out to look after a mine to which the title was not clear, and there were counter-machinations to take it away from him. This much may be told without breach, for, as it turned out, I was not to write that story, after all; at least, not in the lifetime of the Woman at the Eighteen-Mile. And the crux of the story to her was one little, so little, moment, that owing to Whitmark's having been taken with pneumonia within a week afterward, was rendered fixed beyond change or tarnish of time.

When all this was going forward the Mayers kept a miner's boarding-house at Tio Juan, where Whitmark was in and out; and the Woman, who from the first had been attracted by the certain stamp of competency and power, began to help him with warnings, intimations of character and local prejudice, afterward with information which got him the reputation of almost supernatural penetration.

There were reasons why, during his darkest time, Whitmark could find nobody but the Indians and the Woman to trust. Well, he had been wise enough to trust her, and it was plain to see from her account of it that this was the one occasion in life when her soul had stretched itself, observed, judged, wrought, and felt to the full of its power.

She loved him; yes, perhaps—I do not know—if you call love that soul service of a good woman to a man she may not touch. Whitmark had children back East, and a wife whom he had married for all the traditions of niceness and denial and abnegation which men demand of the women they expect to marry, and find savorless so often when they are married to it. He had never known what it meant to have a woman concerned in his work, running neck and neck with it, divining his need, supplementing it not with the merely feminine trick of making him more complacent with himself, but with vital remedies and aids. And once he had struck the note of the West, he kindled to the event and enlarged his spirit. The two must have had great moments at the heart of that tremendous coil of circumstance. All this the Woman conveyed to me by the simplest telling of the story as it happened: "I said . . . and he did . . . the Indian went . . ."

I sat within the shallow shadow of the eaves experiencing the full-throated satisfaction of old prospectors over the feel of pay dirt, rubbing it between the thumb and palm, swearing over it softly below the breath. It was as good as that. And I was never to have it! For one thing the Woman made plain to me in the telling was the guilt of Whitmark. Though there was no evidence by which the court could hold him, though she did not believe it, though the fulness of her conviction intrigued me into believing that it did not matter so much what he was—the only way to write that story successfully was to fix forever against Whitmark's name its damning circumstance. The affair had been a good deal noised about at the time, and through whatever illusion of altered name and detail, was bound to be recognized and made much of in the newspapers. The Woman of the Eighteen-Mile saw that. Suddenly she broke off the telling to show me her poor heart, shrivelling as I knew hearts to warp and shrink in the aching wilderness, this one occasion rendering it serviceable like a hearth-fire in an empty room.

"It was a night like this he went away," said the Woman, stirring to point to the solemn moonlight poured over all the world.

That was after twenty-two months of struggle had left Whitmark in possession of the property. He was on his way then to visit his family, whom he had seen but once in that time, and was to come again to put in operation the mine he had so hardly won. It was, it should have been, an hour ripe with satisfaction.

"He was to take the stage which passed through Bitter Wells at ten that night," said she, "and I rode out with him—he had asked me—from Tio Juan, to bring back the horses. We started at sunset and reached the Wells a quarter of an hour before the time.

"The moon was half high when the sun went down, and I was very happy, because it had all come out so well, and he was to come again in two months. We talked as we rode. I told you he was a cheerful man. All the time when it looked as if he might be tried for his life, the worse it looked the more his spirits rose. He would have laughed if he had heard he was to be hung. But that night there was a trouble upon him. It grew as we rode. His face drew, his breath came sighing. He seemed always on the point of speaking and did not. It was as if he had something to say that must be said, and at the moment of opening his lips it escaped him. In the moonlight I saw his mouth working, and nothing came from it. If I spoke the trouble went out of his face, and when I left off it came again, puzzled wonder and pain. I know now!" said the Woman, shaking forward her thick hair, "that it was a warning, a presentiment. I have heard of such things, and it seems as if I should have felt it too, hovering in the air like that. But I was glad because it had all come out so well and I had had a hand in it. Besides, it was not for me." She turned toward me then for the first time, her hair falling forward to encompass all her face but the eyes, wistful with the desire to have me understand how fine this man was in every worldly point, how far above her, and how honored she was to have been the witness of the intimation of his destiny. I said quickly the thing that was expected of me, which was not the thing I thought, and gave her courage for going on.

"Yet," she said, "I was not entirely out of it, because—because the thing he said at the last, *when* he said it, did not seem the least strange to me, though afterward, of course, when I thought of it, it was the strangest good-bye I had ever heard.

"We had got down and stood between the horses, and the stage was coming in. We heard the sand fret under it, and the moonlight was a cold weight laid upon the world. He took my hand and held it against his breast so—and said— Oh, I am perfectly sure of the words; he said, 'I have *missed* you so.' Just that, not good-bye, and not *shall* miss you, but 'I *have* missed you *so*.'

"Like that," she said, her hands still clasped above her wasted bosom, the quick spirit glowing through it like wine in a turgid glass—"like that," she said. But, no; whatever the phrase implied of the failure of the utterly safe and respectable life to satisfy the inmost hunger of the man, it could never have had in it the pain of her impassioned, lonely years. If it had been the one essential word the desert strives to say it would have been pronounced like that.

"And it was not until the next day," she went on, "it occurred to me that was a strange thing to say to a woman he had seen two or three times a week for nearly two years. But somehow it seemed to me clearer when I heard a week later that he was dead. He had taken cold on the way home, and died after three days. His wife wrote me; it was a very nice letter; she said he told her I had been kind to him. Kind!" She broke off, and far out under the moon rose the thin howl of coyotes running together in the pack. "And that," said the Woman, "is why I made you promise at the beginning that if I told you all I knew about Whitmark and Lang you would not use it."

I jumped. She had done that, and I had promised light-heartedly. People nearly always exact that sort of an assurance in the beginning of confidences, like a woman wanting to be told she is of nobler courage at the moment of committing an indiscretion, a concession to the sacredness of personal experience which always seems so much less once it is delivererd, they can be persuaded to forego the promise of inviolateness. I always promise and afterward persuade. But not the Woman of the Eighteen-Mile. If Whitmark had lived he would have come back and proved his worth, cleared himself by his life and works. As it stood, by the facts against him, he was most utterly given over to ill-repute. The singularity of the incident, the impossibility of its occurring in any place but Death Valley, conspired to fix the ineffaceable stain upon his wife and his children, for, by the story as I should write it, he ought to have been hung. No use to say modestly that the scratchings of my pen would never reach them. If it were not the biggest story of the desert ever written, I had no wish to write it. And there was the Woman. The story was all she had, absolutely all of a heart-stretching, of enlargement and sustenance. What she thought about it was that that last elusive moment when she touched the forecast shadow of his destiny was to bind her to save his credit for his children's sake. One must needs be faithful to one's experiences when there are so few of them.

She said something like that, gathering up her hair in both hands, standing before me in the wan revealing light. The mark of the desert was on her. Heart of desolation! But I knew what pinchings of the spirit went to make that mark!

"It was a promise," she said.

"It is a promise."

But I caught myself in the reservation that it should not mean beyond the term of her life.

The Fakir

Like "The Woman at the Eighteen-Mile," "The Fakir" is a story about two women and the relationship they develop, hidden within the story of a familiar western male character type, a con man. Although the narrator is fascinated and appalled by how readily she and Netta respond to the charm of the man, she realizes that the story isn't really his. Nor is it Netta's. The narrator's susceptibility to the Fakir and her growing sympathy with Netta teach her a good deal about herself.

Austin, who felt judged and rejected by her Methodist mother and liberated by the Indian concept of religion, often explored the powerful repressive influence of the church, especially in A Woman of Genius *and* Earth Horizon. *Told that the church is "an excellent thing for women," Olivia Lattimore thinks about how she was taught not to question:*

*If you were careful about reading the Bible and doing good to people—that is, persuading them to go to church and to leave off swearing—all the more serious details such as making a living, marrying and having children would take care of themselves; and the trouble was, as I have said, that I believed it (*A Woman of Genius, 63*).*

In "The Fakir," as in "The Return of Mr. Wills," Austin suggests that institutional religion controls women's actions and judgments. Mrs. Wills cannot defy her minister and divorce Mr. Wills, but the narrator of "The Fakir" does overcome her self-righteous feeling of superiority to Netta.

Whenever I come up to judgment, and am hard pushed to make good on my own account (as I expect to be), I shall mention the case of Netta Saybrick, for on the face of it, and by all the traditions in which I was bred, I behaved rather handsomely. I say on the face of it, for except in the matter of keeping my mouth shut afterward, I am not so sure I had anything to do with the affair. It was one of those incidents that from some crest of sheer inexplicableness seems about to direct the imagination over vast tracts of human experience, only to fall away into a pit of its own digging, all fouled with weed and sand. But, by keeping memory and attention fixed on its pellucid instant as it mounted against the sun, I can still see the Figure shining through it as I saw it that day at Posada, with the glimmering rails of the P. and S. running out behind it, thin lines of light toward the bar of Heaven.

Up till that time Netta Saybrick had never liked me, though I never laid it to any other account than Netta's being naturally a little fool; afterward she explained to me that it was because she thought I gave myself airs. The Saybricks lived in the third house from mine, around the corner, so that our back doors overlooked each other, and up till the coming of Doctor Challoner there had never been anything in Netta's conduct that the most censorious of the villagers could remark upon. Nor afterward, for that matter. The Saybricks had been married four years, and the baby was about two. He was not an interesting child to anybody but his mother, and even Netta was sometimes thought to be not quite absorbed in him.

Saybrick was a miner, one of the best drillers in our district, and consequently away from home much of the time. Their house was rather larger than their needs, and Netta, to avoid loneliness more than for profit, let out a room or two. That was the way she happened to fall into the hands of the Fakir.

Franklin Challoner had begun by being a brilliant and promising student of medicine. I had known him when his natural gifts prophesied the unusual, but I had known him rather better than most, and I was not surprised to have him turn up five years later at Maverick as a Fakir.

It had begun in his being poor, and having to work his way through the Medical College at the cost of endless pains and mortification to himself. Like most brilliant people, Challoner was sensitive and had an enormous egotism, and, what nearly always goes with it, the faculty of being horribly fascinating to women. It was thought very creditable of him to have put himself through college at his own charge, though in reality it proved a great social waste. I have a notion that the courage, endurance, and steadfastness which should have done Frank Challoner a lifetime was squeezed out of him by the stress of those overworked, starved, mortifying years. His egotism made it important to his happiness to keep the centre of any stage, and this he could do in school by sheer brilliance of scholarship and the distinction of his struggles. But afterward, when he had to establish himself without capital among strangers, he found himself impoverished of manliness. Always there was the compelling need of his temperament to stand well with people, and almost the only means of accomplishing it his poverty allowed was the dreadful facility with which he made himself master of women. I suppose this got his real ability discredited among his professional fellows. Between that and the sharp need of money, and the incredible appetite which people have for being fooled, somewhere in the Plateau of Fatigue between promise and accomplishment, Frank Challoner lost himself. Therefore, I was not surprised when he turned up finally at Maverick, lecturing on phrenology, and from the shape of their craniums advising country people of their proper careers at three dollars a sitting. He advertised to do various things in the way of medical practice that had a dubious sound.

It was court week when he came, and the only possible lodging to be found at Netta Saybrick's. Doctor Challoner took the two front rooms as being best suited to his clients and himself, and I believe he did very well. I was not particularly pleased to see him, on account of having known him before, not wishing to prosecute the acquaintance; and about that time Indian George brought me word that a variety of *redivivus* long sought was blooming that year on a certain clayey tract over toward Waban. It was not supposed to flower oftener than once in seven years, and I was five days finding it. That was why I never knew what went on at Mrs. Saybrick's. Nobody else did, apparently, for I never heard a breath of gossip, and *that* must have been Doctor Challoner's concern, for I am sure Netta would never have known how to avoid it.

Netta was pretty, and Saybrick had been gone five months. Challoner had a thin, romantic face, and eyes—even I had to admit the compelling attraction of his eyes; and his hands were fine and white. Saybrick's hands were cracked, broken-nailed, a driller's hands, and one of them was twisted from the time he was leaded, working on the Lucky Jim. If it came to that, though, Netta's husband might have been anything he pleased, and Challoner would still have had his way with her. He always did with women, as if to make up for not having it with the world. And the life at Maverick was deadly, appallingly dull. The stark houses, the rubbishy streets, the women who went about in them in calico wrappers, the draggling speech of the men, the wide, shadowless table-lands, the hard, bright skies, and the days all of one pattern, that went so stilly by that you only knew it was after-noon when you smelled the fried cabbage Mrs. Mulligan was cooking for supper.

At this distance I cannot say that I blamed Netta, am not sure of not being glad that she had her hour of the rose-red glow—*if* she had it. You are to bear in mind that all this time I was camping out in the creosote belt on the slope of Waban, and as to what had really happened neither Netta nor Challoner ever said a word. I keep saying things like this about Netta's being pretty and all, just as if I thought they had anything to do with it; truth is, the man had just a gift of taking souls, and I, even I, judicious and disapproving—but you shall hear.

At that time the stage from Maverick was a local affair going down to Posada, where passengers from the P. and S. booked for the Mojave line, returning after a wait of hours on the same day.

It happened that the morning I came back from Waban, Doctor Challoner left Maverick. Being saddle weary, I had planned to send on the horses by Indian George, and take the stage where it crossed my trail an hour out from Posada, going home on it in the afternoon. I remember poking the botany-case under the front seat and turning round to be hit straight between the eyes, as it were, by Netta Saybrick and Doctor Challoner. The doctor was wearing his usual air of romantic mystery; wearing it a little awry—or perhaps it was only knowing the man that made me read the perturbation under it. But it was plain to see what Netta was about. Her hat was tilted by the jolting of the stage, white alkali dust lay heavy on the folds of her dress, and she never *would* wear hair-pins enough; but there was that in every turn and posture, in every note of her flat, childish voice, that acknowledged the man beside her. Her excitement was almost febrile. It was part of Netta's unsophistication that she seemed not to know that she gave herself away, and the witness of it was that she had brought the baby.

You would not have believed that any woman would plan to run away with a man like Frank Challoner and take that great, heavy-headed, drooling child. But that is what Netta had done. I am not sure it was maternal instinct, either; she probably did not know what else to do with him. He had pale, protruding eyes and reddish hair, and every time he clawed at the doctor's sleeve I could see the man withhold a shudder.

I suppose it was my being in a manner confounded by this extraordinary situation that made it possible for Doctor Challoner to renew his acquaintance with more warmth than the facts allowed. He fairly pitched himself into an intimacy of reminiscence, and it was partly to pay him for this, I suppose, and partly to gratify a natural curiosity, that made me so abrupt with him afterward. I remember looking around, when we got down, at the little station where I must wait two hours for the return stage, at the seven unpainted pine cabins, at the eating-house, and the store, and the two saloons, in the instant hope of refuge, and then out across the alkali flat fringed with sparse, unwholesome pickle-weed, and deciding that that would not do, and then turning round to take the situation by the throat, as it were. There was Netta, with that great child dragging on her arm and her hat still on one side, with a silly consciousness of Doctor Challoner's movements, and he still trying for the jovial note of old acquaintances met by chance. In a moment more I had him around the corner of the station-house and out with my question.

"Doctor Challoner, are you running away with Netta Saybrick?"

"Well, no," trying to carry it jauntily; "I think she is running away with me." Then, all his pretension suddenly sagging on him like an empty ca-yaque: "On my soul, I don't know what's got into the woman. I was as surprised as you were when she got on the stage with me"—on my continuing to look steadily at him—"she was a pretty little thing . . . and the life is devilish dull there. . . . I suppose I flirted a little"—blowing himself out, as it were, with an assumption of honesty—"on my word, there was nothing more than that."

Flirted! He called it that; but women do not take their babies and run away from home for the sake of a little flirting. The life was devilish dull—did he need to tell me that! And she was pretty—well, whatever had happened he was bound to tell me that it was nothing, and I was bound to behave as if I believed him.

"She will go back," he began to say, looking bleak and drawn in the searching light. "She must go back! She must!"

"Well, maybe you can persuade her," said I; but I relented after that enough to take care of the baby while he and Netta went for a walk.

The whole mesa and the flat crawled with heat, and the steel rails ran on either side of them like thin fires, as if the slagged track were the appointed way that Netta had chosen to walk. They went out as far as the section-house and back toward the deserted station till I could almost read their faces clear, and turned again, back and forth through the heat-fogged atmosphere like the figures in a dream. I could see this much from their postures, that Challoner was trying to hold to some consistent attitude which he had adopted, and Netta wasn't understanding it. I could see her throw out her hands in a gesture of abandonment, and then I saw her stand as if the Pit yawned under her feet. The baby slept on a station bench, and I kept the flies from him with a branch of pickle-weed. I was out of it, smitten anew with the utter inutility of all the standards which were not bred of experience, but merely came down to me with the family teaspoons. Seen by the fierce desert light they looked like the spoons, thin and worn at the edges. I should have been ashamed to offer them to

Netta Saybrick. It was this sense of detached helplessness toward the life at Maverick that Netta afterward explained she and the other women sensed but misread in me. They couldn't account for it on any grounds except that I felt myself above them. And all the time I was sick with the strained, meticulous inadequacy of my own soul. I understood well enough, then, that the sense of personal virtue comes to most women through an intervening medium of sedulous social guardianship. It is only when they love that it reaches directly to the centre of consciousness, as if it were ultimately nothing more than the instinctive movement of right love to preserve itself by a voluntary seclusion. It was not her faithlessness to Saybrick that tormented Netta out there between the burning rails; it was going back to him that was the intolerable offence. Passion had come upon her like a flame-burst, heaven-sent; she justified it on the grounds of its completeness, and lacked the sophistication for any other interpretation.

Challoner was a bad man, but he was not bad enough to reveal to Netta Saybrick the vulgar cheapness of his own relation to the incident. Besides, he hadn't time. In two hours the return stage for Maverick left the station, and he could never in that time get Netta Saybrick to realize the gulf between his situation and hers.

He came back to the station after a while on some pretext, and said, with his back to Netta, moving his lips with hardly any sound: "She must go back on the stage. She must!" Then with a sudden setting of his jaws, "You've got to help me." He sat down beside me, and began to devote himself to the baby and the flies.

Netta stood out for a while expecting him, and then came and sat provisionally on the edge of the station platform, ready at the slightest hint of an opportunity to carry him away into the glimmering heat out toward the station-house, and resume the supremacy of her poor charms.

She was resenting my presence as an interference, and I believe always cherished a thought that but for the accident of my being there the incident might have turned out differently. I could see that Challoner's attitude, whatever it was, was beginning to make itself felt. She was looking years older, and yet somehow pitifully puzzled and young, as if the self of her had had a wound which her intelligence had failed to grasp. I could see, too, that Challoner had made up his mind to be quit of her, quietly if he could, but at any risk of a scene, still to be quit. And it was forty minutes till stage-time.

Challoner sat on the bare station bench with his arm out above the baby protectingly—it was a manner always effective—and began to talk about "goodness," of all things in the world. Don't ask me what he said. It was the sort of talk many women would have called beautiful, and though it was mostly addressed to me, it was every word of it directed to Netta Saybrick's soul. Much of it went high and wide, but I could catch the pale reflection of it in her face like a miner guessing the sort of day it is from the glimmer of it on a puddle at the bottom of a shaft. In it, Netta saw a pair of heroic figures renouncing a treasure they had found for the sake of the bitter goodness by which the world is saved. They had had the courage to take it while they could, but were much too exemplary to enjoy it at the cost of pain to any other heart. He started with the assumption that she meant to go back to Maverick, and recurred to it with a skilful and hyp-notic insistence, painting upon her mind by large and general inference the picture of himself, helped greatly in his career by her noble renunciation of him. As a matter of fact, Saybrick, if his wife really had gone away with Doctor Challoner, would have followed him up and shot him, I suppose, and no end of vulgar and disagreeable things might have come from the affair; but Challoner managed to keep it on so high a plane that even I never thought of them until long afterward. And right here is where the uncertainty as to the part I really played begins. I can never make up my mind whether Challoner, from long practice in such affairs, had hit upon just the right note of extrication, or whether, cornered, he fell back des-perately on the eternal rightness. And what was he, to know rightness at his need?

He was terribly in earnest, holding Netta's eyes with his own; his fore-head sweated, hollows showed about his eyes, and the dreadful slackness of the corner of the mouth that comes of the whole mind being drawn away upon the object of attack to the neglect of its defences. He was so bent on getting Netta fixed in the idea that she must go back to Maverick that if she had not been a good deal of a fool she must have seen that he had given away the whole situation into my hands. I believed—I hope—I did the right thing, but I am not sure I could have helped taking the cue which was pressed upon me; he was as bad as they made them, but there I was lend-ing my whole soul to the accomplishment of his purpose, which was, briefly, to get comfortably off from an occasion in which he had behaved very badly.

All this time Challoner kept a conscious attention on the stage stables far at the other end of the shadeless street. The moment he saw the driver come out of it with the horses, the man's soul fairly creaked with the release of tension. It released, too, an accession of that power of personal fascination for which he was remarkable.

Netta sat with her back to the street, and the beautiful solicitude with which he took up the baby at that moment, smoothed its dress and tied on its little cap, had no significance for her. It was not until she heard the rattle of the stage turning into the road that she stood up suddenly, alarmed. Challoner put the baby into my arms.

Did I tell you that all this time between me and this man there ran the inexplicable sense of being bonded together; the same suggestion of a superior and exclusive intimacy which ensnared poor Netta Saybrick no doubt, the absolute call of self and sex by which a man, past all reasonableness and belief, ranges a woman on his side. He was a Fakir, a common quack, a scoundrel if you will, but there was the call. I had answered it. I was under the impression, though not remembering what he said, when he had handed me that great lump of a child, that I had received a command to hold on to it, to get into the stage with it, and not to give it up on any consideration; and without saying anything, I had promised.

I do not know if it was the look that must have passed between us at that, or the squeal of the running-gear that shattered her dream, but I perceived on the instant that Netta had had a glimpse of where she stood. She saw herself for the moment a fallen woman, forsaken, despised. There was the Pit before her which Challoner's desertion and my knowledge of it had digged. She clutched once at her bosom and at her skirts as if already she heard the hiss of crawling shame. Then it was that Challoner turned toward her with the Look.

It rose in his face and streamed to her from his eyes as though it were the one thing in the world of a completeness equal to the anguish in her breast, as though, before it rested there, it had been through all the troubled intricacies of sin, and come upon the root of a superior fineness that every soul feels piteously to lie at the back of all its own affronting vagaries, brooding over it in a large, gentle way. It was the forgiveness—nay, the obliteration of offence—and the most Challoner could have known of forgiveness was his own great need of it. Out of that Look I could see the woman's soul rising rehabilitated, astonished, and on the instant, out there beyond the man and the woman, between the thin fiery lines of the rails, leading back to the horizon, the tall, robed Figure writing in the sand.

Oh, it was a hallucination, if you like, of the hour, the place, the perturbed mind, the dazzling glimmer of the alkali flat, of the incident of a sinful woman and a common Fakir, faking an absolution that he might the more easily avoid an inconvenience, and I the tool made to see incredibly by some trick of suggestion how impossible it should be that any but the chief of sinners should understand forgiveness. But the Look continued to hold the moment in solution, while the woman climbed out of the Pit. I saw her put out her hand with the instinctive gesture of the sinking, and Challoner take it with the formality of farewell; and as the dust of the arriving stage billowed up between them, the Figure turned, fading, dissolving . . . but with the Look, consoling obliterating. . . He too . . . !

"It was very good of you, Mrs. Saybrick, to give me so much of a good-bye . . ." Challoner was saying as he put Netta into the stage; and then to me, "You must take good care of her . . . good-bye."

"Good-bye, Frank"—I had never called Doctor Challoner by his name before. I did not like him well enough to call him by it at any time, but there was the Look; it had reached out and enwrapped me in a kind of rarefied intimacy of extenuation and understanding. He stood on the station platform staring steadily after us, and as long as we had sight of him in the thick, bitter dust, the Look held.

If this were a story merely, or a story of Franklin Challoner, it would end there. He never thought of us again, you may depend, except to thank his stars for getting so lightly off, and to go on in the security of his success to other episodes from which he returned as scatheless.

But I found out in a very few days that whether it was to take rank as an incident or an event in Netta Saybrick's life depended on whether or not I said anything about it. Nobody had taken any notice of her day's ride to Posada. Saybrick came home in about ten days, and Netta seemed uncommonly glad to see him, as if in the preoccupation of his presence she found a solace for her fears.

But from the day of our return she had evinced an extraordinary liking for my company. She would be running in and out of the house at all hours, offering to help me with my sewing or to stir up a cake, kindly offices that had to be paid in kind; and if I slipped into the neighbors' on an errand, there a moment after would come Netta. Very soon it became clear to me that she was afraid of what I might tell. So long as she had me under her immediate eye she could be sure I was not taking away her character, but when I was not, she must have suffered horribly. I might have told, too, by the woman's code; she was really not respectable, and we made a great deal of that in Maverick. I might refuse to have anything to do with her and justified myself explaining why.

But Netta was not sure how much I knew, and could not risk betrayal by a plea. She had, too, the natural reticence of the villager, and though she must have been aching for news of Doctor Challoner, touch of him, the very sound of his name, she rarely ever mentioned it, but grew strained and thinner; watching, watching.

If that incident was known, Netta would have been ostracized and Saybrick might have divorced her. And I was going dumb with amazement to discover that nothing had come of it, nothing *could* come of it so long as I kept still. It was a deadly sin, as I had been taught, as I believed—of damnable potentiality; and as long as nobody told it was as if it had never been, as if that look of Challoner's had really the power as it had the seeming of absolving her from all soil and stain.

I cannot now remember if I was ever tempted to tell on Netta Saybrick, but I know with the obsession of that look upon my soul I never did. And in the mean time, from being so much in each other's company, Netta and I became very good friends. That was why, a little more than a year afterward, she chose to have me with her when her second child was born. In Maverick we did things for one another that in more sophisticated communities go to the service of paid attendants. That was the time when the suspicion that had lain at the bottom of Netta's shallow eyes whenever she looked at me went out of them forever.

It was along about midnight and the worst yet to come. I sat holding Netta's hands, and beyond in the room where the lamp was, the doctor lifted Saybrick through his stressful hour with cribbage and toddy. I could see the gleam of the light on Saybrick's red, hairy hands, a driller's hands, and whenever a sound came from the inner room, the uneasy lift of his shoulders and the twitching of his lip; then the doctor pushed the whiskey over toward him and jovially dealt the cards anew.

Netta, tossing on her pillow, came into range with Saybrick's blunt profile outlined against the cheaply papered wall, and I suppose her husband's distress was good to her to see. She looked at him a long time quietly.

"Henry's a good man," she said at last.

"Yes," I said; and then she turned to me narrowly with the expiring spark of anxious cunning in her eyes.

"And I've been a good wife to him," said she. It was half a challenge. And I, trapped by the hour, became a Fakir in my turn, called instantly on all my soul and answered—with the Look—"Everybody knows that, Netta"—held on steadily until the spark went out. However I had done it I could not tell, but I saw the trouble go out of the woman's soul as the lids drooped, and with it out of my own heart the last of the virtuous resentment of the untempted. I had really forgiven her; how then was it possible for the sin to rise up and trouble her more? Mind you, I grew up in a church that makes a great deal of the forgiveness of sins and signifies it by a tremendous particularity about behavior, and the most I had learned of the efficient exercise of forgiveness was from the worst man I had ever known.

About an hour before dawn, when a wind began to stir, and out on the mesa the coyotes howled returning from the hunt, stooping to tuck the baby in her arms, I felt Netta's lips brush against my hand.

"You've been mighty good to me," she said. Well—if I were pushed for it, I should think it worth mentioning—but I am not so sure.

Bitterness of Women

Like a later story, "Frustrate," "Bitterness of Women" explores the fate of the unattractive woman. Although Austin eventually came to believe that she "had never been so homely or gauche in appearance as she had grown up thinking herself," she was bitter about her culture's emphasis on physical beauty as woman's main value (Earth Horizon, 171). In her essays she argued again and again that women should be valued for what they can offer to society and not for their appeal to a man, even claiming that feminism is the demand of modern women to be valued rather than desired.

Yet Austin was never naive, about herself or other women, and she knew that women had fully internalized cultural attitudes about beauty. Her woman characters are often unable to escape the feeling that their worth is determined by the love of a man. Marguerita Dupré is such a woman. Austin distanced herself from this autobiographical theme by writing about a woman of another culture in an ironic tone; yet irony, like black humor, is often a defense.

L ouis Chabot was sitting under the fig-tree in her father's garden at Tres Piños when he told Marguerita Dupré that he could not love her. This sort of thing happened so often to Louis that he did it very well and rather enjoyed it, for he was one of those before whom women bloomed instinctively and preened themselves; and that Marguerita loved him very much was known not only to Louis but to all Tres Piños.

It was bright mid-afternoon, and there was no sound in Dupré's garden louder than the dropping of ripe figs and the drip of the hydrant under the Castilian roses. A mile out of town Chabot's flock dozed on their feet, with their heads under one another's bellies, and his herders dozed on the ground, with their heads under the plaited tops of the sage. Old Dupré sat out in front of his own front yard with a handkerchief over his face, and slept very soundly. Chabot finished his claret to the last drop (it was excellent claret, this of Dupré's), turned the tumbler upside down, sat back in his chair, and explained to Marguerita point by point why he did not love her.

Marguerita leaned her fat arms on the table, wrapped in her blue reboza; it was light blue, and she was too dark for it; but it was such a pretty color. She leaned forward, looking steadily and quietly at Louis, because she was afraid if she so much as let her lids droop the tears would come, and if she smiled her lips would quiver. Marguerita felt that she had not invited this, neither had she known how to avoid it. She would have given anything to have told Louis to his face that he need not concern himself so much on her account, as she was not the least interested in him; she had called on all her pride to that end, but nothing came.

She was a good girl, Louis told her, such as, if she had pleased him he would gladly have married. She was a very good girl, and she understood about sheep. *Tres-bien!* Old Dupré had taught her that; but she lacked a trifle—a nuance—but everything where love is concerned, *l'art d'être désiré,* explained the little Frenchman; for though he was only a sheepherder of Lost Borders, if he had been a boulevardier he could not have been more of a Frenchman nor less of a cad. He leaned back in his chair with the air of having delivered himself very well.

"Salty Bill loves me," ventured Marguerita.

"Eh, Bill!" Louis looked hurt, for though he frequently disposed of his ladies in this negligent fashion, he did not care to have them snapped up so quickly. Marguerita felt convicted of *lèse-majesté* by the look, and hastened to reassure him that she cared nothing whatever for Salty Bill. It was a false move, and she knew it as soon as it was done; but she could not bear to have Louis look at her like that, and Marguerita had never in her life learned the good of pretending. Chabot poured himself another glass of claret, and returned to his point.

There was Suzon Moynier, he explained. Such an eye as Suzon had! there was a spark for you! And an ankle! more lovers than few had been won by an ankle. Marguerita, under cover of the table, drew her feet together beneath her skirts. Her ankles were thick and there was no disguising it.

"So it is Suzon you love?"

"Eh," said the herder, "that is as may be. I have loved many women." Then perhaps because the particular woman did not matter so much as that there should be womanhood, and perhaps because he could no more help it than she could help being wondrously flooded by it, he threw her a look from the tail of his eye and such a smile as drew all the blood from her heart, bent above her, brushing her hair with his lips in such a lingering tenderness of farewell, that though he had just told her she was not to be loved, the poor girl was not sure but he was beginning to love her. Women suffered things like that from Louis Chabot, each being perfectly sure she was the only one, and perhaps, like Marguerita, finding it worth while to be made to suffer if it could be done so exquisitely.

Marguerita was only half French herself, old Dupré having married her mother, Señorita Carrasco, who was only half a señorita, since, in fact, most people in Tres Piños were a little this or that, with no chance for name-calling. Dupré had been a herder of sheep, risen to an owner whom the desert had bitten. The natural consequence was that when he was old, instead of returning to France, he had married Marguerita's mother, and settled down in Tres Piños to live on the interest of his money. It was a fact that his daughter had at heart all the fire and tenderness that promised in Suzon's glance; but of what use to Louis Chabot that she had a soul warm and alight if no glow of it suffused her cheek and no spark of it drew him in her eye. She was swarthy and heavy of face; she had no figure, which means she had a great deal too much of it, and there was a light shadow, like a finger-smudge, on her upper lip. Not that the girl did not have her good points. She could cook, that was the French strain in her father; she could dance, that was Castilian from her mother; and such as she was Salty Bill wanted her. Bill drove an eighteen-mule team for the borax works and was seven times a better man that Chabot, but she would have no more of him than Louis would have of her. She continued to say her prayers regularly, and told Tia Juana, who reproached her with losing a good marriage, that she believed yet the saints would give her the desire of her heart, whereat Tia Juana pitied her.

Chabot brought his sheep up from the spring shearing at Bakersfield each year, and made three loops about Tres Piños, so that it brought him to the town about once in three months to replenish his supplies, and the only reason there was not a new object of his attentions each time was that there were not girls enough, for Chabot's taste required them young, pretty, and possessed of the difficult art of being desired. Therefore, he had time to keep hope alive in Marguerita with the glint of his flattering eyes and the trick of his flattering lips, which was such very common coin with him that he did not quite know himself how free he was with it. And after old Dupré died and his daughter inherited his house and the interest on his money, she was enough of a figure in Tres Piños to make a little attention worth while, even though she had a smudge of black on her upper lip and no art but that of being faithful. She lived in the house under the fig-tree with old Tia Juana for a companion, and was much respected. She was said to have more clothes than anybody, though they never became her.

Marguerita kept a candle burning before the saints and another in her heart for the handsome little herder who went on making love to ladies and being loved by them for three years. Then the saints took a hand in his affairs, though, of course, it did not look that way to Louis.

He was sleeping out on Black Mountain in the spring of the year with his flock. The herder whose business it was to have done that was at Tres Piños on a two days' leave, confessing himself, and getting a nice, jolly little claret drunk. Somewhere up in the blown lava-holes of Black Mountain there was a bear with two cubs, who had said to them, bear fashion: "Come down to the flock with me tonight, and I will show you how killing is done. There will be dogs there and men; but do not be afraid, I will see to it that they do not hurt you."

Along about the time Orion's sword sloped down the west, Chabot heard their gruntled noises and the scurry of the flock. Chabot was not a coward; perhaps because he knew that in general bears are; he got up and laid about him with his staff. This he never would have done if he had known about the cubs; he trod on the foot of one in the dark, and the bear mother heard it. She came lumbering up in the soft blackness and took Chabot in her arms.

Toward four of the next afternoon, the herder coming back, still very merry and very comfortable in his mind, found a maimed, bleeding thing by the water-hole that moaned and babbled. One of its arms was gone to the elbow, its face was laid open, and long, red gashes lay along its sides and down one thigh. After a while, when he had washed away the blood and dust, he discovered that this thing was Chabot. The herder laid it as tenderly as he could on the camp burro and took it in to Tres Piños. If there was any question of the propriety of the care of Chabot falling to Marguerita Dupré, it counted for nothing against the fact that nobody was found willing to do it in her stead, and Marguerita was very discreet. Tia Juana was put in charge of the sick-room, and Marguerita gave her whole soul to the cooking.

And if any question had arisen later when Chabot began to hobble about with a crutch under his good arm, and his sleeve pinned up where the other had been, he put an end to it by marrying her. He was thought to have done very well in this, since he could get no more good of himself;

and since Marguerita wanted him it was a handsome way of paying her, but there had something gone before that. Tia Juana had been careful there should be no scrap of a mirror about when Chabot began to slip his bandages, and perhaps he had not had the courage to ask for it; certainly there had been no change in Marguerita's face for any change she saw in him. And the day that he knew the thing he was, he asked her to marry him. He had slipped out into the street for the first time, wearying a little of the solicitations of the two women, and, to say truth, wholly misinterpreting Marguerita's reasons for screening him so much from the public gaze, for she, poor girl, when he had asked her, could only tell him that he was quite as handsome as ever in her eyes. He felt the pleasant tingle of the air and the sun and the smell of grapes and dropping leafage from the little arbors of Tres Piños, and at the turn of the street in old Moynier's garden the flirt of skirts and the graceful reach of young round arms. Louis straightened himself on his crutches; he felt the stir and excitement of the game . . . he was divided between his old swagger and the pathetic droop of weakness . . . he swung slowly past the garden, and suddenly Suzon looked up . . . looked dully at first . . . with dawning recognition. Then she threw her apron over her face and shrieked and fled into the house. There was something more than coquetry in the way she ran.

Louis turned into the lane and sat down under the black sage, he was not so strong as he had thought, and tried to be quite clear in his mind what this should mean. In a little while he was quite clear. Some children playing in the dust of the roadway at his approach had scuttled away like quail, and now he heard behind him the rustle of the sage, the intimation of hunched shoulders and fingers held over giggles of irrepressible excitement as they dared one another to come and peek at a fearsome thing.

It was that afternoon, when she came in with his soup and claret, that he asked Marguerita. The poor girl put down the bowl, and came and knelt by him very humble and gentle.

"Are you quite sure, Louis?" she asked, with her cheek upon his hand.

"I am sure of nothing," said he, "except that I cannot live without you."

It was very curious that no sooner had he said that than he began to discover it would be very hard to live with her; for to lose an ear and an eye and to have one's mouth drawn twisty by a scar does not make a kiss relish better if it falls not in with the natural desire.

Marguerita did not grow prettier after she was married, but showed a tendency to take on fat, and she did not dress quite so well because she could not afford it, though there are times, as, for instance, when he has gone out in company and seen the young married women hustled out of sight of his scars, that her plain face looks almost good to him. Marguerita insists on their going out a great deal, to cock-fights and to *bailes*, where he sits in the corner with his good side carefully disposed toward the guests, and his wife has given up dancing, though she is very fond of it, to sit beside him and keep him company; though, to tell the truth, Chabot could bear very well to do without that if only he could find himself surrounded by the lightness, the laughter, the half-revealing draperies, the delicious disputed moves of the game he loves—as he will not any more, for he knows now that such as these are not given save when there is something to be got by them, and though he is only thirty-four, poor Louis is no longer possessed of *l'art d'être désiré*.

For the rest of his life he will have to make the best of knowing that his wife carries his name with credit, and does not cost him anything. They are not without their comfortable hours. Marguerita takes excellent care of him, and she understands about sheep; if she sees the dust of a flock arising can tuck up her skirts and away to the edge of the town, getting back as much news of where they go, whence they come, and the conditions of the weather as Chabot could have brought himself, and not even her husband knows the extent of her devices for keeping him surrounded with the sense and stir of life. For it was not long after his marriage that Chabot made the discovery that all the quick desire of him toward lovely women warms in his wife's spirit toward the maimed and twisted thing that he is, and thwarted of the subtle play of lip and limb and eye, spends itself in offices of homely comfort.

And this is the bitterness of women which has come to him: that it matters not so much that they should have passion as the power to provoke it, and lacking the spark of a glance, the turn of an ankle, the treasures of tenderness in them wither unfulfilled. Shut behind his wife's fat, commonplace exterior lies the pulse of music, the delight of motion, the swimming sense, the quick, white burning fenced within his scars. Times like this he remembers what has passed between him and many women, and finds his complacency sicken and die in him. Knowing what he does of the state of her heart, and not being quite a cad, he does not make her an altogether bad husband, and if sometimes, looking at her with abhorring eyes—the shaking bosom, the arms enormous, the shade of her upper lip no longer to be mistaken for a smudge—resenting her lack of power to move him, he gives her a bad quarter of an hour, even there she has the best of him. For however unhappy he makes her, with one kiss of his crooked mouth he can set it all right again. But for Louis, the lift, the exultation, the exquisite, unmatched wonder of the world will not happen any more; never any more.

The House of Offence

This story, like many other Austin stories, contrasts a conventional and unconventional woman. Ironically, Mrs. Henby, the "good" woman, is drawn to Mag and her offensive house because she has no need to support herself and nothing to do. As is often the case, the two women have more in common than Mrs. Henby assumes, and each struggles to see the other woman's point of view.

The prostitute is a familiar woman character in western literature, but Austin provides some subtle details about her life. Knowing that she was an unwanted baby and ignorant about her own sexuality when she married, Austin wrote often about the need for birth control and for accurate information about sex; such information might have saved Mag the unwanted pregnancy that apparently led her into prostitution.

It began to be called the House when it was the only frame building in the camp, and wore its offence upon its front—long and low, little rooms, each with its own door opening upon the shallow veranda. Such a house in a mining country is the dial finger of prosperity. All the ores thereabout were argent, and as the lords of far market-places made silver to go up a few points, you were aware of it in the silken rustle and the heel-click of satin slippers in the House. When the Jews got their heads together and whispered in the Bourse, the gay skirts would flit and the lights go out in the little rooms behind the two cottonwood-trees that should have screened their entrances, but clacking their leaves as if forever fluttered and aghast at what went on in them, betrayed it all the more.

Inmates came and went; sometimes they had names and personalities, but mostly they were simply the women of the House. It was always spoken of in that way, as if but to pass the door-sill were to be seized of its full inheritance of turbulence and shame; and as the town poised and hung upon the turn of the appointed fortune of mining-camps, the House passed from being an outburst, an excess, to a backwater pool of enticement, wherein men swam or sunk themselves, and at last, as the quality of its attractions fell off with the grade of ores, it became merely the overt sign of an admitted and ineradicable baseness.

Always it served to keep alive in the camp the consciousness of style and the allurement of finery; for when the House was at its best, the conditions in desert camps, the price freight was, scrub-water to be bought by the gallon, the prohibitive cost of service, ground terribly the faces of good women. But they could always tell what kind of sleeves were being worn in San Francisco by watching the House. They all watched it; women whose lean breasts sagged from the lips of many children, virtuous slattern in calico, petted wives secure in a traditional honor; and their comment kept a stir about it like the pattering trail of the wind in the cottonwoods. In time, as the springs of mining interest drew away from that district to flash and rise again in some unguessed other side of the world, even that fell off before the dead weight of stable interests and a respectability too stale to be curious; the ground about it was parcelled off; all the accustomed activities of small towns went on around it screened from its contamination by no more than a high board fence, from which in time the palings rotted away. Good women exercised themselves no more against it than to prevent their children from playing under the shade of the two cottonwoods that broadened before it, like the shadow of professional impropriety, behind which the House had shrunk, and, in its condition of unregarded sordidness, pointed the last turn of the dial.

About this time it came into the sole possession of Hard Mag, who was handsome enough to have done much better by herself, and concerning whom nothing worth recording might have transpired had it not been for Mrs. Henby.

The Henbys had taken the place which faced the adjacent street and abutted on the back yard of the House. Henby was blast foreman at the Eclipse, and came home every other Sunday; and his wife, who was very fond of him, found a consolation for the lack of his company in the ordered life of the town. To wash on Monday, iron on Tuesday, bake on Wednesday, and keep the front room always looking as if nobody lived in it, gave Mrs. Henby a virtuous sense of well-being that she had not known in twenty years of scrambled existence at the mines. The trouble with Mrs. Henby was that she had no children. If there had been small footsteps going about the rooms and small finger-clutchings at her dress she would have been perfectly happy, and consequently had no time to trouble about the doings of the House. There had been hopes—but at forty, though her cheeks were smooth and bright, her hair still black, and her figure looking as if it had been melted and poured into her neat print wrapper, Mrs. Henby did not hope any more. She made a silk crazy-quilt for the bed-lounge in the parlor, and began to take an interest in Hard Mag and the draggled birds of passage that preened themselves occasionally in the dismantled rooms of the House, though being the most virtuous of women she would never have admitted the faintest distraction in the affairs of "such like."

It began by Mrs. Henby discovering, through the cracks of the fence, that Mag, in the intervals of sinning, was largely occupied with the tasks of widowed and neglected women. Mrs. Henby cut kindlings for herself sometimes if Henby was detained at the mine beyond his week-end visits, but to see Mag of the hard, red lips, the bright, unglinting hair, and the burnt-out blackness of her eyes under the pale, long lids, so employed made it of an amazing opprobriousness. For, as Mrs. Henby understood it, the root of sin lay in self-indulgence, and might be fostered by such small matters as sitting too much in rocking-chairs and wearing too becoming hats; she saw it now as the sign of an essential incompetency in the offices of creditable living. Mag, she perceived, did not even know how to pin up her skirts properly when she swept the back stoop. To see her thus fumbling at the mechanism of existence was to put her forever beyond the reach of resentment into the region of pitiable humanness. In time it grew upon Mrs. Henby that the poor creatures, who took the air of late afternoons in the yard behind the House, might have possibilities even of being interested in the crazy-quilt and the garden, and being prevented by some mysterious law of their profession from doing so. She went so far upon this supposition as to offer Mag a bunch of radishes out of her minute vegetable plot, which Mag, to her relief, refused. Mrs. Henby could no more refrain from neighborliness than she could help being large at the waist, but she really would not like to be seen handing things through the fence to the inmates of the House. She came to that in time, though.

Some wretched consort of Mag's fell sick at the House of the lead poisoning common in the mines when the doctor was away at Maverick, and nobody in the neighborhood was so skilled in the remedies proper to the occasion as Mrs. Henby. This led to several conferences, and the passage between the palings of sundry preparations of hot milk and soups and custards. Mrs. Henby would hand them out after nightfall, and find the dishes on her side of the fence in the morning. She was so ashamed of it that she never told even her husband, and the man having gone away to his own place and died there, Mag had nobody to tell it to in any case. But

Mrs. Henby always entertained a subconscious sureness that something unpleasant was likely to come of her condonings of iniquity, and one morning, when she came out of the kitchen door to find Mag furtively waiting at the fence, she roughed forward all the quills of her respectability at once. Mag leaned her breast upon the point of a broken paling, as though the sharpness of it stayed her. She had no right to the desultory courtesies of back-fence neighborliness, and did not attempt them.

"I've had a letter," she said, abruptly, showing it clinched against her side; the knuckles of her hand were strained and white.

"A letter?"

"From Kansas. My daughter's coming." She lowered her voice and looked back cautiously at the shut House, as if the thing could overhear.

So she had a daughter—this painted piece; and God-fearing women might long and long! Twenty years' resentment began to burn in Mrs. Henby's cushiony bosom.

"What are you doin' with a daughter?" she said.

"Oh," cried Mag, impatiently, "I had her years ago—ten—eleven years! She has been living with my aunt in Kansas: and now my aunt is dead, and they are sending her."

"Who is sending her?"

"I don't know—the neighbors. I've nobody belonging to me back there. They have to do something with her, so they are sending her to me. Here!" She struck upon the paling wickedly with her hand.

"Where's her father?" Mrs. Henby's interest rose superior to her resentment.

"How should I know? I tell you it was a long time ago. I came away when she was a little, little baby. My aunt was religious and couldn't have anything to do with me, but she took care of—her! I sent money."

Mrs. Henby recalled herself to the aloofness of entire respectability. "If your aunt wouldn't have you, I don't see how she could feel to abide your money."

"I told her I was married," said Mag, "and respectable." She leaned upon the paling and laughed a hard, sharp laugh.

Mrs. Henby gathered up her apron full of kindlings.

"Well, you've made your bed," she said. "I guess you will lie in it."

But she sat down trembling as soon as she had shut the door. A daughter—to that woman—and she—Mrs. Henby went about shaking her head and talking to herself with indignation. All day the House remained shut and slumbering, its patched and unwashed windows staring blankly on the yard; but if ever Mrs. Henby came out of her kitchen door, as if she were the cuckoo on the striking of the hour, Mag appeared from the House. It was evident she had ordered a clear field for herself, for no one came out in draggled finery to take the air that day. It was dusk before Mrs. Henby's humanness got the better of her. She went out to the woodpile and whispered to the stirring of Mag's dress:

"When's she coming?"

"Wednesday. She will be started before I can get a letter to her."

"Well, I reckon you'll have to take her," said Mrs. Henby, unconsolingly. A flash of Mag's insuperable hardness broke from her.

"She'll spoil trade," she said.

Mrs. Henby looked up the dusky bulk of the House beyond her, lines of light at the windows like the red lids of distempered eyes. All at once, and, as she said afterward, without for the moment any conscious relativity, she recalled the quagmires of unwarned water-holes where cattle sink and flounder, and the choking call of warning that sounds to the last above the stifling slime. When Mag said that about the child and her way of making a living, Mrs. Henby jumped. She thought she heard the smothering suck of the mire. Somebody in the House laughed and cried out coarsely, and then she heard Mag's voice going on hurriedly behind the palings:

"Mrs. Henby! Mrs. Henby! you've got to help me— I must find some place for her to board— She has been well brought up, I tell you. My aunt is religious— She would be a comfort to some good person."

Meaning me, I suppose," sniffed Mrs. Henby. Mag had not meant anybody in particular, but she swept it up urgently.

"Oh, if you would—she'd be a comfort to you! She's real sweet-looking— they sent me her picture once." She felt for phrases to touch the other woman, but they rang insincerely. "You'd be the saving of her—if you would."

"Well, I won't!" snapped Mrs. Henby; and as soon as she was inside she locked the door against even the suggestion. "Me to take anything off that painted piece!" she quivered, angrily.

It was five days until Wednesday, and Mag struck to her trail insistently.

"You been thinking of what I said last night?" she questioned in the morning interval at the woodpile.

Mrs. Henby denied it, but she had. She had thought of what Henby would say to it, and wondered if Mag's daughter had hard eyes, and bright, unglinting, canary-colored hair. She thought of what explanation she might make to the neighbors in case she decided suddenly to adopt the daughter of—of an old friend in Kansas; then she thought of the faces of the women who went in and out of the House, and resolved not to think any more.

She kept away from the woodpile as much as possible during Saturday and Sunday, but Monday evening she heard Mag calling her from the back of the yard. This was the worst yet, for there was no telling who might overhear.

"Mrs. Henby," demanded the painted piece, "are you going to see that innocent child brought to this place and never lift a hand to it?"

"I don't know as I got any call to interfere," said Mrs. Henby.

"And you with a good home, and calling yourself Christian, and all," went on the hard one. "Besides, I'd pay you."

"I don't feel to need any of your money," thrust in Mrs. Henby, resentfully. "I guess I could take care of one child without—but I ain't going to." She broke off, and moved rapidly toward the house.

"Mrs. Henby, listen to me!" cried Mag, shaking at the palings as though they had been the bars of a cage and she trapped in it. "For God's sake, Mrs. Henby, you must! Mrs. Henby, if you won't listen to me here, I shall come to your house."

Mrs. Henby heard the crack of the rotten palings as she shut the door.

"Mrs. Henby! Mrs. Henby!" threatened the voice, "I'm coming in!"

Then the crash of splintering wood, and Mag's hand on the knob. The vehemence of her mood, her tragic movements, the bright vividness of her lips and hair seemed to force Mrs. Henby into the attitude of the offender. She sat limply in a chair twisting her hands in her fat lap while the other assailed her. Behind her on the wall Mag's shadow shook and threatened like the shape of an uncouth destiny.

"I know what you are thinking, Mrs. Henby. You think there's bad blood, and she will turn out like me maybe, but I tell you it's no such thing. Look here—if it's any satisfaction to you to know—I was good when I had her, and her father was good—only we were young and didn't know any better—we hadn't any feelings except what we'd have had if we had been married—only we didn't happen to— It's the truth, Mrs. Henby, if I die for it. Bad blood!" she said, hardness augmenting upon her. "How many a man comes to the House and goes away to raise a family, and not a word said about bad blood! You don't reckon—"

But Mrs. Henby had her apron over her face, and was crying into it. Mag floundered back to the other woman's point of view.

"If it is a question what she'll come to, you know well enough if I have to take her with me. *Me!*" she said. She threw round herself an indescribable air of lascivious deviltry, as though she had been blown upon by the blast of an unseen furnace, and the shadow upon the wall shook and confirmed it. "That's what she will come to unless you save her from it. It's up to you, Mrs. Henby."

"I—I don't know what Henby will say," whimpered Mrs. Henby, afresh.

"Say?" urged Mag, with the scorn of her kind for the well-regulated husband. "He'll say anything he thinks you want him to say. He'll be as fond as anything of her—and you can bring her up to be a comfort to him." The poverty of Mag's experience furnished her with no phrases to express what a child might become.

"A nice time I'd have," burst out the other woman, in a last throb of resentment, "bringing her up to be a comfort to anybody, with her own mother living a sinful life right under her eyes."

"Oh," said Mag, with enlightenment, "so that's what is troubling you! Well—if you say the word—I'll clear out. The girls will kick—but they have to do what I say. Look here, then! If you'll take the kid—I'll go."

"And never come back—nor let her know?"

"Cross my heart to die," said Mag.

"Well, then"—Mrs. Henby let her apron fall tremulously—"I'll take her."

"For keeps?"

"For keeps," vowed Mrs. Henby, solemnly.

They were silent, regarding each other for a time, neither knowing how to terminate the interview without offence.

"What's her name?" asked Mrs. Henby, timidly, at last.

"Marietta."

Mag searched her scant remembrances and brought up this: "She's got dark hair."

Mrs. Henby was visibly comforted.

Mrs. Henby found, after all, that she was not put to any great strain of inventiveness to account for the little girl she had decided to adopt, the event being overshadowed, in the estimation of the townspeople, by the more memorable one which occurred on the very night of Marietta's arrival. This was no less than the departure of Hard Mag and the women of the House. They went out of it as they came, with scant warning, helped by coarse laughter of the creatures they had preyed upon, and with so much of careless haste that about two hours after their flitting—caught, it was supposed, from their neglected fires—the whole shell of the House burst into flame. It made a red flare in the windows in the middle of the night, but, as none of the townspeople had any interest in it and no property was endangered, it was allowed to burn quite out, which it did as quickly as the passions it had thrived upon, to an inconsiderable heap of cinders. The next year the Henbys took over the place where it had stood for a garden, and Henby made a swing under the cottonwood-trees for his adopted daughter.

❖ ❖ ❖

The Walking Woman

Many of Austin's stories about the desert regions are based on personal experience, on desert characters she met in her wanderings. In one of her Tejon notebooks from 1888, she described meeting "The Walking Woman":

> Over on the Temblor we met the Walking Woman. I had heard of her. The cow-boys call her Mrs. Walker but nobody knows her name. She told one of the women at Temblor that her first name is Jenny, but she answers to Mrs. Walker. She is not very tall, but her hair is thick and greyish and it is impossible to tell how old she is. She has a black bag which she carries over her shoulder on a stick. The men say she

does not allow any liberties. They say she has just as good sense as anybody, except that she is a little bit crazy. Mother says she looks like a woman who has had a child.[1]

Austin well knew what it was like to be called crazy, and her story about the Walking Woman suggests her admiration for those able to walk "off all sense of society-made values." Although Austin leaves ambiguous whether her narrator agrees with the Walking Woman's assessment of what is indispensable to self-awareness, she implies through her story's final image that the Walking Woman's trail is one worth following.

The first time of my hearing of her was at Temblor. We had come all one day between blunt, whitish bluffs rising from mirage water, with a thick, pale wake of dust billowing from the wheels, all the dead wall of the foothills sliding and shimmering with heat, to learn that the Walking Woman had passed us somewhere in the dizzying dimness, going down to the Tulares on her own feet. We heard of her again in the Carrisal, and again at Adobe Station, where she had passed a week before the shearing, and at last I had a glimpse of her at the Eighteen-Mile House as I went hurriedly northward on the Mojave stage; and afterward, sheepherders at whose camps she slept, and cowboys at rodeos, told me as much of her way of life as they could understand. Like enough they told her as much of

1. The Tejon notebooks are part of the Huntington Library's Austin Collection (box 24c).

mine. That was very little. She was the Walking Woman, and no one knew her name, but because she was a sort of whom men speak respectfully, they called her to her face Mrs. Walker, and she answered to it if she was so inclined. She came and went about our western world on no discoverable errand, and whether she had some place of refuge where she lay by in the interim, or whether between her seldom, unaccountable appearances in our quarter she went on steadily walking, was never learned. She came and went, oftenest in a kind of muse of travel which the untrammelled space begets, or at rare intervals flooding wondrously with talk, never of herself, but of things she had known and seen. She must have seen some rare happenings, too—by report. She was at Maverick the time of the Big Snow, and at Tres Piños when they brought home the body of Morena; and if anybody could have told whether De Borba killed Mariana for spite or defence, it would have been she, only she could not be found when most wanted. She was at Tunawai at the time of the cloud-burst, and if she had cared for it could have known most desirable things of the ways of trail-making, burrow-habiting small things.

All of which should have made her worth meeting, though it was not, in fact, for such things I was wishful to meet her; and as it turned out, it was not of these things we talked when at last we came together. For one thing, she was a woman, not old, who had gone about alone in a country where the number of women is as one in fifteen. She had eaten and slept at the herder's camps, and laid by for days at one-man stations whose masters had no other touch of human kind than the passing of chance prospectors, or the halting of the tri-weekly stage. She had been set on her way by teamsters who lifted her out of white, hot desertness and put her down at the crossing of unnamed ways, days distant from anywhere. And through all this she passed unarmed and unoffended. I had the best testimony to this, the witness of the men themselves. I think they talked of it because they were so much surprised at it. It was not, on the whole, what they expected of themselves.

Well I understand that nature which wastes its borders with too eager burning, beyond which rim of desolation it flares forever quick and white, and have had some inkling of the isolating calm of a desire too high to stoop to satisfaction. But you could not think of these things pertaining to the Walking Woman; and if there were ever any truth in the exemption from offence residing in a frame of behavior called ladylike, it should have been inoperative here. What this really means is that you get no affront so long as your behavior in the estimate of the particular audience invites none. In the estimate of the immediate audience—conduct which affords protection in Mayfair gets you no consideration in Maverick. And by no canon could it be considered ladylike to go about on your own feet, with a blanket and a black bag and almost no money in your purse, in and about the haunts of rude and solitary men.

There were other things that pointed the wish for a personal encounter with the Walking Woman. One of them was the contradiction of reports of her—as to whether she was comely, for example. Report said yes, and again, plain to the point of deformity. She had a twist to her face, some said; a hitch to one shoulder; they averred she limped as she walked. But by the distance she covered she should have been straight and young. As to sanity, equal incertitude. On the mere evidence of her way of life she was cracked; not quite broken, but unserviceable. Yet in her talk there was both wisdom and information, and the word she brought about trails and water-holes was as reliable as an Indian's.

By her own account she had begun by walking off an illness. There had been an invalid to be taken care of for years, leaving her at last broken in body, and with no recourse but her own feet to carry her out of that predicament. It seemed there had been, besides the death of her invalid, some other worrying affairs, upon which, and the nature of her illness, she was never quite clear, so that it might very well have been an unsoundness of mind which drove her to the open, sobered and healed at last by the large soundness of nature. It must have been about that time that she lost her name. I am convinced that she never told it because she did not know it herself. She was the Walking Woman, and the country people called her Mrs. Walker. At the time I knew her, though she wore short hair and a man's boots, and had a fine down over all her face from exposure to the weather, she was perfectly sweet and sane.

I had met her occasionally at ranch-houses and road-stations, and had got as much acquaintance as the place allowed; but for the things I wished to know there wanted a time of leisure and isolation. And when the occasion came we talked altogether of other things.

It was at Warm Spring in the Little Antelope I came upon her in the heart of a clear forenoon. The spring lies off a mile from the main trail, and has the only trees about it known in that country. First you come upon a pool of waste full of weeds of a poisonous dark green, every reed ringed about the water-level with a muddy white incrustation. Then the three oaks appear staggering on the slope, and the spring sobs and blubbers below them in ashy-colored mud. All the hills of that country have the down plunge toward the desert and back abruptly toward the Sierra. The grass is thick and brittle and bleached straw-color toward the end of the season. As I rode up the swale of the spring I saw the Walking Woman sitting where the grass was deepest, with her black bag and blanket, which she carried on a stick, beside her. It was one of those days when the genius of talk flows as smoothly as the rivers of mirage through the blue hot desert morning.

You are not to suppose that in my report of a Borderer I give you the words only, but the full meaning of the speech. Very often the words are merely the punctuation of thought; rather, the crests of the long waves of intercommunicative silences. Yet the speech of the Walking Woman was fuller than most.

The best of our talk that day began in some dropped word of hers from which I inferred that she had had a child. I was surprised at that, and then wondered why I should have been surprised, for it is the most natural of all experiences to have children. I said something of that purport, and also that it was one of the perquisites of living I should be least willing to do without. And that led to the Walking Woman saying that there were three things which if you had known you could cut out all the rest, and they were good any way you got them, but best if, as in her case, they were related to and grew each one out of the others. It was while she talked that I decided that she really did have a twist to her face, a sort of natural warp or skew into which it fell when it was worn merely as a countenance, but which disappeared the moment it became the vehicle of thought or feeling.

The first of the experiences the Walking Woman had found most worth while had come to her in a sand-storm on the south slope of Tehachapi in a dateless spring. I judged it should have been about the time she began to find herself, after the period of worry and loss in which her wandering began. She had come, in a day pricked full of intimations of a storm, to the camp of Filon Geraud, whose companion shepherd had gone a three days' *pasear* to Mojave for supplies. Geraud was of great hardihood, red-blooded, of a full laughing eye, and an indubitable spark for women. It was the season of the year when there is a soft bloom on the days, but the nights are cowering cold and the lambs tender, not yet flockwise. At such times a sand-storm works incalculable disaster. The lift of the wind is so great that the whole surface of the ground appears to travel upon it slantwise, thinning out miles high in air. In the intolerable smother the lambs are lost from the ewes; neither dogs nor man make headway against it.

The morning flared through a horizon of yellow smudge, and by mid-forenoon the flock broke.

"There were but the two of us to deal with the trouble," said the Walking Woman. "Until that time I had not known how strong I was, nor how good it is to run when running is worth while. The flock travelled down the wind, the sand bit our faces; we called, and after a time heard the words broken and beaten small by the wind. But after a little we had not to call. All the time of our running in the yellow dusk of day and the black dark of night, I knew where Filon was. A flock-length away, I knew him. Feel? What should I feel? I knew. I ran with the flock and turned it this way and that as Filon would have.

"Such was the force of the wind that when we came together we held by one another and talked a little between pantings. We snatched and ate what we could as we ran. All that day and night until the next afternoon the camp kit was not out of the cayaques. But we held the flock. We herded them under a butte when the wind fell off a little, and the lambs sucked; when the storm rose they broke, but we kept upon their track and brought them together again. At night the wind quieted, and we slept by turns; at least Filon slept. I lay on the ground when my turn was and beat with the storm. I was no more tired than the earth was. The sand filled in the creases of the blanket, and where I turned, dripped back upon the ground. But we saved the sheep. Some ewes there were that would not give down their milk because of the worry of the storm, and the lambs died. But we kept the flock together. And I was not tired."

The Walking Woman stretched out her arms and clasped herself, rocking in them as if she would have hugged the recollection to her breast.

"For you see," said she, "I worked with a man, without excusing, without any burden on me of looking or seeming. Not fiddling or fumbling as women work, and hoping it will all turn out for the best. It was not for Filon to ask, Can you, or Will you. He said, Do, and I did. And my work was good. We held the flock. And that," said the Walking Woman, the twists coming in her face again, "is one of the things that make you able to do without the others."

"Yes," I said; and then, "What others?"

"Oh," she said, as if it pricked her, "the looking and the seeming."

And I had not thought until that time that one who had the courage to be the Walking Woman would have cared! We sat and looked at the pattern of the thick crushed grass on the slope, wavering in the fierce noon like the waterings in the coat of a tranquil beast; the ache of a world-old bitterness sobbed and whispered in the spring. At last—

"It is by the looking and the seeming," said I, "that the opportunity finds you out."

"Filon found out," said the Walking Woman. She smiled; and went on from that to tell me how, when the wind went down about four o'clock and left the afternoon clear and tender, the flock began to feed, and they had out the kit from the cayaques, and cooked a meal. When it was over, and Filon had his pipe between his teeth, he came over from his side of the fire, of his own notion, and stretched himself on the ground beside her. Of his own notion. There was that in the way she said it that made it seem as if nothing of the sort had happened before to the Walking Woman, and for a moment I thought she was about to tell me one of the things I wished to know; but she went on to say what Filon had said to her of her work with the flock. Obvious, kindly things, such as any man in sheer decency would have said, so that there must have something more gone with the words to make them so treasured of the Walking Woman.

"We were very comfortable," said she, "and not so tired as we expected to be. Filon leaned up on his elbow. I had not noticed until then how broad he was in the shoulders, and how strong in the arms. And we had saved the flock together. We felt that. There was something that said together, in the slope of his shoulders toward me. It was around his mouth and on the cheek high up under the shine of his eyes. And under the shine the look—the look that said, 'We are of one sort and one mind'—his eyes that were the color of the flat water in the tulares—do you know the look?"

"I know it."

"The wind was stopped and all the earth smelled of dust, and Filon understood very well that what I had done with him I could not have done so well with another. And the look—the look in the eyes—"

"Ah-ah—!"

I have always said, I will say again, I do not know why at this point the Walking Woman touched me. If it were merely a response to my unconscious throb of sympathy, or the unpremeditated way of her heart to declare that this, after all, was the best of all indispensable experiences; or if in some flash of forward vision, encompassing the unimpassioned years, the stir, the movement of tenderness were for *me*—but no; as often as I have thought of it, I have thought of a different reason, but no conclusive one, why the Walking Woman should have put out her hand and laid it on my arm.

"To work together, to love together," said the Walking Woman, withdrawing her hand again; "there you have two of the things; the other you know."

"The mouth at the breast," said I.

"The lips and the hands," said the Walking Woman. "The little, pushing hands and the small cry." There ensued a pause of fullest understanding, while the land before us swam in the noon, and a dove in the oaks behind the spring began to call. A little red fox came out of the hills and lapped delicately at the pool.

"I stayed with Filon until the fall," said she. "All that summer in the Sierra, until it was time to turn south on the trail. It was a good time, and longer than he could be expected to have loved one like me. And besides, I was no longer able to keep the trail. My baby was born in October."

Whatever more there was to say to this, the Walking Woman's hand said it, straying with remembering gesture to her breast. There are so many ways of loving and working, but only one way of the first-born. She added after an interval, that she did not know if she would have given up her walking to keep at home and tend him, or whether the thought of her son's small feet running beside her in the trails would have driven her to the open again. The baby had not stayed long enough for that. "And whenever the wind blows in the night," said the Walking Woman, "I wake and wonder if he is well covered."

She took up her black bag and her blanket; there was the ranch-house of Dos Palos to be made before night, and she went as outliers do, without a hope expressed of another meeting and no word of good-bye. She was the Walking Woman. That was it. She had walked off all sense of society-made values, and, knowing the best when the best came to her, was able to take it. Work—as I believed; love—as the Walking Woman had proved it; a child—as you subscribe to it. But look you: it was the naked thing the Walking Woman grasped, not dressed and tricked out, for instance, by prejudices in favor of certain occupations; and love, man love, taken as it came, not picked over and rejected if it carried no obligation of permanency; and a child; *any* way you get it, a child is good to have, say nature and the Walking Woman; to have it and not to wait upon a proper concurrence of so many decorations that the event may not come at all.

At least one of us is wrong. To work and to love and to bear children. *That* sounds easy enough. But the way we live establishes so many things of much more importance.

Far down the dim, hot valley I could see the Walking Woman with her blanket and black bag over her shoulder. She had a queer, sidelong gait, as if in fact she had a twist all through her.

Recollecting suddenly that people called her lame, I ran down to the open space below the spring where she had passed. There in the bare, hot sand the track of her two feet bore evenly and white.

❖   ❖   ❖

The Basket Woman

Some of Austin's earliest publications were in such periodicals as *St. Nicholas Magazine* and *The Youth's Companion*. She wrote two collections of stories for children, *The Basket Woman* (1910) and *The Trail Book* (1918), and a poetry collection, *The Children Sing in the Far West* (1928). Perhaps she was so interested in nurturing children's imaginations because she felt her childhood was so constricted, because she was deprived of books and discouraged from "storying." During her years of teaching in California, she discovered that the stories and poems she made up about the region appealed more immediately to her pupils than did classic myths or tales of far-off places, and she later complained that children were "brought up [exclusively] . . . in the literature and lore of New England" (*Earth Horizon*, 97). Believing as she did that literature reflects the land and regional culture from which it is generated, she thought that children would come to realize what she called "the continuity of natu-ral forces and their relativity to the life of man" more readily if they were exposed to literature native to their region (*The Basket Woman*, vii). Regional literature, she felt, was also an introduction to the great themes of American culture: democracy, individualism, the social experiment.

Austin also sought to introduce children to "the first-born literature of our native land," to the "literary heritage" of Native Americans. "It is still easier to know more of Beowulf than of the Red Score of the Delaware," she said, "more of Homer than of the Creation Myth of the Zuni, more of Icelandic sagas than of the hero myths of the Iroquois and Navajo."[1] *The Basket Woman* contains a series of western myths, many of them stories she heard in the campoodies of the West. Although the stories are intended to awaken children to "the larger significance of things," they contain ambiguities and ironies whose larger significance will appeal to adults as well.

1. "Aboriginal American Literature," in *American Writers of American Literature,* ed. John Macy (New York: Horace Liveright, 1931), 426–41.

The Basket Woman: First Story

The Basket Woman *begins by introducing a storyteller, a compassionate and insightful Indian woman known as the Basket Woman, and her audience, Alan, a young boy who has recently moved to a western ranch. Alan comes west with a fear of Indians from what "he had heard" about them. His initial dislike of the Basket Woman, Austin shows, stems from this fear based on inexperience and prejudice. Eventually, through her stories, he comes to know and trust her, to empathize with her, and she comes "to understand that the boy really loved her tales and believed them" (109). The stories enter "his mind when he lay in his bed at night, and saw the stars in the windy sky shine through the cabin window," and they eventually become so much a part of his experience that he feels "part of the story himself" and even believes he dreams them (109–10). The Basket Woman becomes an important influence on Alan's consciousness, an inner voice that shapes his perceptions and responds to his inner needs. She tells him tales of her tribe, transporting him into the past through her vision, she personifies the natural world to emphasize that it is alive with spiritual meaning, and she teaches him what Austin felt to be* a central value of Indian life—consideration for the interrelationships of all living things.

The structure of The Basket Woman *is a clever one, for Austin initiates her reader into Native American culture as the Basket Woman initiates Alan. The little boy becomes someone with whom her young readers can identify, a representative reader of these western myths. Although not all the stories are explicitly framed by the Basket Woman, she is the implicit storyteller, the source of tradition, and the stories are told within the framework of a developing human relationship. The collection's structure thus attempts to echo the oral tradition Austin so values, and it conveys the feeling that stories, emblems of culture, help create human bonds. In her preface to* The Basket Woman, *Austin encouraged mothers to read her stories to their children, and the Basket Woman becomes a mother figure, nurturing and protecting Alan and even saving his life in one story, "The Merry-Go-Round." Most importantly, she expands his imagination.*

Like her creator, the Basket Woman sings the "Wolf's Song."

The homesteader's cabin stood in a moon-shaped hollow between the hills and the high mesa; and the land before it stretched away golden and dusky green, and was lost in a blue haze about where the river settlements began. The hills had a flowing outline and melted softly into each other and higher hills behind, until the range broke in a ragged crest of thin peaks white with snow. A clean, wide sky bent over that country, and the air that moved in it was warm and sweet.

The homesteader's son had run out on the trail that led toward the spring, with half a mind to go to it, but ran back again when he saw the Basket Woman coming. He was afraid of her, and ashamed because he was afraid, so he did not tell his mother that he had changed his mind.

"There is the mahala coming for the wash," said his mother; "now you will have company at the spring." But Alan only held tighter to a fold of her dress. This was the third time the Indian woman had come to wash for the homesteader's wife; and, though she was slow and quiet and had a pleasant smile, Alan was still afraid of her. All that he had heard of Indians before coming to this country was very frightful, and he did not understand yet that it was not so. Beyond a certain point of hills on clear days he could see smoke rising from the campoodie, and though he knew nothing but his dreams of what went on there, he would not so much as play in that direction.

The Basket Woman was the only Indian that he had seen. She would come walking across the mesa with a great cone-shaped carrier basket heaped with brushwood on her shoulders, stooping under it and easing the weight by a buckskin band about her forehead. Sometimes it would be a smaller basket carried in the same fashion, and she would be filling it with bulbs of wild hyacinth or taboose; often she carried a bottle-necked water basket to and from the spring, and always wore a bowl-shaped basket on her head for a hat. Her long hair hung down from under it, and her black eyes glittered beadily below the rim. Alan had a fancy that any moment she might pick him up with a quick toss as if he had been a bit of brushwood, and drop him over her shoulder into the great carrier, and walk away across the mesa with him. So when he saw her that morning coming down the trail from the spring, he hung close by his mother's skirts.

"You must not be afraid of her, Alan," said his mother; "she is very kind, and no doubt has had a boy of her own."

The Basket Woman showed them her white, even teeth in a smile. "This one very pretty boy," she said; but Alan had made up his mind not to trust her. He was thinking of what the teamster had said when he had driven them up from the railroad station with their belongings the day they came to their new home and found the Basket Woman spying curiously in at the cabin windows.

"You wanter watch out how you behaves yourself, sonny," said the teamster, wagging a solemn jaw, "she's likely to pack you away in that basket o' her'n one of these days." And Alan had watched out very carefully indeed.

It was not a great while after they came to the foothill claim that the homesteader went over to the campoodie to get an Indian to help at fence building, and Alan went with him, holding fast by his father's hand. They found the Indians living in low, foul huts; their clothes were also dirty, and they sat about on the ground, fat and good-natured. The dogs and children lay sleeping in the sun. It was all very disappointing.

"Will they not hurt us, father?" Alan had said at starting.

"Oh, no, my boy; you must not get any such notion as that," said the homesteader; "Indians are not at all now what they were once."

Alan thought of this as he looked at the campoodie, and pulled at his father's hand.

"I do not like Indians the way they are now," he said; and immediately saw that he had made a mistake, for he was standing directly in front of the Basket Woman's hut, and as she suddenly put her head out of the door he thought by the look of her mysterious, bright eyes that she had understood. He did not venture to say anything more, and all the way home kept looking back toward the campoodie to see if anything came of it.

"Why do you not eat your supper?" said his mother. "I am afraid the long walk in the hot sun was too much for you." Alan dared not say anything to her of what troubled him, though perhaps it would have been better if he had, for that night the Basket Woman came for him.

She did not pick him up and toss him over her shoulder as he expected; but let down the basket, and he stepped into it of his own accord. Alan was surprised to find that he was not so much afraid of her after all.

"What will you do with me?" he said.

"I will show you Indians as they used to be," said she.

Alan could feel the play of her strong shoulders as they went out across the lower mesa and began to climb the hills.

"Where do you go?" said the boy.

"To Pahrump, the valley of Corn Water. It was there my people were happiest in old days."

They went on between the oaks, and smelled the musky sweet smell of the wild grapevines along the water borders. The sagebrush began to fail from the slopes, and buckthorn to grow up tall and thicker; the wind brought them a long sigh from the lowest pines. They came up with the silver firs and passed them, passed the drooping spruces, the wet meadows, and the wood of thimble-cone pines. The air under them had an earthy smell. Presently they came out upon a cleared space very high up where the rocks were sharp and steep.

"Why are there no trees here?" asked Alan.

"I will tell you about that," said the Basket Woman. "In the old flood time, and that is longer ago than is worth counting, the water came up and covered the land, all but the high tops of mountains. Here then the Indians fled and lived, and with them the animals that escaped from the flood. There were trees growing then over all the high places, but because the waters were long on the earth the Indians were obliged to cut them down for firewood. Also they killed all the large animals for food, but the small ones hid in the rocks. After that the waters went down; trees and grass began to grow over all the earth, but never any more on the tops of high mountains. They had all been burned off. You can see that it is so."

From the top of the mountain Alan could see all the hills on the other side shouldering and peering down toward the happy valley of Corn Water.

"Here," said the Basket Woman, "my people came of old time in the growing season of the year; they planted corn, and the streams came down from the hills and watered it. Now we, too, will go down."

They went by a winding trail, steep and stony. The pines stood up around and locked them closely in.

"I see smoke arising," said Alan, "blue smoke above the pines."

"It is the smoke of their hearth fires," said the Basket Woman, and they went down and down.

"I hear a sound of singing," said the boy.

"It is the women singing and grinding at the quern," she said, and her feet went faster.

"I hear laughter," he said again, "it mixes with the running of the water."

"It is the maidens washing their knee-long hair. They kneel by the water and stoop down, they dip in the running water and shake out bright drops in the sun."

"There is a pleasant smell," said Alan.

"It is pine nuts roasting in the cones," said the Basket Woman; "so it was of old time."

They came out of the cleft of the hills in a pleasant place by singing water. "There you will see the rows of wickiups," said the Basket Woman, "with the doors all opening eastward to the sun. Let us sit here and see what we shall see."

The women sat by the wickiups weaving baskets of willow and stems of fern. They made patterns of bright feathers and strung wampum about the rims. Some sewed with sinew and needles of cactus thorn on deerskin white and fine; others winnowed the corn. They stood up tossing it in baskets like grains of gold, and the wind carried away the chaff. All this time the young girls were laughing as they dried their hair in the sun. They bound it with flowers and gay strings of beads, and made their cheeks bright with red earth. The children romped and shouted about the camp, and ran bare-legged in the stream.

"Do they do nothing but play?" said Alan.

"You shall see," said the Basket Woman.

Away up the mountain sounded a faint halloo. In a moment all the camp was bustle and delight. The children clapped their hands; they left off playing and began to drag up brushwood for the fires. The women put away their weaving and brought out the cooking-pots; they heard the men returning from the hunt. The young men brought deer upon their shoulders; one had grouse and one held up a great basket of trout. The women made the meat ready for cooking. Some of them took meal and made cakes for baking in the ashes. The men rested in the glow of the fires, feathering arrows and restringing their bows.

"That is well," said the Basket Woman, "to make ready for to-morrow's meat before to-day's is eaten."

"How happy they are!" said the boy.

"They will be happier when they have eaten," said she.

After supper the Indians gathered together for singing and dancing. The old men told tales one after the other, and the children thought each one was the best. Between the tales the Indians all sang together, or one sang a new song that he had made. There was one of them who did better than all. He had streaked his body with colored earth and had a band of eagle feathers in his hair. In his hand was a rattle of wild sheep's horn and small stones; he kept time with it as he leapt and sang in the light of the fire. He sang of old wars, sang of the deer that was killed, sang of the dove and the young grass that grew on the mountain; and the people were well pleased, for when the heart is in the singing it does not matter much what the song is about. The men beat their hands together to keep time to his dancing, and the earth under his feet was stamped to a fine dust.

"He is one that has found the wolf's song," said the Basket Woman.

"What is that?" asked Alan.

"It is an old tale of my people," said she. "Once there was a man who could not make any songs, so he got no praise from the tribe, and it troubled him much. Then, as he was gathering taboose by the river, a wolf went by, and the wolf said to him, 'What will you have me to give you for your taboose?' Then said the man, 'I will have you to give me a song.'

"'That will I gladly,' said the wolf. So the wolf taught him, and that night he sang the wolf's song in the presence of all the people, and it made their hearts to burn within them. Then the man fell down as if he were dead, for the pure joy of singing, and when deep sleep was upon him the wolf came in the night and stole his song away. Neither the man nor any one who had heard it remembered it any more. So we say when a man sings as no other sang before him, 'He has the wolf's song.' It is a good saying. Now we must go, for the children are all asleep by their mothers, and the day comes soon," said the Basket Woman.

"Shall we come again?" said Alan. "And will it all be as it is now?"

"My people come often to the valley of Corn Water," said she, "but it is never as it is now except in dreams. Now we must go quickly." Far up the trail they saw a grayness in the eastern sky where the day was about to come in.

"Hark," said the Basket Woman, "they will sing together the coyote song. It is so that they sing it when the coyote goes home from his hunting, and the morning is near.

> The coyote cries . . .
> He cries at daybreak . . .
> He cries . . .
> The coyote cries . . .

sang the Basket Woman, but all the spaces in between the words were filled with long howls,—weird, wicked noises that seemed to hunt and double in a half-human throat. It made the hair on Alan's neck stand up, and cold shivers creep along his back. He began to shake, for the wild howls drew near and louder, and he felt the bed under him tremble with his trembling.

"Mother, mother," he cried, "what is that?"

"It is only the coyotes," said she; "they always howl about this time of night. It is nothing; go to sleep again."

"But I am afraid."

"They cannot hurt you," said his mother; "it is only the little gray beasts that you see trotting about the mesa of afternoons; hear them now."

"I am afraid," said Alan.

"Then you must come in my bed," said she; and in a few minutes he was fast asleep again.

❖   ❖   ❖

The Basket Woman: Second Story

In the Basket Woman's first story, she shows Alan that the poverty and listlessness of her tribe's present life is a result of its contact with whites, that its culture was rich and food plentiful in a past that is now only a dream. Her second story, told in response to Alan's sorrow over the wishful and sad eyes of the Indians he meets in town, is far more ambiguous. Well aware of the tradition of Cooper, Austin was unwilling to romanticize Native American lives; she considered the noble savage to be as stereotypical as the bloodthirsty demon. "The Basket Woman: Second Story" suggests that there are two sides to every story, though in this case both originate from the Basket Woman's point of view.

Yet it is unnerving that Alan's mother gets the last word, as if her conclusion is the right one, and that the Basket Woman seems to suggest that intertribal warfare led to the Paiutes' departure from their homeland. Austin spent her entire adult life trying to preserve Native American culture, and she surely did not believe that Indians were "better off" without it. An adult reader can see the naïveté of Alan's neat either/or conclusion, can understand Austin's efforts to present a multifaceted historical treatment of what caused the "dwindling away" of the Paiutes. The Basket Woman's story shows the costs of war from a woman's point of view, and since the Basket Woman is based on Paiute women Austin knew, her story may well reflect their view of their history before whites appeared. Nevertheless, it is surprising that Austin did not more overtly undercut the final message of this story. Perhaps the Basket Woman should have told Alan some of the stories she is too sad to tell in order to help him interpret what he sees in a more complex way.*

The next time Alan saw the Basket Woman he was not nearly so much afraid of her, though he did not venture to speak of their journey to Pahrump. He said to his mother, "Do you not wish the Indians could have stayed the way they were?" and his mother laughed.

"Why, no, child," she said, "I do not think that I do. I think they are much better off as they are now." Alan, however, was not to be convinced. The next time he saw the Basket Woman he was even troubled about it.

The homesteader had taken his family to the town for a day, and the first thing Alan saw when he got down from the wagon was the Basket Woman. She was sitting in a corner of the sidewalk with a group of other mahalas, with her blanket drawn over her shoulders, looking out upon the town, and her eyes were dull and strange.

A stream of people went by them in the street, and minded them no more than the dogs they stepped over, sprawling at the doors of the stores. Some of the Indian women had children with them, but they neither shouted nor ran as they had done in the camp of Corn Water; they sat quietly by their mothers, and Alan noticed how worn and poor were the clothes of all of them, and how wishful all the eyes. He could not get his mind off them because he could not get them out of his sight for very long at a time. It was a very small town, and as he went with his mother in and about the stores he would be coming face to face with the mahalas every little while, and the Basket Woman's eyes were always sad.

His mother, when she had finished her shopping, gave him a silver dime and told him that he might spend it as he wished. As soon as Alan had turned the corner on that errand there was the Basket Woman with her chin upon her knees and her blanket drawn over her shoulders. Alan stopped a moment in front of her; he would have liked to say something comforting, but found himself still afraid.

Her eyes looked on beyond him, blurred and dim; he supposed she must be thinking of the happy valley, and grew so very sorry for her that, as he could not get the courage to speak, he threw his dime into her lap and ran as fast as he could away. It seemed to him as he ran that she called to him, but he could not be sure.

That night, almost as soon as he had touched the pillow, she came and stood beside him without motion or sound, and let down the basket from her back.

"Do we go to Corn Water?" asked Alan as he stepped into it.

"To my people of old time," said the Basket Woman, "so that you need not be so much sorry."

Then they went out by the mesa trail, where the sage showed duskily under a thin rim of moon. It seemed to Alan that they went slowly, almost heavily. When they came to the parting of the ways, she let down the basket to rest. A rabbit popped, startled, out of the brush, and scurried into the dark; its white tail, like a signal, showed the way it went.

"What was that?" asked Alan.

"Only little Tavwots, whom we scared out of his nest. Lean forward," she said, "and I will tell you a tale about him." So the boy leaned his head against the Basket Woman's long black hair, and heard the story of Little Tavwots and How He Caught the Sun in a Snare.

"It was long ago," said the Basket Woman. "Tavwots was the largest of all four-footed things, and a mighty hunter. He would get up as soon as it was day and go to his hunting, but always before him was the track of a great foot on the trail; and this troubled him, for his pride was as big as his body and greater than his fame.

"'Who is this?' cried Tavwots, 'that goes with so great a stride before me to the hunting? Does he think to put me to shame?'

"'T'-sst!' said his mother, 'there is none greater than thee.'

"'Nevertheless,' said Tavwots, 'there are the footprints in the trail.' The next morning he got up earlier but there were always the great footprints and the long stride before him.

"'Now I will set me a trap for this impudent fellow,' said Tavwots, for he was very cunning. So he made a snare of his bowstring and set it in the trail overnight, and in the morning when he went to look, behold, he had caught the sun in his snare. All that quarter of the earth was beginning to smoke with the heat of it.

"'Is it you?' cried Tavwots, 'who made the tracks in my trail?'

"'It is I,' said the sun. 'Come now and set me free before the whole earth is afire.' Then Tavwots saw what he had to do, so he drew his knife and ran to cut the bowstring. But the heat was so great that he ran back before he had done it, and was melted down to one half his size. Then the smoke of the burning earth began to curl up against the sky.

"'Come again, Tavwots,' cried the sun. So he ran again and ran back, and the third time he ran he cut the bowstring, and the sun was set free from the snare. But by that time Tavwots was melted down to as small as he is now, and so he remains. Still you may see by the print of his feet as he leaps in the trail how great his stride was when he caught the sun in his snare.

"So it is always," said the Basket Woman, "that which is large grows less, and my people, which were great, have dwindled away."

After that she became quiet, and they went on over the mountain. Because he was beginning to be acquainted with it, the way seemed shorter to Alan than before. They passed over the high barren ridges, and he began to look for the camp at Corn Water.

"I see no smoke," said Alan.

"It would bring down their enemies like buzzards on carrion," said the Basket Woman.

"There is no sound of singing nor of laughter," said the boy.

"Who laughs in the time of war?" said she.

"Is there war?" asked Alan.

"Long and bitter," said the Basket Woman. "Let us go softly and come upon them unawares."

So they went, light of foot, among the pines until they saw the wickiups opening eastward to the sun, but many of them stood ruined and awry. There were only the very old and the children in the camp, and these did not run and play. They stole about like mice in the meadow sod, and if so much as a twig snapped in the forest, they huddled motionless as young quail. The women worked in the growing corn; they dug roots on the hill slope and caught grasshoppers for food. One made a noose of her long black hair plucked out, and snared the bright lizards that ran among the rocks. It seemed to Alan that the Indians looked wishful and thinner than they should; but such food as they found was all put by.

"Why do they do this?" asked the boy.

"That the men who go to war may not go fasting," said the Basket Woman. "Look, now we shall have news of them."

A young man came noiselessly out of the wood, and it was he who had sung the new song on the night of feasting and dancing. He had eagle feathers in his hair, but they were draggled; there was beadwork on his leggings, but it was torn with thorns; there was paint on his face and his body, but it was smeared over red, and as he came into the camp he broke his bow across his knee.

"It is a token of defeat," said the Basket Woman; "the others will come soon." But some came feebly because of wounds, and it seemed the women looked for some who might never come. They cast up their arms and cried with a terrible wailing sound that rose and shuddered among the pines.

"Be still," said the young man; "would you bring our enemies down upon us with your screeching?" Then the women threw themselves quietly in the dust, and rocked to and fro with sobbing; their stillness was more bitter than their crying.

Suddenly out of the wood came a storm of arrows, a rush of strange, painted braves, and the din of fighting.

"Shut your eyes," said the Basket Woman, "it is not good for you to see." Alan hid his face in the Basket Woman's dress, and heard the noise of fighting rage and die away. When he ventured to look again on the ruined huts and the trampled harvest, there were few left in the camp of Corn Water, and they had enough to do to find food for their poor bodies. They winnowed the creek with basketwork weirs for every finger-long troutling that came down in it, and tore the bark off the pine trees to get at the grubs underneath.

"Why do they not go out and kill deer as before?" asked Alan.

"Their enemies lurk in the wood and drive away the game," said the Basket Woman.

"Why do they not go to another place?"

"Where shall they go, when their foes watch every pass?" said she.

It seemed to Alan that many days and nights passed while they watched by the camp; and the days were all sorrowful, and always, as before, the best meat was set aside for the strongest.

"Why is this so?" asked the boy.

"Because," said the Basket Woman, "those who are strong must stay so to care for the rest. It is the way of my people. You see that the others do not complain." And it was so that the feeble ones tottered silently about the camp or sat still a long time in one place with their heads upon their knees.

"How will it end?" asked Alan.

"They must go away at last," said she, "though the cords of their hearts are fastened here. But there is no seed corn, and the winter is close at hand."

Then there began to be a tang of frost in the air, and the people gathered up their household goods, and, though there was not much of them, they staggered and bent under the burden as they went up out of the once happy valley to another home. The women let down their long hair and smeared ashes upon it; they threw up their lean arms and wailed long and mournfully as they passed among the pines. Alan began to tremble with crying, and felt the Basket Woman patting him on the shoulder. Her voice sounded to him like the voice of his mother telling him to go to sleep again, for there was nothing for him to be troubled about. After he grew quieter, the Indan woman lifted him up. "We must be going," she said, "it is not good for us to be here."

Alan wished as they went up over the mountain that she would help him with talk toward forgetting what he had seen, but the long hair fell over her face and she would not talk. He shivered in the basket, and the night felt colder and full of fearsome noises.

"What is that?" he whispered, as a falling star trailed all across the dark.

"It is the coyote people that brought the fire to my people," said the Basket Woman. Alan hoped she would tell him a tale about it, but she would not. They went on down the mountain until they came to the borders of the long-leaved pines. Alan heard the sough of the wind in the needles, and it seemed as if it called.

"What is that?" he whispererd.

"It is Hí-no-no, the wind, mourning for his brother, the pine tree," but she would not tell him that tale, either. She went faster and faster, and Alan felt the stir of her shoulders under him. He listened to the wind, and it grew fierce and louder until he heard the house beams creak, for he was awake in his own bed. A strong wind drove gustily across the mesa and laid hold of the corners of the roof.

The next morning the homesteader said that he must go to the campoodie and Alan might go with him. Alan was quite pleased, and said to his mother while she was getting him ready, "Do you know, I think Indians are a great deal better off as they are now."

"Why, yes," said his mother, smiling, "I think so, too."

❖ ❖ ❖

The Coyote-Spirit and the Weaving Woman

"The Coyote-Spirit and the Weaving Woman" is a western tall tale from a woman's point of view; it turns upon emotional rather than physical strength, on vision, the ability to look deeper and deeper into things rather than the desire to control others and keep them out of one's territory. The Weaving Woman, who does not realize that she looks at the world differently from others, is yet another of Austin's chiseras; she has the power to make others see more in the world and in themselves. The story presents a particularly rich treatment of how the artist expresses herself and her relationship to nature in her art. Also typical of Austin's chisera stories is the contrast between the Goat-Girl, the traditional woman who "always stayed in the safe open places,"

and the Weaving Woman, who, like her creator, seeks the place where all the trails converge.

Eventually the Weaving Woman wanders into the Coyote-Spirit's range and, in his view, "must expect to take the consequences." His coyote side expresses the violence and possessiveness often associated with the western male, but the Weaving Woman only laughs at his blustering, refusing to see that side of him, insisting that he is "only a man." By refusing to acknowledge the beast, she helps him to affirm his humanity. The story becomes a parable about what the nontraditional woman can offer men. In this light, the Coyote-Spirit's conventional choice at the story's end becomes all the more ironic.[1]

The Weaving Woman lived under the bank of the stony wash that cut through the country of the mesquite dunes. The Coyote-Spirit, which, you understand, is an Indian whose form has been changed to fit with his evil behavior, ranged from the Black Rock where the wash began to the white sands beyond Pahranagat; and the Goat-Girl kept her flock among the mesquites, or along the windy stretch of sage below the cam-

---

1. I am indebted to my student Robert Schirmer for his insights about this story.

poodie; but as the Coyote-Spirit never came near the wickiups by day, and the Goat-Girl went home the moment the sun dropped behind Pahrana-gat, they never met. These three are all that have to do with the story.

The Weaving Woman, whose work was the making of fine baskets of split willow and roots of yucca and brown grass, lived alone, because there was nobody found who wished to live with her, and because it was whis-pered among the wickiups that she was different from other people. It was reported that she had an infirmity of the eyes which caused her to see everything with rainbow fringes, bigger and brighter and better than it was. All her days were fruitful, a handful of pine nuts as much to make merry over as a feast; every lad who went by a-hunting with his bow at his back looked to be a painted brave, and every old woman digging roots as fine as a medicine man in all his feathers. All the faces at the campoodie, dark as the mingled sand and lava of the Black Rock country, deep lined with work and weather, shone for this singular old woman with the glory of the late evening light on Pahranagat. The door of her wickiup opened toward the campoodie with the smoke going up from cheerful hearths, and from the shadow of the bank where she sat to make baskets she looked down the stony wash where all the trails converged that led every way among the dunes, and saw an enchanted mesa covered with misty bloom and gentle creatures moving on trails that seemed to lead to the places where one had always wished to be.

Since all this was so, it was not surprising that her baskets turned out to be such wonderful affairs, and the tribesmen, though they winked and wagged their heads, were very glad to buy them for a haunch of venison or a bagful of mesquite meal. Sometimes, as they stroked the perfect curves of the bowls or traced out the patterns, they were heard to sigh, thinking how fine life would be if it were so rich and bright as she made it seem, instead of the dull occasion they had found it. There were some who even said it was a pity, since she was so clever at the craft, that the weaver was not more like other people, and no one thought to suggest that in that case her weaving would be no better than theirs. For all this the basket-maker did not care, sitting always happily at her weaving or wandering far into the desert in search of withes and barks and dyes, where the wild things showed her many a wonder hid from those who have not rainbow fringes to their eyes; and because she was not afraid of anything, she went farther and farther into the silent places until in the course of time she met the Coyote-Spirit.

Now a Coyote-Spirit, from having been a man, is continually thinking about men and wishing to be with them, and, being a coyote and of the wolf's breed, no sooner does he have his wish than he thinks of devouring. So as soon as this one had met the Weaving Woman he desired to eat her up, or to work her some evil according to the evil of his nature. He did not see any opportunity to begin at the first meeting, for on account of the infirmity of her eyes the woman did not see him as a coyote, but as a man, and let down her wicker water bottle for him to drink, so kindly that he was quite abashed. She did not seem in the least afraid of him, which is disconcerting even to a real coyote; though if he had been, she need not have been afraid of him in any case. Whatever pestiferous beast the Indian may think the dog of the wilderness, he has no reason to fear him except when by certain signs, as having a larger and leaner body, a sharper muzzle, and more evilly pointed ears, he knows him the soul of a bad-hearted man going about in that guise. There are enough of these Coyote-Spirits ranging in Mesquite Valley and over towards Funeral Mountains and about Pahranagat to give certain learned folk surmise as to whether there may not be a strange breed of wolves in that region; but the Indians know better.

When the Coyote-Spirit who had met the basket woman thought about it afterward, he said to himself that she deserved all the mischance that might come upon her for that meeting. "She knows," he said, "that this is my range, and whoever walks in a Coyote-Spirit's range must expect to take the consequences. She is not at all like the Goat-Girl."

The Coyote-Spirit had often watched the Goat-Girl from the top of Pahranagat, but because she was always in the open where no lurking-places were, and never far from the corn lands where the old men might be working, he had made himself believe he would not like that kind of a girl. Every morning he saw her come out of her leafy hut, loose the goats from the corral, which was all of cactus stems and broad leaves of prickly-pear, and lead them out among the wind-blown hillocks of sand under which the trunks of the mesquite flourished for a hundred years, and out of the tops of which the green twigs bore leaves and fruit; or along the mesa to browse on bitterbrush and the tops of scrubby sage. Sometimes she plaited willows for the coarser kinds of basketwork, or, in hot noonings while the flock dozed, worked herself collars and necklaces of white and red and turquoise-colored beads, and other times sat dreaming on the sand. But whatever she did, she kept far enough from the place of the Coyote-Spirit, who, now that he had met the Weaving Woman, could not keep his mind off her. Her hut was far enough from the campoodie so that every morning he went around by the Black Rock to see if she was still there, and there she sat weaving patterns in her baskets of all that she saw or thought. Now it would be the winding wash and the wattled huts beside it, now the mottled skin of the rattlesnake or the curled plumes of the quail.

At last the Coyote-Spirit grew so bold that when there was no one passing on the trail he would go and walk up and down in front of the wickiup. Then the Weaving Woman would look up from her work and give him the news of the season and the tribesmen in so friendly a fashion that he grew less and less troubled in his mind about working her mischief. He said in his evil heart that since the ways of such as he were known to the Indians,—as indeed they were, with many a charm and spell to keep them safe,—it could be no fault of his if they came to harm through too much familiarity. As for the Weaving Woman, he said, "She sees me as I am, and ought to know better," for he had not heard about the infirmity of her eyes.

Finally he made up his mind to ask her to go with him to dig for roots around the foot of Pahranagat, and if she consented,—and of course she did, for she was a friendly soul,—he knew in his heart what he would do. They went out by the mesa trail, and it was a soft and blossomy day of spring. Long wands of the creosote with shining fretted foliage were hung with creamy bells of bloom, and doves called softly from the Dripping Spring. They passed rows of owlets sitting by their burrows and saw young rabbits playing in their shallow forms. The Weaving Woman talked gayly as they went, as Indian women talk, with soft mellow voices and laughter breaking in between the words like smooth water flowing over stones. She talked of how the deer had shifted their feeding-grounds and of whether the quail had mated early that year as a sign of a good season, matters of which the Coyote-Spirit knew more than she, only he was not thinking of those things just then. Whenever her back was turned he licked his cruel jaws and whetted his appetite. They passed the level mesa, passed the tumbled fragments of the Black Rock and came to the sharp wall-sided cañons that showed the stars at noon from their deep wells of sombre shade, where no wild creature made its home and no birds ever sang. Then the Weaving Woman grew still at last because of the great stillness, and the Coyote-Spirit said in a hungry, whining voice,—

"Do you know why I brought you here?"

"To show me how still and beautiful the world is here," said the Weaving Woman, and even then she did not seem afraid.

"To eat you up," said the Coyote. With that he looked to see her fall quaking at his feet, and he had it in mind to tell her it was no fault but her own for coming so far astray with one of his kind, but the woman only looked at him and laughed. The sound of her laughter was like water in a bubbling spring.

"Why do you laugh?" said the Coyote, and he was so astonished that his jaws remained open when he had done speaking.

"How could you eat me?" said she. "Only wild beasts could do that."

"What am I, then?"

"Oh, you are only a man."

"I am a coyote," said he.

"Do you think I have no eyes?" said the woman. "Come!" For she did not understand that her eyes were different from other people's, what she really thought was that other people's were different from hers, which is quite another matter, so she pulled the Coyote-Spirit over to a rain-fed pool. In that country the rains collect in basins of the solid rock that grow polished with a thousand years of storm and give back from their shining side a reflection like a mirror. One such lay in the bottom of the black cañon, and the Weaving Woman stood beside it.

Now it is true of Coyote-Spirits that they are so only because of their behavior; not only have they power to turn themselves to men if they wish—but they do not wish, or they would not have become coyotes in the first place—but other people in their company, according as they think man-thoughts or beast-thoughts, can throw over them such a change that they have only to choose which they will be. So the basket-weaver contrived to throw the veil of her mind over the Coyote-Spirit, so that when he looked at himself in the pool he could not tell for the life of him whether he was most coyote or most man, which so frightened him that he ran away and left the Weaving Woman to hunt for roots alone. He ran for three days and nights, being afraid of himself, which is the worst possible fear, and then ran back to see if the basket-maker had not changed her mind. He put his head in at the door of her wickiup.

"Tell me, now, am I a coyote or a man?"

"Oh, a man," said she, and he went off to Pahranagat to think it over. In a day or two he came back.

"And what now?" he said.

"Oh, a man, and I think you grow handsomer every day."

That was really true, for what with her insisting upon it and his thinking about it, the beast began to go out of him and the man to come back. That night he went down to the campoodie to try and steal a kid from the corral, but it occurred to him just in time that a man would not do that, so he went back to Pahranagat and ate roots and berries instead, which was a true sign that he had grown into a man again. Then there came a day when the Weaving Woman asked him to stop at her hearth and eat. There was a savory smell going up from the cooking-pots, cakes of mesquite meal baking in the ashes, and sugary white buds of the yucca palm roasting on the coals. The man who had been a coyote lay on a blanket of rabbit skin and heard the cheerful snapping of the fire. It was all so comfortable and bright that somehow it made him think of the Goat-Girl.

"That is the right sort of a girl," he said to himself. "She has always stayed in the safe open places and gone home early. She should be able to tell me what I am," for he was not quite sure, and since he had begun to walk with men a little, he had heard about the Weaving Woman's eyes.

Next day he went out where the flock fed, not far from the corn lands, and the Goat-Girl did not seem in the least afraid of him. So he went again, and the third day he said,—

"Tell me what I seem to you."

"A very handsome man," said she.

"Then will you marry me?" said he; and when the Goat-Girl had taken time to think about it she said yes, she thought she would.

Now, when the man who had been a coyote lay on the blanket of the Weaving Woman's wickiup, he had taken notice how it was made of willows driven into the ground around a pit dug in the earth, and the poles drawn together at the top, and thatched with brush, and he had tried at the foot of Pahranagat until he had built another like it; so when he had married the Goat-Girl, after the fashion of her tribe, he took her there to live. He was not now afraid of anything except that his wife might get to know that he had once been a coyote. It was during the first month of their marriage that he said to her, "Do you know the basket-maker who lives under the bank of the stony wash? They call her the Weaving Woman."

"I have heard something of her and I have bought her baskets. Why do you ask?"

"It is nothing," said the man, "but I hear strange stories of her, that she associates with Coyote-Spirits and such creatures," for he wanted to see what his wife would say to that.

"If that is the case," said she, "the less we see of her the better. One cannot be too careful in such matters."

After that, when the man who had been a coyote and his wife visited the campoodie, they turned out of the stony wash before they reached the wickiup, and came in to the camp by another trail. But I have not heard whether the Weaving Woman noticed it.

Mahala Joe

A main theme in The Basket Woman *is the development of a bond between the Basket Woman and Alan, who come to care about and trust one another. Austin had learned of the compassion and generosity of Paiute women firsthand, and several of her stories explore ties between women of different races and cultures. In "Mahala Joe," the collection's final story, Austin turns to the theme of brotherhood between races. The story pattern for "Mahala Joe" is a familiar one in American literature: two males innocently trust their feelings and create a bond that implicitly challenges racism. Yet from the story's beginning, when Walter names Joe, Austin quietly exposes how whites ignore Indian cultural traditions, how unequal "brothers" can be. It is the Indian boy who is* made to pay for the feelings his brother apparently outgrows, to pay for the relationship as the Indian tribes eventually paid for their initial friendship with white settlers. Austin called "Mahala Joe" a hero myth, and though Joe, like Tom of Uncle Tom's Cabin *and Jim of Huckleberry Finn, is perhaps too long-suffering and self-sacrificing in his tragic heroism, she admired his inability to put abstract hatreds before individual friendships.*

Finally, "Mahala Joe," like many of Austin's children's stories, turns on an irony perhaps too subtle for children: the meaning of the "badge of an all but intolerable shame" for a man, the wearing of a woman's dress, is undercut when the reader realizes that the dress signifies not cowardice but courage.

In the campoodie of Three Pines, which you probably know better by its Spanish name of Tres Pinos, there is an Indian, well thought of among his own people, who goes about wearing a woman's dress, and is known as Mahala Joe. He should be about fifty years old by this time, and has a quiet, kindly face. Sometimes he tucks up the skirt of his woman's dress over a pair of blue overalls when he has a man's work to do, but at feasts and dances he wears a ribbon around his waist and a handkerchief on his head as the other mahalas do. He is much looked to because of his knowledge of white people and their ways, and if it were not for the lines of deep sadness that fall in his face when at rest, one might forget that the woman's gear is the badge of an all but intolerable shame. At least it was so used by the Paiutes, but when you have read this full and true account of how it was first put on, you may not think it so.

Fifty years ago the valley about Tres Pinos was all one sea of moving grass and dusky, greenish sage, cropped over by deer and antelope, north as far as Togobah, and south to the Bitter Lake. Beside every considerable stream which flowed into it from the Sierras was a Paiute campoodie, and all they knew of white people was by hearsay from the tribes across the mountains. But soon enough cattlemen began to push their herds through the Sierra passes to the Paiutes' feeding-ground. The Indians saw them come, and though they were not very well pleased, they held still by the counsel of their old men; night and day they made medicine and prayed that the white men might go away.

Among the first of the cattlemen in the valley about Tres Pinos was Joe Baker, who brought a young wife, and built his house not far from the campoodie. The Indian women watched her curiously from afar because of a whisper that ran among the wattled huts. When the year was far gone, and the sun-cured grasses curled whitish brown, a doctor came riding hard from the fort at Edswick, forty miles to the south, and though they watched, they did not see him ride away. It was the third day at evening when Joe Baker came walking towards the campoodie, and his face was set and sad. He carried something rolled in a blanket, and looked anxiously at the women as he went between the huts. It was about the hour of the evening meal, and the mahalas sat about the fires watching the cooking-pots. He came at last opposite a young woman who sat nursing her child. She had a bright, pleasant face, and her little one seemed about six months old. Her husband stood near and watched them with great pride. Joe Baker knelt down in front of the mahala, and opened the roll of blankets. He showed her a day-old baby that wrinkled up its small face and cried.

"Its mother is dead," said the cattleman. The young Indian mother did not know English, but she did not need speech to know what had happened. She looked pitifully at the child, and at her husband timidly. Joe Baker went and laid his rifle and cartridge belt at the Paiute's feet. The Indian picked up the gun and fingered it; his wife smiled. She put down her own child, and lifted the little white stranger to her breast. It nuzzled against her and hushed its crying; the young mother laughed.

"See how greedy it is," she said; "it is truly white." She drew up the blanket around the child and comforted it.

The cattleman called to him one of the Indians who could speak a little English.

"Tell her," he said, "that I wish her to care for the child. His name is Walter. Tell her that she is to come to my house for everything he needs, and for every month that he keeps fat and well she shall have a fat steer from my herd." So it was agreed.

As soon as Walter was old enough he came to sleep at his father's house, but the Indian woman, whom he called *Ebia,* came every day to tend him. Her son was his brother, and Walter learned to speak Paiute before he learned English. The two boys were always together, but as yet the little Indian had no name. It is not the custom among Paiutes to give names to those who have not done anything worth naming.

"But I have a name," said Walter, "and so shall he. I will call him Joe. That is my father's name, and it is a good name, too."

When Mr. Baker was away with the cattle, Walter slept at the campoo-die, and Joe's mother made him a buckskin shirt. At that time he was so brown with the sun and the wind that only by his eyes could you tell that he was white; he was also very happy. But as this is to be the story of how Joe came to the wearing of a woman's dress, I cannot tell you all the plays they had, how they went on their first hunting, nor what they found in the creek of Tres Pinos.

The beginning of the whole affair of Mahala Joe must be laid to the arrow-maker. The arrow-maker had a stiff knee from a wound in a long-gone battle, and for that reason he sat in the shade of his wickiup, and chipped arrow points from flakes of obsidian that the young men brought him from Togobah, fitting them to shafts of reeds from the river marsh. He used to coax the boys to wade in the brown water and cut the reeds, for the dampness made his knee ache. They drove bargains with him for arrows for their own hunting, or for the sake of the stories he could tell. For an armful of reeds he would make three arrows, and for a double armful he would tell tales. These were mostly of great huntings and old wars, but when it was winter, and no snakes in the long grass to overhear, he would tell Wonder-stories. The boys would lie with their toes in the warm ashes, and the arrow-maker would begin.

"You can see," said the arrow-maker, "on the top of Waban the tall boul-der looking on the valleys east and west. That is the very boundary be-tween the Paiute country and Shoshone land. The boulder is a hundred times taller than the tallest man, and thicker through than six horses stand-ing nose to tail; the shadow of it falls all down the slope. At mornings it falls toward the Paiute peoples, and evenings it falls on Shoshone land.

Now on this side of the valley, beginning at the campoodie, you will see a row of pine trees standing all upstream one behind another. See, the long branches grow on the side toward the hill; and some may tell you it is because of the way the wind blows, but I say it is because they reach out in a hurry to get up the mountain. Now I will tell you how these things came about.

"Very long ago all the Paiutes of this valley were ruled by two brothers, a chief and a medicine man, Winnedumah and Tinnemaha. They were both very wise, and one of them never did anything without the other. They taught the tribes not to war upon each other, but to stand fast as brothers, and so they brought peace into the land. At that time there were no white people heard of, and game was plenty. The young honored the old, and nothing was as it is now."

When the arrow-maker came to this point, the boys fidgeted with their toes, and made believe to steal the old man's arrows to distract his attention. They did not care to hear about the falling off of the Paiutes; they wished to have the tale. Then the arrow-maker would hurry on to the time when there arose a war between the Paiutes and the Shoshones. Then Winnedumah put on his war bonnet, and Tinnemaha made medicine. Word went around among the braves that if they stood together man to man as brothers, then they should have this war.

"And so they might," said the arrow-maker, "but at last their hearts turned to water. The tribes came together on the top of Waban. Yes; where the boulder now stands, for that is the boundary of our lands, for no brave would fight off his own ground for fear of the other's medicine. So they fought. The eagles heard the twang of the bowstring, and swung down from White Mountain. The vultures smelled the smell of battle, and came in from Shoshone land. Their wings were dark like a cloud, and underneath the arrows flew like hail. The Paiutes were the better bowmen, and they caught the Shoshone arrows where they struck in the earth and shot them back again. Then the Shoshones were ashamed, and about the time of the sun going down they called upon their medicine men, and one let fly a magic arrow,—for none other would touch him,—and it struck in the throat of Tinnemaha.

"Now when that befell," went on the arrow-maker, "the braves forgot the word that had gone before the battle, for they turned their backs to the medicine man, all but Winnedumah, his brother, and fled this way from Waban. Then stood Winnedumah by Tinnemaha, for that was the way of those two; whatever happened, one would not leave the other. There was none left to carry on the fight, and yet since he was so great a chief the Shoshones were afraid to take him, and the sun went down. In the dusk they saw a bulk, and they said, 'He is still standing'; but when it was morning light they saw only a great rock, so you see it to this day. As for the braves who ran away, they were changed to pine trees, but in their hearts they are cowards yet, therefore they stretch out their arms and strive toward the mountain. And that," said the arrow-maker, "is how the tall stones came to be on the top of Waban. But it was not in my day nor my father's." Then the boys would look up at Winnedumah, and were half afraid, and as for the tale, they quite believed it.

The arrow-maker was growing old. His knee hurt him in cold weather, and he could not make arrow points fast enough to satisfy the boys, who lost a great many in the winter season shooting at ducks in the tulares. Walter's father promised him a rifle when he was fifteen, but that was years away. There was a rock in the cañon behind Tres Pinos with a great crack in the top. When the young men rode to the hunting, they shot each an arrow at it, and if it stuck it was a promise of good luck. The boys scaled the rock by means of a grapevine ladder, and pried out the old points. This gave them an idea.

"Upon Waban where the fighting was, there must be a great many arrow points," said Walter.

"So there must be," said Joe.

"Let us go after them," said the white boy; but the other dared not, for no Paiute would go within a bowshot of Winnedumah; nevertheless, they talked the matter over.

"How near would you go?" asked Walter.

"As near as a strong man might shoot an arrow," said Joe.

"If you will go so far," said Walter, "I will go the rest of the way."

"It is a two days' journey," said the Paiute, but he did not make any other objection.

It was a warm day of spring when they set out. The cattleman was off to the river meadow, and Joe's mother was out with the other mahalas gathering taboose.

"If I were fifteen, and had my rifle, I would not be afraid of anything," said Walter.

"But in that case we would not need to go after arrow points," said the Indian boy.

They climbed all day in a bewildering waste of boulders and scrubby trees. They could see Winnedumah shining whitely on the ridge ahead, but when they had gone down into the gully with great labor, and up the other side, there it stood whitely just another ridge away.

"It is like the false water in the desert," said Walter. "It goes farther from you, and when you get to it there is no water there."

"It is magic medicine," said Indian Joe. "No good comes of going against medicine."

"If you are afraid," said Walter, "why do you not say so? You may go back if you like, and I will go on by myself."

Joe would not make any answer to that. They were hot and tired, and awed by the stillness of the hills. They kept on after that, angry and apart; sometimes they lost sight of each other among the boulders and underbrush. But it seemed that it must really have been as one or the other of them had said, for when they came out on a high mesa presently, there was no Winnedumah anywhere in sight. They would have stopped then and taken counsel, but they were too angry for that, so they walked on in silence, and the day failed rapidly, as it will do in high places. They began to draw near together and to be afraid. At last the Indian boy stopped and gathered the tops of bushes together, and began to weave a shelter for the night, and when Walter saw that he made it large enough for two, he spoke to him.

"Are we lost?" he said.

"We are lost for to-night," said Joe, "but in the morning we will find ourselves."

They ate dried venison and drank from the wicker bottle, and huddled together because of the dark and the chill.

"Why do we not see the stone any more?" asked Walter in a whisper.

"I do not know," said Joe. "I think it has gone away."

"Will he come after us?"

"I do not know. I have on my elk's tooth," said Joe, and he clasped the charm that hung about his neck. They started and shivered, hearing a stone crash far away as it rolled down the mountain-side, and the wind began to move among the pines.

"Joe," said Walter, "I am sorry I said that you were afraid."

"It is nothing," said the Paiute. "Besides, I am afraid."

"So am I," whispered the other. "Joe," he said again after a long silence, "if he comes after us, what shall we do?"

"We will stay by each other."

"Like the two brothers, whatever happens," said the white boy, "forever and ever."

"We are two brothers," said Joe.

"Will you swear it?"

"On my elk's tooth."

Then they each took the elk's tooth in his hand and made a vow that whether Winnedumah came down from his rock, or whether the Shoshones found them, come what would, they would stand together. Then they were comforted, and lay down, holding each other's hands.

"I hear some one walking," said Walter.

"It is the wind among the pines," said Joe.

A twig snapped. "What is that?" said the one boy.

"It is a fox or a coyote passing," said the other, but he knew better. They lay still, scarcely breathing, and throbbed with fear. They felt a sense of a presence approaching in the night, the whisper of a moccasin on the gravelly soil, the swish of displaced bushes springing back to place. They saw a bulk shape itself out of the dark; it came and stood over them, and they saw that it was an Indian looking larger in the gloom. He spoke to them, and whether he spoke in a strange tongue, or they were too frightened to understand, they could not tell.

"Do not kill us!" cried Walter, but the Indian boy made no sound. The man took Walter by the shoulders and lifted him up.

"White," said he.

"We are brothers," said Joe; "we have sworn it."

"So," said the man, and it seemed as if he smiled.

"Until we die," said both the boys. The Indian gave a grunt.

"A white man," he said, "is—white." It did not seem as if that was what he meant to say.

"Come, I will take you to your people. They search for you about the foot of Waban. These three hours I have watched you and them." The boys clutched at each other in the dark. They were sure now who spoke to them, and between fear and fatigue and the cramp of cold they staggered and stumbled as they walked. The Indian stopped and considered them.

"I cannot carry both," he said.

"I am the older," said Joe; "I can walk." Without any more words the man picked up Walter, who trembled, and walked off down the slope. They went a long way through the scrub and under the tamarack pines. The man was naked to the waist, and had a quiver full of arrows on his shoulder.

The buckthorn branches whipped and scraped against his skin, but he did not seem to mind. At last they came to a place where they could see a dull red spark across an open flat.

"That," said the Indian, "is the fire of your people. They missed you at afternoon, and have been looking for you. From my station on the hill I saw." Then he took the boy by the shoulders.

"Look you," he said, "no good comes of mixing white and brown, but now that the vow is made, see to the keeping of it." Then he stepped back from them and seemed to melt into the dark. Ahead of them the boys saw the light of the fire flare up with new fuel, and shadows, which they knew for the figures of their friends, moved between them and the flame. Swiftly as two scared rabbits they ran on toward the glow.

When Walter and Joe had told them the story at the campoodie, the Paiutes made a great deal of it, especially the arrow-maker.

"Without a doubt," he said, "it was Winnedumah who came to you, and not, as some think, a Shoshone who was spying on our land. It is a great mystery. But since you have made a vow of brothers, you should keep it after the ancient use." Then he took a knife of obsidian and cut their arms, and rubbed a little of the blood of each upon the other.

"Now," he said, "you are one fellowship and one blood, and that is as it should be, for you were both nursed at one breast. See that you keep the vow."

"We will," said the boys solemnly, and they went out into the sunlight very proud of the blood upon their bared arms, holding by each other's hands.

I I

When Walter was fifteen his father gave him a rifle, as he had promised, and a word of advice with it.

"Learn to shoot quickly and well," he said, "and never ride out from home without it. No one can tell what this trouble with the Indians may come to in the end."

Walter rode straight to the campoodie. He was never happy in any of his gifts until he had showed them to Joe. There was a group of older men at the camp, quartering a deer which they had brought in. One of them, called Scar-Face, looked at Walter with a leering frown.

"See," he said, "they are arming the very children with guns."

"My father promised it to me many years ago," said Walter. "It is my birthday gift."

He could not explain why, and he grew angry at the man's accusing tone, but after it he did not like showing his present to the Indians.

He called Joe, and they went over to a cave in the black rock where they had kept their boyish treasures and planned their plays since they were children. Joe thought the rifle a beauty, and turned it over admiringly in the shadow of the cave. They tried shooting at a mark, and then decided to go up Oak Creek for a shot at the gray squirrels. There they sighted a band of antelope that led them over a tongue of hills into Little Round Valley, where they found themselves at noon twelve miles from home and very hungry. They had no antelope, but four squirrels and a grouse. The two boys made a fire for cooking in a quiet place by a spring of sweet water.

"You may have my rifle to use as often as you like," said Walter, "but you must not lend it to any one in the campoodie, especially to Scar-Face. My father says he is the one who is stirring up all this trouble with the whites."

"The white men do not need any one to help them get into trouble," said Joe. "They can do that for themselves."

"It is the fault of the Indians," said Walter. "If they did not shoot the cattle, the white men would leave them alone."

"But if the white men come first to our lands with noise and trampling and scare away the game, what then will they shoot?" asked the Paiute.

Walter did not make any answer to that. He had often gone hunting with Joe and his father, and he knew what it meant to walk far, and fasting, after game made shy by the rifles of cattlemen, and at last to return empty to the campoodie where there were women and children with hungry eyes.

"Is it true," he said after a while, "that Scar-Face is stirring up all the Indians in the valley?"

"How should I know?" said Joe; "I am only a boy, and have not killed big game. I am not admitted to the counsels of the old men. What does it matter to us whether of old feuds or new? Are we not brothers sworn?"

Then, as the dinner was done, they ate each of the other's kill, for it was the custom of the Paiutes at that time that no youth should eat game of his own killing until he was fully grown. As they walked homeward the boys planned to get permission to go up on Waban for a week, after mountain sheep, before the snows began.

Mr. Baker looked grave when Walter spoke to him.

"My boy," he said, "I wish you would not plan long trips like this without first speaking to me. It is hardly safe in the present state of feeling among the Indians to let you go with them in this fashion. A whole week, too. But as you have already spoken of it, and it has probably been talked over in the campoodie, for me to refuse now would look as if I suspected something, and might bring about the thing I most fear."

"You should not be afraid for me with Joe, father, for we are brothers sworn," said Walter, and he told his father how they had mixed the blood of their arms in the arrow-maker's hut after they had come back from their first journey on Waban.

"Well," said Mr. Baker, who had not heard of this before, "I know that they set great store by these superstitious customs, but I have not much faith in the word of a Paiute when he is dealing with a white man. However, you had better go on with this hunting trip. Take Hank with you, and Joe's father, and do not be gone more than five days at the outside."

Hank was one of Mr. Baker's vaqueros, and very glad to get off for a few days' hunting on the blunt top of Waban. On the Monday following they left the Baker ranch for the mountain. As the two boys rode up the boulder-strewn slope it set them talking of the first time they had gone that way on their fruitless hunt for arrow points about the foot of Winnedumah, and of all that happened to them at that time. The valley lay below them full of purple mist, and away by the creek of Tres Pinos the brown, wattled huts of the campoodie like great wasps' nests stuck in the sage. Hank and Joe's father, with the pack horses, were ahead of them far up the trail; Joe and Walter let their own ponies lag, and the nose of one touched the flank of the other as they climbed slowly up the steep, and the boys turned their faces to each other, as if they had some vague warning that they would not ride so and talk familiarly again, as if the boiling anger of the tribes in the valley had brewed a sort of mist that rose up and gloomed the pleasant air on the slope of Waban.

"Joe," said Walter, "my father says if it came to a fight between the white settlers and the Paiutes, that you would not hold by the word we have passed."

"That is the speech of a white man," said Joe.

"But would you?" the other insisted.

"I am a Paiute," said Joe; "I will hold by my people, also by my word; I will not fight against you."

"Nor I against you, but I would not like to have my father think you had broken your word."

"Have no care," said the Indian, "I will not break it."

Mr. Baker looked anxiously after his son as he rode to the hunting on

Waban; he looked anxiously up that trail every hour until the boy came again, and that, as it turned out, was at the end of three days. For the trouble among the Indians had come to something at last,—the wasps were all out of nest by the brown creeks, and with them a flight of stinging arrows. The trouble began at Cottonwood, and the hunting party on Waban the second day out saw a tall, pale column of smoke that rose up from the notch of the hill behind the settlement, and fanned out slowly into the pale blueness of the sky.

It went on evenly, neither more nor less, thick smoke from a fire of green wood steadily tended. Before noon another rose from the mouth of Oak Creek, and a third from Tunawai. They waved and beckoned to one another, calling to counsel.

"Signal fires," said Hank; "that means mischief."

And from that on he went with his rifle half cocked, and walked always so that he might keep Joe's father in full view. By night that same day there were seven smoke trees growing up in the long valley, and spreading thin, pale branches to the sky. There was no zest left in the hunt, and in the morning they owned it. Walter was worried by what he knew his father's anxiety must be. Then the party began to ride down again, and always Hank made the Indian go before. Away by the foot of Oppapago rose a black volume of smoke, thick, and lighted underneath by flames. It might be the reek of a burning ranch house. The boys were excited and afraid. They talked softly and crowded their ponies together on the trail.

"Joe," said Walter whisperingly, "if there is battle, you will have to go to it."

"Yes," said Joe.

"And you will fight; otherwise they will call you a coward, and if you run away, they will kill you."

"So I suppose," said Joe.

"Or they will make you wear a woman's dress like To-go-na-tee, the man who got up too late." This was a reminder from one of the arrow-maker's tales. "But you have promised not to fight."

"Look you," said the Indian boy; "if a white man came to kill me, I would kill him. That is right. But I will not fight you nor your father's house. That is my vow."

The white boy put out his hand, and laid it on the flank of the foremost pony. The Indian boy's fingers came behind him, and crept along the pony's back until they reached the other hand. They rode forward without talking.

Toward noon they made out horsemen riding on the trail below them. As it wound in and out around the blind gullies they saw and lost sight of them a dozen times. At last, where the fringe of the tall trees began, they came face to face. It was Mr. Baker and a party of five men; they carried rifles and had set and anxious looks.

"What will you have?" said Indian Joe's father as they drew up before him under a tamarack pine.

"My son," said the cattleman.

"Is there war?" said the Indian.

"There is war. Come, Walter."

The boys were still and scared. Slowly Hank and Walter drew their horses out of the path and joined the men. Indian Joe and his father passed forward on the trail.

"Do them no harm," said Joe Baker to those that were with him.

"Good-bye, Joe," said Walter half aloud.

The other did not turn his head, but as he went they noticed that he had bared his right arm from the hunting shirt, and an inch above the elbow showed a thin, white scar. Walter had the twin of that mark under his flannels.

Mr. Baker did not mind fighting Indians; he thought it a good thing to have their troubles settled all at once in this way, but he did not want his son mixed up in it. The first thing he did when he got home was to send him off secretly by night to the fort, and from there he passed over the mountains with other of the settlers' families under strong escort, and finally went to his mother's people in the East, and was put to school. As it turned out he never came back to Tres Pinos, he does not come into this story any more.

When the first smoke rose up that showed where the fierce hate of the Paiutes had broken into flame, the Indians took their women and children away from the pleasant open slopes, and hid them in deep cañons in secret places of the rocks. There they feathered arrows, and twisted bowstrings of the sinew of deer. And because there were so many grave things done, and it was not the custom for boys to question their elders, Joe never heard how Walter had been sent away. He thought him still at the ranch with his father, and it is because of this mistake that there is any more story at all.

You may be sure that, of those two boys, Joe's was the deeper loving, for, besides having grown up together, Walter was white, therefore thinking himself, and making the other believe it, the better of the two. But for this

Walter made no difference in his behavior; had Joe to eat at his table, and would have him sleep in his bed, but Joe laughed, and lay on the floor. All this was counted a kindness and a great honor in the campoodie. Walter could find out things by looking in a book, which was sheer magic, and had taught Joe to write a little, so that he could sent word by means of a piece of paper, which was cleverer than the tricks Joe had taught him of reading the signs of antelope and elk and deer.

The white boy was to the Indian a little of all the heroes and bright ones of the arrow-maker's tales come alive again. Therefore he quaked in his heart when he heard the rumors that ran about the camp.

The war began about Cottonwood, and ran like wildfire that licked up all the ranches in its course. Then the whites came strongly against the Paiutes at the Stone Corral, and made an end of the best of their fighting men. Then the Indians broke out in the north, and at last it came to such a pass that the very boys must do fighting, and the women make bowstrings. The cattlemen turned in to Baker's ranch as a centre, and all the northern campoodies gathered together to attack them. They had not much to hope for, only to do as much killing as possible before the winter set in with the hunger and the deep snows.

By this time Joe's father was dead, and his mother had brought the boy a quiver full of arrows and a new bowstring, and sent him down to the battle.

And Joe went hotly enough to join the men of the other village, nursing his bow with great care, remembering his father, but when he came to counsel and found where the fight must be, his heart turned again, for he remembered his friend. The braves camped by Little Round Valley, and he thought of the talk he and Walter had there; the war party went over the tongue of hills, and Joe saw Winnedumah shining whitely on Waban, and remembered his boyish errand, the mystery of the tall, strange warrior that came upon them in the night, their talk in the hut of the arrow-maker, and the vow that came afterward.

The Indians came down a ravine toward Tres Pinos, and there met a band of horses which some of their party had run in from the ranches; among them was a pinto pony which Walter had used to ride, and it came to Joe's hand when he called. Then the boy wondered if Walter might be dead, and leaned his head against the pony's mane; it turned its head and nickered softly at his ear.

The war party stayed in the ravine until it grew dark, and Joe watched how Winnedumah swam in a mist above the hills long after the sun had gone quite down, as if in his faithfulness he would outwatch the dark; and then the boy's heart was lifted up to the great chief standing still by Tin-nemaha. "I will not forget," he said. "I, too, will be faithful." Perhaps at this moment he expected a miracle to help him in his vow as it had helped Winnedumah.

In the dusk the mounted Indians rode down by the creek of Tres Pinos. When they came by the ruined hut where his father had lived, Joe's heart grew hot again, and when he passed the arrow-maker's, he remembered his vow. Suddenly he wheeled his pony in the trail, hardly knowing what he would do. The man next to him laid an arrow across his bow and pointed it at the boy's breast.

"Coward," he whispered, but an older Indian laid his hand on the man's arm.

"Save your arrows," he said. Then the ponies swept forward in the charge, but Joe knew in an instant how it would be with him. He would be called false and a coward, killed for it, driven from the tribe, but he would not fight against his sworn brother. He would keep his vow.

A sudden rain of arrows flew from the advancing Paiutes; Joe fumbled his and dropped it on the ground. He was wondering if any of the many aimed would find his brother. Bullets answered the arrow flight. He saw the braves pitch forward, and heard the scream of wounded ponies.

He hoped he would be shot; he would not have minded that; it would be better than being called a coward. And then it occurred to him, if Walter and his father came out and found him when the fight was done, they would think that he had broken his word. The Paiutes began to seek cover, but Joe drove out wildly from them, and rode back in the friendly dark, and past the ruined campoodie, to the black rocks. There he crept into the cave which only he and Walter knew, and lay on his face and cried, for though he was an Indian he was only a boy, and he had seen his first fight. He was sick with the thought of his vow. He lay in the black rocks all the night and the day, and watched the cattlemen and the soldiers ranging all that county for the stragglers of his people, and guessed that the Paiutes had made the last stand. Then in the second night he began to work back by secret paths to the mountain camp. It never occurred to him not to go. He had the courage to meet what waited for him there, but he had not the heart to go to it in the full light of day. He came in by his mother's place, and she spat upon him for she had heard how he had carried himself in the fight.

"No son of mine," said she.

He went by the women and children and heard their jeers. His heart was very sick. He went apart and sat down and waited what the men would say. There were few of them left about the dying fire. They had washed off their war paint, and their bows were broken. When they spoke at last, it was with mocking and sad scorn.

"We have enough of killing," said the one called Scar-Face. "Let him have a woman's dress and stay to mend the fire."

So it was done in the presence of all the camp; and because he was a boy, and because he was an Indian, he said nothing of his vow, nor opened his mouth in his defense, though his heart quaked and his knees shook. He had the courage to wear the badge of being afraid all his life. They brought him a woman's dress, though they were all too sad for much laughter, and in the morning he set to bringing the wood for the fire.

Afterward there was a treaty made between the Paiutes and the settlers, and the remnant went back to the campoodie of Tres Pinos, and Joe learned how Walter had been sent out of the valley in the beginning of the war, but that did not make any difference about the woman's dress. He and Walter never met again. He continued to go about in dresses, though in time he was allowed to do a man's work, and his knowledge of English helped to restore a friendly footing with the cattlemen. The valley filled very rapidly with settlers after that, and under the slack usage of the tribe, Mahala Joe, as he came to be known, might have thrown aside his woman's gear without offense, but he had the courage to wear it to his life's end. He kept his sentence as he kept his vow, and yet it is certain that Walter never knew.

California, Land of the Sun

In *Earth Horizon,* Austin wrote that "people used to fret at me because I would not do another 'Land of Little Rain.' I couldn't, of course, I had used up all I had in the first one. I should have had to find another country like that, and pay out ten thousand dollars to live in it ten or twelve years. I wrote what I lived, what I had observed and understood. Then I stopped" (320). She did eventually find another country, Arizona and New Mexico, the subject of *The Land of Journey's Ending.* But she also wrote a little-known book, *California, Land of the Sun,* that demonstrates she had not "used up" everything she had to say about California in *The Land of Little Rain.*

California, Land of the Sun was originally published in London by A. and C. Black in 1914, where Austin had been asked to write a text to accompany a series of watercolor paintings of California by Sutton Palmer. It is an evocative lyrical description of coastal and mountain California. As Austin makes clear in her preface, the tone of the book is elegiac for she believed that "on the life there, the unforgettable life, modern America has laid a greedy, vulgarizing hand" (*Earth Horizon,* 234).

Like *The Land of Little Rain,* *California, Land of the Sun* is a series of nature and character sketches suggesting the ties between landscape, human character, and culture that so fascinated Austin. "Old Spanish Gardens" introduces the reader to California's bygone culture through a representative of that culture, Doña Ina Manuelita Echivarra, a woman who is a relic of the past enshrined in a sort of natural history museum, her patio. Old herself, Doña Ina's "conversation wanders in the past" to figures in California history like the Pathfinder, John C. Frémont, but most especially to her mother. Social history, "Old Spanish Gardens" might be seen as a forerunner to Alice Walker's "In Search of Our Mother's Gardens," for Austin sees Doña Ina and her mother as artists enclosed within domestic walls. Doña Ina's life is symbolized by her garden, with all its beauty, healing herbs, and strict boundaries.

"Old Spanish Gardens" also shows Austin's interest in Spanish cultural traditions and in Hispanic women, an interest revealed in early works like "The Castro Baby" and *Isidro* and in her wonderful late story "Blue Roses." Although other writers, like Gertrude Atherton and Charles Lummis, also explored the influence of Spanish culture in California, Austin's attention to the domestic art of the Hispanic woman is unique during her time period and reflects her special concern with women's art.

Old Spanish Gardens

Dona Ina Manuelita Echivarra had come to the time of life when waists were not to be mentioned. It took all the evidence of her name to convince you that her cheek had once known tints of the olive and apricot. Tio Juan, who sunned himself daily in her patio, had achieved the richness of weathered teak; his moustachios were whitened as with the rime that collects on old adobes sometimes near the sea-shore. But Dona Ina, who missed by a score of years his mark of the days of *mañana por la mañana,* was muddily dark, and her moustache—but one does not suggest such things of a lady, and that Dona Ina was a lady could be proved by a foot so delicately arched and pointed, an ankle so neat that there was not another like it in your acquaintance save the mate to it.

Once you had seen it peeping forth from under the black skirt—have not Castilian ladies worn black immemorially?—you did not require the assurance of Tio Juan that there was no one in her day could have danced *la jota* with Dona Ina Manuelita.

She would clack the castanets for you occasionally still, just to show how it was done, or with the guitar resting on the arm of her chair—laps were no more to be thought of than waists were—she would quaver a song, *La Golindrina* for choice, or *La Noche esta Serena.* But unquestionably Dona Ina's time had gone by for shining at anything but conversation. She would talk, and never so fruitfully as when the subject was her garden.

A Spanish garden is a very intimate affair. It is the innermost undergarment of the family life. Dona Ina's was walled away from the world by six feet of adobe, around the top of which still lingered the curved red tiles of Mission manufacture. It was not spoken of as the garden at all, it was the patio, an integral part of the dwelling. There was, in fact, a raw hide cot on the long gallery which gave access to it, and Dona Ina's drawn-work chemises bleaching in the sun. The patio is a gift to us from Andalusia; it is more Greek than Oriental, and the English porch has about as much relation to it as the buttons on the back of a man's coat to the sword-belt they were once supposed to accommodate. The patio is the original mud-walled enclosure of a people who preferred living in the open but were driven to protection; the rooms about three sides of it were an afterthought.

The Echivarra patio did not lack the indispensable features of the early California establishment, the raised grill or cooking platform, and the ramada, the long vine-covered trellis where one took wine with one's friends, or the ladies of the family sat sewing at their interminable drawn work, *enramada*. The single vine which covered the twenty-foot trellis was of Mission stock, and had been planted by Dona Ina's father in the year the Pathfinder came over Tejon Pass into the great twin valleys. In Dona Ina's childhood a wine-press had stood in the corner of the patio where now there was a row of artichokes, which had been allowed to seed in order that their stiff silken tassels, dyed blue and crimson, might adorn the pair of china vases on either side the high altar. Dona Ina was nothing if not religious. In the corner of the patio farthest from the gallery, a fig-tree—this also is indispensable—hung over the tiled wall like a cloud. There was a weeping willow in the midst of the garden, and just outside, on either side the door, two great pepper trees of the very stock of the parent of all pepper trees in Alta California, which a sea captain from South America gave to the Padre at San Luis Rey. Along the east wall there were pomegranates.

A pomegranate is the one thing that makes me understand what a pretty woman is to some men—the kind of prettiness that was Dona Ina's in the days when she danced *la jota*. The flower of the pomegranate has the crumpled scarlet of lips that find their excuse in simply being scarlet and folded like the petals of a flower; and then the fruit, warm from the sunny wall, faintly odorous, dusky flushed! It is so tempting when broken open—that sort opens of its own accord if you leave it long enough on the bush—the rich heart colour, and the pleasant uncloying, sweet, sub-acid taste. One tastes and tastes—but when all is said and done there is nothing to a pomegranate except colour and flavour, and at least if it does not nourish neither does it give you indigestion. That is what suggests the comparison; there are so many people who would like to find a pretty woman in the same category. Always when we sat together nibbling the rosy seeds, I could believe, even without the evidence of the ankles, that Dona Ina had had her pomegranate days. Only, of course, she would not have smelled so of musk and—there is no denying it—of garlic. Thick-walled old adobes of the period of the Spanish Occupation give off a faint reek of this compelling condiment at every pore, and as for the musk, it was always about the gallery in saucers and broken flower-pots.

And yet Dona Ina was sensitive to odours: she told me that she had had the datura moved from the place where her mother had planted it, to the far end of the patio, where after nightfall its heavy, slightly fetid perfume, unnoticeable by day, scented all the air. She added that she felt convicted by this aversion of a want of sentiment toward a plant whose wide, papery-white bells went by the name of "Angels' trumpets."

On the day that she told me about the datura, which I had only recognised by its resemblance to its offensive wayside congener, the "jimson weed," the Señora Echivarra had been washing her hair with a tonic made of oil expressed from the seeds of the megharizza after a recipe which her mother had had from *her* mother, who had it from an Indian who used to peddle vegetables from the Mission, driving in every Saturday in an ancient caretta. I was interested to know if it were any more efficacious than the young shoots of the golden poppy fried in olive oil, which I had already tried. So we fell to talking of the virtues of plants and their application.

We began with the blessed "herb of the saints," dried bunches of which hung up under the rafters of the gallery as an unfailing resort in affections of the respiratory tract, and *yerba buena,* in which she was careful to distinguish between the creeping, aromatic *del campo* of the woodlands and the *yerba buena del poso,* "herb of the well," the common mint of damp places. When she added that the buckskin bag on the wall contained shavings of *cascara sagrada,* the sacred bark of the native buckthorn, indispensable to all nurseries, I knew that she had named two of the three most important contributions of the west to the modern pharmacopoeia. This particular bag of bark had been sent from Sonoma County, for south of Monterey it grows too thin to be worth the gathering. The Grindelia, she told me, had come from the salt marshes about the mouth of the Pajaro, where Don Gaspar de Portola must have crossed going northward.

"And were you then at such pains to secure them?"

"In the old days, yes," she assured me. In her mother's time there was a regular traffic carried on by means of roving Indians in healing herbs and simples; things you could get now by no means whatever.

"As for instance—?" I was curious.

Well, there was creosote gum, which came from the desert beyond the Sierra Wall, valuable for sores and for rheumatism. It took me a moment or two, however, to recognise in her appellation of it (*hideondo,* stinking) the shiny, shellac-covered *larrea* of the arid regions. There were roots also of the holly-leaved barberry, which came from wet mountains northward,

and of the "skunk cabbage," which were to be found only in soggy mountain meadows, where any early spring, almost before the frost was out of
the ground, bears could be seen rooting it from the sod, fairly burying
themselves in the black, peaty loam.

But when it came to *yerba mansa*, Dona Ina averred, her mother would
trust nobody for its gathering. She would take an Indian or two and as
many of her ten children as could not be trusted to be left at home, and
make long *pasears* into the coast ranges for this succulent cure-all. I knew it
well for one of the loveliest of meadow-haunting plants; wherever springs
babbled, wherever a mountain stream lost itself under the roble oaks,
the *yerba mansa* lifted above its heart-shaped leaves of pale green, quaint,
winged cones on pink, pellucid stems. But I had never heard one half of
the curative wonders which Dona Ina related of it. Efficacious in rheumatism, invaluable in pulmonary complaints, its bruised leaves reduced swell-
ings, the roots were tonic and alterative.

I spare you the whole list, for Dona Ina was directly of the line of that
lovely Señorita who had disdainfully described the English as the race who
"pay for everything," and to her mind it took a whole category of virtues
to induce so much effort as a trip into the mountains which had not a *baile*
or a *fiesta* at the end of it. Other things that were sought for by the housewives of the Spanish Occupation were *amole,* or soaproot, the bulbs of
a delicate, orchid-like lily which comes up in the late summer among the
stems of the chaparral, and the roots of the wild gourd, the *chili-cojote,*
a powerful purgative. Green fruit of this most common pest, said Dona
Ina, pounded to a pulp, did wonders in the way of removing stains from
clothing.

Then there was artemisia, romero, azalea, the blue-eyed grass of our
meadows, upon an infusion of which fever patients can subsist for days,
and elder, potent against spells, and there was Virgin's bower, which
brought us back to the patio, for a great heap of it lay on the roof of the
gallery, contesting the space there with the yellow banksia roses. I had
supposed, until the Señora Echivarra mentioned it, that its purpose was
purely ornamental, but I was to learn that it had come into the garden as
yerba de chivato about the time the barbed-wire fences of the gringo began
to make a remedy for cuts indispensable to the ranchero who valued the
appearance of his live stock. When the eye, travelling along its twisty stems
and twining leaf-stalks, came to a clump of yarrow growing at the root of it
I began at once to suspect the whole garden. Was not the virtue of yarrow
known even to the Greeks?

There was thyme flowering in the damp corner beyond the dripping faucet, and pot-marigold, lavender, rosemary, and lemon verbena, all plants that grow deep into the use and remembrance of man.

No friend of our race, not even the dog, has been more faithful. The stock of these had come overseas from Spain—were not the Phoenicians credited with introducing the pomegranate into Hispaniola?—and thence by way of the Missions.

All the borders of Dona Ina's garden were edged with rosy thrift, a European variety; and out on the headlands, a mile away, a paler, native cousin of it bloomed gaily with beach asters and yellow sand verbenas, but there was no one who knew by what winds, what communicating rootlets, they had exchanged greetings.

Observation, travelling by way of the borders, came to the datura, which was to set the conversation off again, this time not of plants curative, but hurtful. We knew of the stupefying effects of the bruised pods and roots of this species, and—this was my contribution—how the Paiute Indians used to administer the commoner variety, called *main-oph-weep,* to their warriors to produce the proper battle frenzy, and especially to young women about to undergo the annual ordeal of the "Dance of Marriageable Maidens."

Every year, at the spring gathering of the tribes, the maidens piled their dowries in a heap, and for three days, fasting, danced about it. If they fell or fainted, it was a sure sign they were not yet equal to the duties of housekeeping and childbearing; but I had had Paiute women tell me that they would never have endured the trial without a mild decoction of *main-oph-weep.*

"It was different with us," insisted Dona Ina; "many a time we have danced the sun up over the mountain, and been ready to begin again the next evening. . . ." But I wished to talk of the properties of plants, not of young ladies.

The mystery of poison plants oppressed me. One may understand how a scorpion stings in self-protection, but what profit has the "poison oak" of its virulence? It is not oak at all, but *Rhus trilobata,* and in the spring whole hillsides are enlivened by the shining bronze of its young foliage, or made crimson in September. But the pollen that floats from it in May in clouds, the sticky sap, or even the acrid smoke from the clearing where it is being exterminated, is an active poison to the human skin, though I had not heard that any animal suffered similarly. Dona Ina opined that there was never an evil plant let loose in the gardens of the Lord but the remedy was set to grow beside it. A wash of manzanita tea, Grindelia, or even buckthorn, she insisted, was excellent for poison oak. Best of all was a paste of pounded "soaproot." She knew a plant, too, which was corrective of the form of madness induced by the "loco" weed, whose pale foliage and delicately tinted, bladdery pods may be found always about the borders of the chaparral. For the convulsions caused by wild parsnip there was the wonder-working *yerba del pasmo*. This she knew also as a specific for snake-bite and tetanus. So greatly was it valued by mothers of families in the time of the Spanish Occupation, that when a clearing was made for a house and patio, in any country where it grew, a plant or two was always left standing. But it was not until I had looked for it, where she said I would find it between the oleander and the lemon verbena, that I recognised the common "grease-wood," the chamise of the mesa country.

"But were there no plants, Dona Ina, which had another meaning, flowers of affection, corrective to the spirit?"

"Angelica," she considered doubtfully. Young maids, on occasions of indecision, would pin a sprig of it across their bosoms, she said, and after they had been to church would find their doubts resolved; and there was yarrow, which kept your lover true, particularly if you plucked it with the proper ceremony from a young man's grave.

Dona Ina remembered a fascinating volume of her mother's time, the *Album Mexicana,* in which the sentimental properties of all flowers were set forth. "There was the camelia, a beautiful woman without virtue, and the pomegranate—"

"But the flowers of New Spain, Dona Ina, was there nothing of these?" I insisted.

"Of a truth, yes, there was the cactus flower, not the opunta, the broad-leaved spiny sort, of which hedges were built in the old days, but the low, flamy-blossomed, prickly variety of hot sandy places. If a young man wore such a one pinned upon his velvet jacket it signified, 'I burn for you.'"

"And if he wore no flower at all, how then?"

Dona Ina laughed, "*Si me quieros, no me quieros*"; she referred to the common yellow composite which goes by the name of "sunshine," or in the San Joaquin, where miles of it mixed with blue phacelias brighten with the spring, as "flyflower." "In the old Spanish playing-cards," said Dona Ina, "the Jack of spades had such a one in his hand, but when I was a girl no caballero would have been caught saying, 'Love me, love me not!' They left all that to the señoritas."

There was a Castilian rose growing beside me. Now a Castilian rose is not in the least what you expect it to be. It is a thick, cabbagy florescence, the petals short and not recurved, the pink hardly deeper than that of the common wild rose, the leafage uninteresting. One has to remember that it distinguished itself long before the time of the tea and garden hybrids, and, I suspect, borrowed half its charm from the faces it set off. For there was never but one way in the world for a rose to be worn, and that is the way Castilian beauties discovered so long ago that centuries have not made any improvement in it. Set just behind the ear and discreetly veiled by the mantilla, it suggests the effulgent charm of Spain, tempered by mystery. The Señora Echivarra had followed my glance, and nodded acquiescence to my thought. "In dressing for a *baile,* one would have as soon left off the rose as one's fan. One wore it even when the dress was wreathed with other flowers."

"And did you, then, go wreathed in flowers?"

"Assuredly; from the garden if we had them, or from the field. I remember once I was all blue larkspurs, here and here . . ." she illustrated on her person, "and long flat festoons of the *yerba buena* holding them together."

"It would have taken hoop skirts for that?" I opined.

"That also. It was the time that the waltz had been learned from the officers of the American ships, and we were quite wild about it. The good Padre had threatened to excommunicate us all if we danced it . . . but we danced . . . we danced. . . ." Dona Ina's pretty feet twitched reminiscently. The converation wandered a long time in the past before it came back to the patio lying so still, divided from the street by the high wall, the clouding fig, and the gnarly pear tree. Beyond the artichokes a low partition wall shut off the vegetable plot; strings of chili reddened against it. There was not a blade of grass in sight, only the flat, black adobe paths worn smooth by generations of treading, house and enclosing walls all of one earth.

"But if so much came into the garden from the field, Señora, did nothing ever go out?"

Ah, yes, yes—the land is gracious; there was mustard of course, and pepper grass and horehound, blessed herb, which spread all over the west with healing. The pimpernel, too, crept out of the enclosing wall, and the tree mallow which came from the Channel Islands by way of the gardens and has become a common hedge plant on the sandy lands about the bay of San Francisco. Along streams which ran down from the unfenced gardens of the *Americanos,* callas had domesticated themselves and lifted their pure white spathes serenely amid a tangle of mint and wild blackberries and painted cup. The almond, the rude stock on which the tender sorts were grafted, if allowed to bear its worthless bitter nuts would take to hillsides naturally. It is not, after all, walls which hold gardens but water. This is all that constrains the commingling of wild and cultivated species; they care little for man, their benefactor. Give them water, said Dona Ina, and they come to your door like a fed dog, or if you like the figure better, like grateful children. They repay you with sweetness and healing.

A swift darted among the fig, marigolds, and portulacca of the inevitable rock-work which was the pride of the old Spanish gardens. Great rockets of tritoma flamed against the wall, on the other side of which traffic went unnoted and unsuspecting.

"But we, Dona Ina, we Americans, when we make a garden, make it in the sight of all so that all may have pleasure in it."

"Eh, the *Americanos* . . ." she shrugged; she moved to give a drink to the spotted musk, flowering in a chipped saucer; the subject did not interest her; her thought, like her flowers, had grown up in an enclosure.

❖   ❖   ❖

The Trail Book

Like *The Basket Woman, The Trail Book* (1918) is intended for children, but Austin's fables, which present a mythic history of the American continent, speak on many levels for adults as well. Oliver and Dorcas Jane, the children of a night engineer at a natural history museum, follow the trails of their guides, the Indians and animals of the exhibits, who magically come alive in response to the children's imaginative curiosity. The structure of the collection reflects Austin's interest in oral storytelling, while the unifying trail metaphor teaches the children the connections between landscape and human experience. They learn that "like the trails . . . every word is an expression of a need" and that "there is a story about everything." The trails lead them through myths about friendships between humans and talking animals into more recent times, "to the place in the Story of the Trails, which is known in the schoolbooks as 'History.'" The trails show them the interrelationships between myth, history, nature, and human culture and identity when they dis-

cover that "all the stories of that country, like the trails, seemed to run into one another."

Austin used the trail metaphor often in her poetry for children, entitling one poem "Wind's Trail I am Seeking" and writing about foggy trails in California in "Dormidera." Her purpose in writing *The Trail Book* is suggested by a poem she published in *The Children Sing in the Far West,* "Western Magic," which begins:

There are no fairy-folk in our
   Southwest;
The cactus spines would tear
   their filmy wings;
There's no dew anywhere for
   them to drink,
And no green grass to make
   them fairy rings.

And ends:

There are no fairy-folk in our
   Southwest,
But there are homes where
   prairie dog and snake,
Black beetle and the tecolote
   owl
Between two winks their

ancient forms will take.
Clad in white skins with shell
    shield glittering
The sun, their chief, the
    Ancient road will walk,
Half in her sleep the mothering
    earth
Of older things than fairy-folk
    will talk.

The Trail Book gives youngsters a mythology of America, a mythology that grows organically from the "mothering earth."

When she was writing *The Trail Book,* Austin convinced the staff of the American Museum of Natural History to let her "go into the Museum at night and take things out of the cases, and wear them and be told things about them" (*Earth Horizon,* 331). She claimed that this period was one of the few times in New York when she could satisfy her interest in Native American culture.

❖　❖　❖

How the Corn Came

"How the Corn Came," a chisera story, is told by the Corn Woman, a follower of "Giver-of-the-Corn who died giving." It is a myth of female heroism based on cunning and courage rather than on physical strength. The story seeks to validate women's contribution to culture. Giver-of-the-Corn, a "wise woman" and a shaman, leads her followers in tribute to the "God of the Seed, a woman god who was served by women," and the source of food. When Giver-of-the-Corn saves her adopted tribe from starvation, she unites her people with the cyclical rhythms of growth and cultivation. Her gift is her offspring, the kernels of corn that give life and die each year only to be reborn the next. The story suggests that women are the source of life in another way: Giver-of-the-Corn makes her women followers "keepers of the seed."

It was one of those holidays, when there isn't any school and the Museum is only opened for a few hours in the afternoon, that Dorcas Jane had come into the north gallery of the Indian room where her father was at work mending the radiators. This was about a week after the children's first adventure on the Buffalo Trail, but it was before the holes had been cut in the Museum wall to let you look straight across the bend in the Colorado and into the Hopi pueblo. Dorcas looked at all the wall cases and wondered how it was the Indians seemed to have so much corn and so many kinds of it, for she had always thought of corn as a civilized sort of thing to have. She sat on a bench against the wall wondering, for the lovely clean stillness of the room encouraged thinking, and the clink of her father's hammers on the pipes fell presently into the regular *tink-tink-a-tink* of tortoise-shell rattles, keeping time to the shuffle and beat of bare feet on the dancing-place by the river. The path to it led across a clearing between little hillocks of freshly turned earth, and the high forest overhead was bursting into tiny green darts of growth like flame. The rattles were sewed to the leggings of the women—little yellow and black land-tortoise shells filled with pebbles—who sang as they danced and cut themselves with flints until they bled.

"Oh," said Dorcas, without waiting to be introduced, "what makes you do that?"

"To make the corn grow," said the tallest and the handsomest of the women, motioning to the others to leave off their dancing while she answered. "Listen! You can hear the men doing their part."

From the forest came a sudden wild whoop, followed by the sound of a drum, little and far off like a heart beating. "They are scaring off the enemies of the corn," said the Corn Woman, for Dorcas could see by her headdress, which was of dried corn tassels dyed in colors, and by a kind of kilt she wore, woven of corn husks, that that was what she represented.

"Oh!" said Dorcas; and then, after a moment, "It sounds as if you were sorry, you know."

"When the seed corn goes into the ground it dies," said the Corn Woman; "the tribe might die also if it never came alive again. Also we lament for the Giver-of-the-Corn who died giving."

"I thought corn just grew," said Dorcas; "I didn't know it came from any place."

"From the People of the Seed, from the Country of Stone Houses. It was bought for us by Given-to-the-Sun. Our people came from the East, from the place where the Earth opened, from the place where the Noise was, where the Mountain thundered. . . . This is what I have heard; this is what the Old Ones have said," finished the Corn Woman, as though it were some sort of song.

She looked about to the others as if asking their consent to tell the story. As they nodded, sitting down to loosen their heavy leggings, Dorcas could see that what she had taken to be a shock of last year's cornstalks, standing in the middle of the dancing-place, was really tied into a rude resemblance to a woman. Around its neck was one of the Indian's sacred bundles; Dorcas thought it might have something to do with the story, but decided to wait and see.

"There was a trail in those days," said the Corn Woman, "from the buffalo pastures to the Country of the Stone House. We used to travel it as far as the ledge where there was red earth for face-painting, and to trade with the Blanket People for salt. But no farther. Hunting-parties that crossed into Chihuahua returned sometimes; more often they were given to the Sun.—On the tops of the hills where their god-houses were," explained the Corn Woman seeing that Dorcas was puzzled. "The Sun was their god to them. Every year they gave captives on the hills they built to the Sun."

Dorcas had heard the guard explaining to visitors in the Aztec room. "Teocales," she suggested.

"That was one of their words," agreed the Corn Woman. "They called themselves Children of the Sun. This much we knew; that there was a Seed. The People of the Cliffs, who came to the edge of the Windswept Plain to trade, would give us cakes sometimes for dried buffalo tongues. This we understood was *mahiz,* but it was not until Given-to-the-Sun came to us that we thought of having it for ours. Our men were hunters. They thought it shame to dig in the ground.

"Shungakela, of the Three Feather band, found her at the fork of the Turtle River, half starved and as fierce as she was hungry, but *he* called her 'Waits-by-the-Fire' when he brought her back to his tipi, and it was a long time before we knew that she had any other name. She belonged to one of the mountain tribes whose villages were raided by the People of the Sun, and because she had been a child at the time, she was made a servant. But in the end, when she had shot up like a red lily and her mistress had grown fond of her, she was taken by the priests of the Sun.

"At first the girl did not know what to make of being dressed so handsomely and fed upon the best of everything, but when they painted her with the sign of the Sun she knew. Over her heart they painted it. Then they put about her neck the Eye of the Sun, and the same day the woman who had been her mistress and was fond of her, slipped her a seed which she said should be eaten as she went up the Hill of the Sun, so she would feel nothing. Given-to-the-Sun hid it in her bosom.

"There was a custom that, in the last days, those who were to go up the Hill of the Sun could have anything they asked for. So the girl asked to walk by the river and hear the birds sing. When they had walked out of sight of the Stone Houses, she gave her watchers the seed in their food and floated down the river on a piece of bark until she came ashore in the thick woods and escaped. She came north, avoiding the trails, and after a year Shungakela found her. Between her breasts there was the sign of the Sun."

The Corn Woman stooped and traced in the dust the ancient sign of the intertwined four corners of the Earth with the Sun in the middle. "Around her neck in a buckskin bag was the charm that is known as the Eye of the Sun. She never showed it to any of us, but when she was in trouble or doubt, she would put her hand over it. It was her Medicine."

"It was good Medicine, too," spoke up the oldest of the dancing women.

"We had need of it," agreed the Corn Woman. "In those days the Earth was too full of people. The tribes swarmed, new chiefs arose, kin hunted against kin. Many hunters made the game shy, and it removed to new pastures. Strong people drove out weaker and took away their hunting-grounds. We had our share of both fighting and starving, but our tribe fared better than most because of the Medicine of Waits-by-the-Fire, the Medicine of the Sun. She was a wise woman. She was made Shaman. When she spoke, even the chiefs listened. But what could the chiefs do except hunt farther and fight harder? So Waits-by-the-Fire talked to the women. She talked of corn, how it was planted and harvested, with what rites and festivals.

"There was a God of the Seed, a woman god who was served by women. When the women of our tribe heard that, they took heart. The men had been afraid that the God of the Corn would not be friendly to us. I think, too, they did not like the idea of leaving off the long season of hunting and roving, for corn is a town-maker. For the tending and harvesting there must be one place, and for the guarding of the winter stores there must be a safe place. So said Waits-by-the-Fire to the women digging roots or boiling old bones in the long winter. She was a wise woman.

"It was the fight we had with the Tenasas that decided us. That was a year of great scarcity and the Tenasas took to sending their young men, two or three at a time, creeping into our hunting-grounds to start the game, and turn it in the direction of their own country. When our young men were sure of this, they went in force and killed inside the borders of the Tenasas. They had surprised a herd of buffaloes at Two Kettle Licks and were cutting up the meat when the Tenasas fell upon them. Waits-by-the-Fire lost her last son by that battle. One she had lost in the fight at Red Buttes and one in a year of Hunger while he was little. This one was swift of foot and was called Last Arrow, for Shungakela had said, 'Once I had a quiver full.' Waits-by-the-Fire brought him back on her shoulders from the place where the fight was. She walked with him into the Council.

"'The quiver is empty,' she said; 'the food bags, also; will you wait for us to fill one again before you fill the other?'

"Mad Wolf, who was chief at the time, threw up his hand as a man does when he is down and craves a mercy he is too proud to ask for. 'We have fought the Tenasas,' he said; 'shall we fight our women also?'

"Waits-by-the-Fire did not wait after that for long speeches in the Council. She gathered her company quickly, seven women well seasoned and not comely,—'The God of the Corn is a woman god,' she said, sharp smiling,—and seven men, keen and hard runners. The rest she appointed to meet her at Painted Rock ten moons from their going."

"So long as that!" said Dorcas Jane. "Was it so far from where you lived to Mex—to the Country of Stone Houses?"

"Not so far, but they had to stay from planting to harvest. Of what use was the seed without knowledge. Traveling hard they crossed the River of the White Rocks and reached, by the end of that moon, the mountain overlooking the Country of Stone Houses. Here the men stayed. Waits-by-the-Fire arranged everything. She thought the people of the towns might hesitate to admit so many men strangers. Also she had the women put on worn moccasins with holes, and old food from the year before in their food bags."

"I should think," began Dorcas Jane, "they would have wanted to put on the best they had to make a good impression."

"She was a wise woman," said the Corn Woman; "she said that if they came from near, the people of the towns might take them for spies, but they would not fear travelers from so far off that their moccasins had holes in them."

The Corn Woman had forgotten that she was telling a story older than the oaks they sat under. When she came to the exciting parts she said "we" and "us" as though it were something that had happened to them all yesterday.

"It was a high white range that looked on the Country of Stone Houses," she said, "with peaks that glittered, dropping down ridge by ridge to where the trees left off at the edge of a wide, basket-colored valley. It hollowed like a meal basket and had a green pattern woven through it by a river. Shungakela went with the women to the foot of the mountain, and then, all at once, he would not let them go until Waits-by-the-Fire promised to come back to the foot of the mountain once in every moon to tell him how things went with us. *We* thought it very childish of him, but afterward we were glad we had not made any objection.

"It was mid-morning when the Seven walked between the fields, with little food in their bags and none whatever in their stomachs, all in rags except Waits-by-the-Fire, who had put on her Shaman's dress, and around her neck, tied in a bag with feathers, the Medicine of the Sun. People stood up in the fields to stare, and we would have stared back again, but we were afraid. Behind the stone house we saw the Hill of the Sun and the priests moving up and down as Waits-by-the-Fire had described it.

"Below the hill, where the ground was made high, at one side of the steps that went up to the Place of Giving, stood the house of the Corn Goddess, which was served by women. There the Seven laid up their offering of poor food before the altar and stood on the steps of the god-house until the head priestess noticed them. Wisps of incense smoke floated out of the carved doorways and the drone of the priestess like bees in a hollow log. All the people came out on their flat roofs to watch— Did I say that they had two and even three houses, one on top of the other, each one smaller than the others, and ladders that went up and down to them?— They stood on the roofs and gathered in the open square between the houses as still and as curious as antelopes, and at last the priestess of the Corn came out and spoke to us. Talk went on between her and Waits-by-the-Fire, purring, spitting talk like water stumbling among stones. Not one word did our women understand, but they saw wonder grow among the Corn Women, respect and amazement.

"Finally, we were taken into the god-house, where in the half dark, we could make out the Goddess of the Corn, cut in stone, with green stones on her forehead. There were long councils between Waits-by-the-Fire and the Corn Woman and the priests that came running from the Temple of the Sun. Outside the rumor and the wonder swelled around the god-house like a sudden flood. Faces bobbed up like rubbish in the flood into the bright blocks of light that fell through the doorway, and were shifted and shunted by other faces peering in. After a long time the note of wonder outside changed to a deep, busy hum; the crowd separated and let through women bearing food in pots and baskets. Then we knew that Waits-by-the-Fire had won."

"But what?" insisted Dorcas; "what was it that she had told them?"

"That she had had a dream which was sent by the Corn Spirit and that she and those with her were under a vow to serve the Corn for the space of one growing year. And to prove that her dream was true the Goddess of the Corn had revealed to her the speech of the Stone House tribe and also many hidden things. These were things which she remembered from her captivity which she told them."

"What sort of things?"

"Why, that in such a year they had had a pestilence and that the father of the Corn Woman had died of eating over-ripe melons. The Corn Women were greatly impressed. But she carried it almost too far . . . perhaps . . . and perhaps it was appointed from the beginning that that was the way the Corn was to come. It was while we were eating that we realized how wise she was to make us come fasting, for first the people pitied us, and then they were pleased with themselves for making us comfortable. But in the middle of it there was a great stir and a man in chief's dress came pushing through. He was the Cacique of the Sun and he was vexed because he had not been called earlier. He was that kind of man.

"He spoke sharply to the Chief Corn Woman to know why strangers were received within the town without his knowledge.

"Waits-by-the-Fire answered quickly. 'We are guests of the Corn, O Cacique, and in my dream I seem to have heard of your hospitality to women of the Corn.' You see there had been an old story when he was young, how one of the Corn Maidens had gone to his house and had been kept there against her will, which was a discredit to him. He was so astonished to hear the strange woman speak of it that he turned and went out of the god-house without another word. The people took up the incident and whispered it from mouth to mouth to prove that the strange Shaman was a great prophet. So we were appointed a house to live in and were permitted to serve the Corn."

"But what did you do?" Dorcas insisted on knowing.

"We dug and planted. All this was new to us. When there was no work in the fields we learned the ways of cooking corn, and to make pots. Hunting-tribes do not make pots. How should we carry them from place to place on our backs? We cooked in baskets with hot stones, and sometimes when the basket was old we plastered it with mud and set it on the fire. But the People of the Corn made pots of coiled clay and burned it hard in the open fires between the houses. Then there was the ceremony of the Corn to learn, the prayers and the dances. Oh, we had work enough! And if ever anything was ever said or done to us which was not pleasant, Waits-by-the-Fire would say to the one who had offended, 'We are only the servants of the Corn, but it would be a pity if the same thing happened to you that happened to the grandfather of your next-door neighbor!'

"And what happened to them?"

"Oh, a plague of sores, a scolding wife," or anything that she chanced to remember from the time she had been Given-to-the-Sun. *That* stopped them. But most of them held us to be under the protection of the Corn Spirit, and when our Shaman would disappear for two or three days—that was when she went to the mountain to visit Shungakela—*we* said that she had gone to pray to her own gods, and they accepted that also."

"And all this time no one recognized her?"

"She had painted her face for a Shaman," said the Corn Woman slowly, "and besides it was nearly forty years. The woman who had been kind to her was dead and there was a new Priest of the Sun. Only the one who had painted her with the sign of the Sun was left, and he was doddering." She seemed about to go on with the story, but the oldest dancing woman interrupted her.

"Those things helped," said the dancing woman, "but it was her thought which hid her. She put on the thought of a Shaman as a man puts on the thought of a deer or a buffalo when he goes to look for them. That which one fears, that it is which betrays one. She was a Shaman in her heart and as a Shaman she appeared to them."

"She certainly had no fear," said the Corn Woman, "though from the first she must have known—

"It was when the seed corn was gathered that we had the first hint of trouble," she went on. "When it was ripe the priests and Caciques went into the fields to select the seed for next year. Then it was laid up in the god-houses for the priestess of the Corn to keep. That was in case of an enemy or a famine when the people might be tempted to eat it. After it was once taken charge of by the priestess of the Corn they would have died rather than give it up. Our women did not know how they should get the seed to bring away from the Stone House except to ask for it as the price of their year's labor."

"But couldn't you have just taken some from the field?" inquired Dorcas. "Wouldn't it have grown just the same?"

"That we were not sure of; and we were afraid to take it without the good-will of the Corn Goddess. Centcotli her name was. Waits-by-the-Fire made up her mind to ask for it on the first day of the Feast of the Corn Harvest, which lasts four days, and is a time of present-giving and good-willing. She would have got it, too, if it had been left to the Corn Women to decide. But the Cacique of the Sun, who was always watching out for a chance to make himself important, insisted that it was a grave matter and should be taken to Council. He had never forgiven the Shaman, you see, for that old story about the Corn Maiden.

"As soon as the townspeople found that the Caciques were considering whether it was proper to give seed corn to the strangers, they began to consider it, too, turning it over in their minds together with a great many things that had nothing to do with it. There had been smut in the corn that year; there was a little every year, but this season there was more of it, and a good many of the bean pods had not filled out. I forgot," said the Corn Woman, "to speak of the beans and squashes. They were the younger sisters of the corn; they grew with the corn and twined about it. Now, every man who was a handful or two short of his crop began to look at us doubtfully. Then they would crowd around the Cacique of the Sun to argue the matter. They remembered how our Shaman had gone apart to pray to her own gods and they thought the Spirit of the Corn might have been offended. And the Cacique would inquire of every one who had a toothache or any such matter, in such a way as to make them think of it in connection with the Shaman.—In every village," the Corn Woman interrupted herself to say, "there is evil enough, if laid at the door of one person, to get her burned for a witch!"

"Was she?" Dorcas Jane squirmed with anxiety.

"She was standing on the steps at the foot of the Hill of the Sun, the last we saw of her," said the Corn Woman. "Of course, our women, not understanding the speech of the Stone Houses, did not know exactly what was going on, but they felt the changed looks of the people. They thought, perhaps, they could steal away from the town unnoticed. Two of them hid in their clothing as much Seed as they could lay hands on and went down toward the river. They were watched and followed. So they came back to the house where Waits-by-the-Fire prayed daily with her hand on the Medicine of the Sun.

"So came the last day of the feast when the sacred seed would be sealed up in the god-house. 'Have no fear,' said Waits-by-the-Fire, 'for my dream has been good. Make yourselves ready for the trail. Take food in your food bags and your carriers empty on your backs.' She put on her Shaman's dress and about the middle of the day the Cacique of the Sun sent for them. He was on the platform in front of the god-house where the steps go up to the Hill of the Sun, and the elders of the town were behind him. Priests of the Sun stood on the steps and the Corn Women came out from the temple of the Corn. As Waits-by-the-Fire went up with the Seven, the people closed in solidly behind them. The Cacique looked at the carriers on their backs and frowned.

"'Why do you come to the god-house with baskets, like laborers of the fields?' he demanded.

"'For the price of our labor, O Cacique,' said the Shaman. 'The gods are not so poor that they accept labor for nothing.'

"'Now, it is come into my heart,' said the Cacique sourly, 'that the gods are not always pleased to be served by strangers. There are signs that this is so.'

"'It may be,' said Waits-by-the-Fire, 'that the gods are not pleased. They have long memories.' She looked at him very straight and somebody in the crowd snickered."

"But wasn't it awfully risky to keep making him mad like that?" asked Dorcas. "They could have just done anything to her!"

"She was a wise woman; she knew what she had to do. The Cacique *was* angry. He began making a long speech at her, about how the smut had come in the corn and the bean crop was a failure,—but that was because there had not been water enough,—and how there had been sickness. And when Waits-by-the-Fire asked him if it were only in that year they had misfortune, the people thought she was trying to prove that she hadn't had anything to do with it. She kept reminding them of things that had happened the year before, and the year before. The Cacique kept growing more and more angry, admitting everything she said, until it showed plainly that the town had had about forty years of bad luck, which the Cacique tried to prove was all because the gods had known in advance that they were going to be foolish and let strangers in to serve the Corn. At first the people grew excited and came crowding against the edge of the platform, shouting, 'Kill her! Kill the witch!' as one and then another of their past misfortunes were recalled to them.

"But, as the Shaman kept on prodding the Cacique, as hunters stir up a bear before killing him, they began to see that there was something more coming, and they stood still, packed solidly in the square to listen. On all the housetops roundabout the women and the children were as still as images. A young priest from the steps of the Hill, who thought he must back up the Cacique, threw up his arms and shouted, 'Give her to the Sun!' and a kind of quiver went over the people like the shiver of still water when the wind smites it. It was only at the time of the New Fire, between harvest and planting, that they give to the Sun, or in great times of war or pestilence. Waits-by-the-Fire moved out to the edge of the platform.

"'It is not, O People of the Sun, for what is given, that the gods grow angry, but for what is withheld,' she said. 'Is there nothing, priests of the Sun, which was given to the Sun and let go again? Think, O priests. Nothing?'

"The priests, huddled on the stairs, began to question among themselves, and Waits-by-the-Fire turned to the people. 'Nothing, O Offspring of the Sun?'

"Then she put off the Shaman's thought which had been a shield to her. 'Nothing, Toto?' she called to a man in the crowd by a name none knew him by except those that had grown up with him. She was Given-to-the-Sun, and she stood by the carved stone corn of the god-house and laughed at them, shuffling and shouldering like buffaloes in the stamping-ground, and not knowing what to think. Voices began to call for the man she had spoken to, 'Toto, O Toto!'

"The crowd swarmed upon itself, parted and gave up the figure of the ancient Priest of the Sun, for they remembered in his day how a girl who was given to the Sun had been snatched away by the gods out of sight of the people. They pushed him forward, doddering and peering. They saw the woman put back her Shaman's bonnet from her head, and the old priest clap his hand to his mouth like one suddenly astonished.

"Over the Cacique's face came a cold glint like the coming of ice on water. 'You,' he said, 'you are Given-to-the-Sun?' And he made a gesture to the guard to close in on her.

"'Given-to-the-Sun,' she said. 'Take care how you touch that which belongs to the gods, O Cacique!'

"And though he still smiled, he took a step backward.

"'So,' he said, 'you are the woman and this is the meaning of those prophecies!'

"'I am that woman and that prophet,' she said with her hand at her throat and looked from priests to people. 'O People of the Sun, I have heard you have a charm,' she said,—'a Medicine of the Sun called the Eye of the Sun, strong Medicine.'

"No one answered for a while, but they began to murmur among themselves, and at last one shouted that they had such a charm, but it was not for witches or for runaway slave women.

"'You *had* such a charm,' she said, for she knew well enough that the sacred charm was kept in the god-house and never shown to the people except on very great occasions. She was sure that the priests had never dared to tell the people that their Sacred Stone had disappeared with the escaped captive.

"Given-to-the-Sun took the Medicine bag from her neck and swung it in her fingers. '*Had!*' she said mockingly. The people gave a growl; another time they would have been furious with fright and anger, but they did not wish to miss a syllable of what was about to happen. The priests whispered angrily with the guard, but Given-to-the-Sun did not care what the priests did so long as she had the people. She signed to the Seven, and they came huddling to her like quail; she put them behind her.

"'Is it not true, Children of the Sun, that the favor of the Sun goes with the Eye of the Sun and it will come back to you when the Stone comes back?'

"They muttered and said that it was so.

"'Then, will your priests show you the Eye of the Sun or shall I show you?'

"There was a shout raised at that, and some called to the priests to show the Stone, and others that the woman would bring trouble on them all with her offenses. But by this time they knew very well where the Stone was, and the priests were too astonished to think of anything. Slowly the Shaman drew it out of the Medicine bag—"

The Corn Woman waited until one of the women handed her the sacred bundle from the neck of the Corn image. Out of it, after a little rummaging, she produced a clear crystal of quartz about the size of a pigeon's egg. It gave back the rays of the Sun in a dazzle that, to any one who had never seen a diamond, would have seemed wonderfully brilliant. Where it lay in the Corn Woman's hand it scattered little flecks of reflected light in rainbow splashes. The Indian women made the sign of the Sun on their foreheads and Dorcas felt a prickle of solemnity along the back of her neck as she looked at it. Nobody spoke until it was back again in the Medicine bundle.

"Given-to-the-Sun held it up to them," the story went on, "and there was a noise in the square like a noise of the stamping-ground at twilight. Some bellowed one thing and some another, and at last a priest of the Sun moved sharply and spoke:—

"'The Eye of the Sun is not for the eyes of the vulgar. Will you let this false Shaman impose on you, O Children of the Sun, with a common pebble?'

"Given-to-the-Sun stooped and picked up a mealing-stone that was used for grinding the sacred meal in the temple of the Corn.

"'If your Stone is in the temple and this is a common pebble,' said she, 'it does not matter what I do with it.' And she seemed about to crush it on the top of the stone balustrade at the edge of the platform. The people groaned. They knew very well that this was their Sacred Stone and that the priests had deceived them. Given-to-the-Sun stood resting one stone upon the other.

"'The Sun has been angry with you,' she said, 'but the Goddess of the Corn saves you. She has brought back the Stone and the Sacrifice. Do not show yourselves ungrateful to the Corn by denying her servants their wages. What! will you have all the gods against you? Priestess of the Corn,' she called toward the temple, 'do you also mislead the people?'

"At that the Corn Women came hurrying, for they saw that the people were both frightened and angry; they brought armsful of corn and seeds for the carriers, they took bracelets from their arms and put them for gifts in the baskets. The priests of the Sun did not say anything. One of the women's headbands slipped and the basket swung sideways. Given-to-the-Sun whipped off her belt and tucked it under the basket rim to make it ride more evenly. The woman felt something hard in the belt pressing her shoulder, but she knew better than to say anything. In silence the crowd parted and let the Seven pass. They went swiftly with their eyes on the ground by the north gate to the mountain. The priests of the Sun stood still on the steps of the Hill of the Sun and their eyes glittered. The Sacrifice of the Sun had come back to them.

"When our women passed the gate, the crowd saw Given-to-the-Sun restore what was in her hand to the Medicine bag; she lifted her arms above her head and began the prayer to the Sun."

"I see," said Dorcas after a long pause; "she stayed to keep the People of the Sun pacified while the women got away with the seed. That was splendid. But, the Eye of the Sun, I thought you saw her put that in the buckskin bag again?"

"She must have had ready another stone of shape and size like it," said the Corn Woman. "She thought of everything. She was a wise woman, and so long as she was called Given-to-the-Sun the Eye of the Sun was hers to give. Shungakela was not surprised to find that his wife had stayed at the Hill of the Sun; so I suppose she must have told him. He asked if there was a token, and the woman whose basket she had propped with her girdle gave it to him with the hard lump that pressed her shoulder. So the Medicine of the Sun came back to us.

"Our men had met the women at the foot of the mountain and they fled all that day to a safe place the men had made for them. It was for that they had stayed, to prepare food for flight, and safe places for hiding in case they were followed. If the pursuit pressed too hard, the men were to stay and fight while the women escaped with the corn. That was how Given-to-the-Sun arranged it.

"Next day as we climbed, we saw smoke rising from the Hill of the Sun, and Shungakela went apart on the mountain, saying, 'Let me alone, for I make a fire to light the feet of my wife's spirit. . . .' They had been married twenty years.

"We found the tribe at Painted Rock, but we thought it safer to come on east beyond the Staked Plains as Given-to-the-Sun had advised us. At Red River we stopped for a whole season to plant corn. But there was not rain enough there, and if we left off watching the fields for a day the buffaloes came and cropped them. So for the sake of the corn we came still north and made friends with the Tenasas. We bought help of them with the half of our seed, and they brought us over the river, the Missi-Sippu, the Father of all Rivers. The Tenasas had boats, round like baskets, covered with buffalo hide, and they floated us over, two swimmers to every boat to keep us from drifting downstream.

"Here we made a town and a god-house, to keep the corn contented. Every year when the seed is gathered seven ears are laid up in the god-house in memory of the Seven, and for the seed which must be kept for next year's crop there are seven watchers"—the Corn Woman included the dancers and herself in a gesture of pride. "We are the keepers of the Seed," she said, "and no man of the tribe knows where it is hidden. For no matter how hungry the people may become the seed corn must not be eaten. But with us there is never any hunger, for every year from planting time till the green corn is ready for picking, we keep all the ceremonies of the corn, so that our cribs are filled to bursting. Look!"

The Corn Woman stood up and the dancers getting up with her shook the rattles of their leggings with a sound very like the noise a radiator makes when some one is hammering on the other end of it. And when Dorcas turned to look for the Indian cribs there was nothing there but the familiar wall cases and her father mending the steam heater.

❖ ❖ ❖

The Secret of the Holy Places

"The Secret of the Holy Places," like all of The Trail Book, *demonstrates Austin's awareness that the history of the West did not begin with white mountain men and pioneers, that the West was settled from the north and south before the east. Austin's West is always multicultural, and "The Secret of the Holy Places" is a story of the conflict of two cultures. This conflict takes place literally as Father Letrado tries to destroy the Zuni religion and is eventually destroyed himself. It also takes place within the breast of Ho-tai, a man torn between two cultures.*

Like so much of Austin's work, this story attempts to give white readers a fuller understanding of the complexity of Native American culture. Father Letrado is the story's villain because he makes no effort to understand the meaning and feeling behind Zuni rituals and beliefs. "White men do not understand about scalping," she writes, and tries to explain the scalp dance, as she later explains the use of peyote to induce visions. Although we never find out whether Ho-Tai tells the secret of the Holy Places—and hope he doesn't—the story reveals many secrets of Zuni life.*

"In the days of our Ancients," said the Road-Runner between short skimming runs, "this was the only trail from the river to the Middle Ant Hill of the World. The eastern end of it changed like the tip of a wild gourd vine as the towns moved up and down the river or the Queres crossed from Katzimo to the rock of Acoma; but always Zuñi was the root, and the end of the first day's journey was the Rock."

Each time he took his runs afresh, like a kicking stick in a race, and waited for the children to catch up. The sands as they went changed from gray to gleaming pearl; on either side great islands of stone thinned and swelled like sails and took on rosy lights and lilac shadows.

They crossed a high plateau with somber cones of extinct volcanoes, crowding between rivers of block rock along its rim. Northward a wilderness of pines guarded the mesa; dark junipers, each one with a secret look, browsed wide apart. They thickened in the cañons from which arose the white bastions of the Rock.

Closer up, El Morro showed as the wedge-shaped end of a high mesa, soaring into cliffs and pinnacles, on the very tip of which they could just make out the hunched figure of the great Condor.

"El Morro, 'the Castle,' the Spaniards called it," said the Road-Runner, casting himself along the laps of the trail like a feathered dart. "But to our Ancients it was always 'The Rock.' On winter journeys they camped on the south side to get the sun, and in summers they took the shade on the north. They carved names and messages for those that were to come after, with flint knives, with swords and Spanish daggers. Men are all very much alike," said the Road-Runner.

On the smooth sandstone cliffs the children could make out strange, weathered picture-writings, and twisty inscriptions in much abbreviated Spanish which they could not read.

The white sand at the foot of the Rock was strewn with flakes of charcoal from the fires of ancient camps. A little to the south of the cliff, that towered two hundred feet and more above them, shallow footholds were cut into the sandstone.

"There were pueblos at the top in the old days," said the Road-Runner, "facing across a deep divide, but nobody goes there now except owls that have their nests in the ruins, and the last of the Condors, who since old time have made their home in the pinnacles of the Rock. He'll have seen us coming." The children looked up as a sailing shadow began to circle about them on the evening-colored sands. "You can see by the frayed edges of his wing feathers that he has a long time for remembering," said the Road-Runner.

The great bird came slowly to earth, close by the lone pine that tasseled out against the south side of El Morro and the Road-Runner ducked several times politely.

"My children, how is it with you these days?" asked the Condor with great dignity.

"Happy, happy, Grandfather. And you?"

The Condor assured them that he was very happy, and seeing that no one made any other remark, he added, after an interval, looking pointedly at the children, "It is not thinking of nothing that strangers come to the house of a stranger."

"True, Grandfather," said the Road-Runner; "we are thinking of the gold, the seed of the Sun, that the Spaniards did not find. Is there left to you any of the remembrance of these things?"

"*Hai, hai!*" The Condor stretched his broad wings and settled himself comfortably on a nubbin of sandstone. "Of which of these who passed will you hear?" He indicated the inscriptions on the rock, and then by way of explanation he said to the children, "I am town-hatched myself. Lads of Zuñi took my egg and hatched it under a turkey hen, at the Ant Hill. They kept my wings clipped, but once they forgot, so I came away to the ancient home of my people. But in the days of my captivity I learned many tales and the best manner of telling them. Also the Tellings of my own people who kept the Rock. They fit into one another like the arrow point to the shaft. Look!"—he pointed to an inscription protected by a little brow of sandstone, near the lone pine. "Juan de Oñate did that when he passed to the discovery of the Sea of the South. He it was who built the towns, even the chief town of Santa Fé.

"There signed with his sword, Vargas, who reconquered the pueblos after the rebellion—yes, they rebelled again and again. On the other side of the Rock you can read how Governor Nieto carried the faith to them. They came and went, the Iron Shirts, through two hundred years. You can see the marks of their iron hats on some of the rafters of Zuñi town to this day, but small was the mark they left on the hearts of the Zuñis."

"Is that so!" said the Road-Runner, which is a polite way of saying that you think the story worth going on with; and then cocking his eye at the inscription, he hinted, "I have heard that the Long Gowns, the Padres who came with them, were master-workers in hearts."

"It is so," said the Condor. "I remember the first of them who managed to build a church here, Padre Francisco Letrado. Here!" He drew their attention to an inscription almost weathered away, and looking more like the native picture-writings than the signature of a Spanish gentleman. He read:—

"They passed on the 23d of March of 1832 years to the avenging of the death of Father Letrado." It was signed simply "Lujan."

"There is a Telling of that passing and of that soldier which has to do with the gold that was never found.

"*Sons eso,*" said the Road-Runner, and they settled themselves to listen.

"About the third of a man's life would have passed between the time when Oñate came to the founding of Santa Fé, and the building of the first church by Father Letrado. There were Padres before that, and many baptizings. The Zuñis were always glad to learn new ways of persuading the gods to be on their side, and they thought the prayers and ceremonies of the Padres very good Medicine indeed. They thought the Iron Shirts were gods themselves, and when they came received them with sprinklings of sacred meal. But it was not until Father Letrado's time that it began to be understood that the new religion was to take the place of their own, for to the Indians there is but one spirit in things, as there is one life in man. They thought their own prayers as good as any that were taught them.

"But Father Letrado was zealous and he was old. He made a rule that all should come to the service of his church and that they should obey him and reverence him when they met, with bowings and kissings of his robe. It is not easy to teach reverence to a free people, and the men of the Ant Hill had been always free. But the worst of Father Letrado's ruling was that there were to be no more prayers in the kivas, no dancings to the gods nor scatterings of sacred pollen and planting of plumes. Also—this is not known, I think—that the sacred places where the Sun had planted the seed of itself should be told to the Padres."

"He means the places where the gold is found mixed with the earth and the sand," explained the Road-Runner to Dorcas Jane and Oliver.

"In the days of the Ancients," said the Condor, "when such a place was found, it was told to the Priests of the Bow, and kept in reverence by the whole people. But since the Zuñis had discovered what things white men will do for gold, there had been fewer and fewer who held the secret. The Spaniards had burnt too many of those who were suspected of knowing, for one thing, and they had a drink which, when they gave to the Indians, let the truth out of their mouths as it would not have gone when they were sober.

"At the time Father Letrado built his first chapel there was but one man in Hawikuh who knew.

"He was a man of two natures. His mother had been a woman of the Matsaki, and his father one of the Oñate's men, so that he was half of the Sun and half of the Moon, as we say,—for the Zuñis called the first half-white children, Moon-children,—and his heart was pulled two ways, as I have heard the World Encompassing Water is pulled two ways by the Sun and the Moon. Therefore, he was called Ho-tai the Two-Hearted.

"What finally pulled his heart out of his bosom was the love he had for his wife. Flower-of-the-Maguey, she was called, and she was beautiful beyond all naming. She was daughter to the Chief Priest of the Bow, and young men from all the seven towns courted her. But though she was lovely and quiet she was not as she seemed to be. She was a Passing Being." The Condor thoughtfully stretched his wings as he considered how to explain this to the children.

"Such there are," he said. "They are shaped from within outward by their own wills. They have the power to take the human form and leave it. But it was not until she had been with her mother to To-yalanne, the sacred Thunder Mountain, as is the custom when maidens reach the marriageable age, that her power came to her. She was weary with gathering the sacred flower pollen; she lay under a maguey in the warm sun and felt the light airs play over her. Her breath came evenly and the wind lifted her long hair as it lay along her sides.

"Strangely she felt the pull of the wind on her hair, all along her body. She looked and saw it turn short and tawny in the sun, and the shape of her limbs fitted to the sandy hollows. Thus she understood that she was become another being, Mokeiche, the puma. She bounded about in the sun and chased the blue and yellow butterflies. After a time she heard the voice of her mother calling, and it pulled at her heart. She let her heart have way and became a maid again. But often she would steal out after that, when the wind brought her the smell of the maguey, or at night when the moon walked low over To-yalanne, and play as puma. Her parents saw that she had power more than is common to maidens, but she was wise and modest, and they loved her and said nothing.

"'Let her have a husband and children,' they said, 'and her strangeness will pass.' But they were very much disappointed at what happened to all the young men who came a-courting.

"This is the fashion of a Zuñi courting: The young man says to his Old Ones, 'I have seen the daughter of the Priest of the Bow at the Middle Ant Hill, what think ye?' And if they said, 'Be it well!' he gathered his presents into a bundle and went to knock at the sky-hole of her father's house.

"'*She!*' he said, and '*Hai!*' they answered from within. 'Help me down,' he would say, which was to tell them that he had a bundle with him and it was a large one. Then the mother of the girl would know what was afoot. She would rise and pull the bundle down through the sky-hole—all pueblo houses are entered from the top, did you not know?" asked the Condor.

The children nodded, not to interrupt; they had seen as they came along the trail the high terraced houses with the ladders sticking out of the door-holes.

"Then there was much politeness on both sides, politeness of food offered and eaten and questions asked, until the girl's parents were satisfied that the match would be a good one. Finally, the Old Ones would stretch themselves out in their corners and begin to scrape their nostrils with their breath—thus," said the Condor, making a gentle sound of snoring; "for it was thought proper for the young people to have a word or two together. The girl would set the young man a task, so as not to seem too easily won, and to prove if he were the sort of man she wished for a husband.

"'Only possibly you love me,' said the daughter of the Chief Priest of the Bow. 'Go out with the light to-morrow to hunt and return with it, bringing your kill, that I may see how much you can do for my sake.'

"But long before light the girl would go out herself as a puma and scare the game away. Thus it happened every time that the young man would return at evening empty-handed, or he would be so mortified that he did not return at all, and the girl's parents would send the bundle back to him. The Chief Priest and his wife began to be uneasy lest their daughter should never marry at all.

"Finally Ho-tai of the pueblo of Matsaki heard of her, and said to his mother, 'That is the wife for me.'

"'*Shoom!*' said his mother; 'what have you to offer her?' for they were very poor.

"'*Shoom* yourself!' said Ho-tai. 'He that is poor in spirit as well as in appearance, is poor indeed. It is plain she is not looking for a bundle, but for a man.' So he took what presents he had to the house of the Chief Priest of the Bow, and everything went as usual; except that when Ho-tai asked them to help him in, the Chief Priest said, 'Be yourself within,' for he was growing tired of courtings that came to nothing. But when Ho-tai came cheerfully down the ladder with his gift, the girl's heart was touched, for he was a fine gold color like a full moon, and his high heart gave him a proud way of walking. So when she had said, 'Only possibly you love me, but that I may know what manner of husband I am getting, I pray you hunt for me one day,' and when they had bidden each other 'wait happily until the morning,' she went out as a puma and searched the hills for game that she might drive toward the young man, instead of away from him. But because she could not take her eyes off of him, she was not so careful as she should be not to let him see her. Then she went home and put on all her best clothes, the white buckskins, the turquoises and silver bracelets, and waited. At evening, Ho-tai, the Two-Hearted, came with a fine buck on his shoulders, and a stiff face. Without a word he gave the buck to the Priest's wife and turned away. '*Hai,*' said the mother, 'when a young man wins a girl he is permitted to say a few words to her!'—for she was pleased to think that her daughter had got a husband at last.

"'I did not kill the buck by myself,' said Ho-tai; and he went off to find the Chief Priest and tell him that he could not marry his daughter. Flower-of-the-Maguey, who was in her room all this time peeking through the curtain, took a water jar and went down to the spring where Ho-tai could not help but pass her on his way back to his own village.

"'I did not bring back your bundle,' she said when she saw him; 'what is a bundle to a woman when she has found a man?'

"Then his two hearts were sore in him, for she was lovely past all naming. 'I do not take what I cannot win by my own labor,' said he; 'there was a puma drove up the game for me.'

"'Who knows,' said she, 'but Those Above sent it to try if you were honest or a braggart?' After which he began to feel differently. And in due course they were married, and Ho-tai came to live in the house of the Chief Priest at Hawikuh, for her parents could not think of parting with her.

"They were very happy," said the Condor, "for she was wisely slow as well as beautiful, and she eased him of the struggle of his two hearts, one against the other, and rested in her life as a woman."

"Does that mean she wasn't a puma any more?" asked Dorcas Jane.

The Condor nodded, turning over the Zuñi words in his mind for just the right phrase. "Understanding of all her former states came to her with the years. There was nothing she dreaded so much as being forced out of this life into the dust and whirl of Becoming. That is one reason why she feared and distrusted the Spanish missionaries when they came, as they did about that time.

"One of her husband's two hearts pulled very strongly toward the religion of the Spanish Padres. He was of the first that were baptized by Father Letrado, and served the altar. He was also the first of those upon whose mind the Padre began to work to persuade him that in taking the new religion he must wholly give up the old.

"At the end of that trail, a day's journey," said the Condor, indicating the narrow foot-tread in the sand, which showed from tree to tree of the dark junipers, and seemed to turn and disappear at every one, "lies the valley of Shiwina, which is Zuñi.

"It is a narrow valley, watered by a muddy river. Red walls of mesas shut it in above the dark wood. To the north lies Thunder Mountain, wall-sided and menacing. Dust devils rise up from the plains and veil the crags. In the winter there are snows. In the summer great clouds gather over Shiwina and grow dark with rain. White corn tassels are waving, blue butterfly maidens flit among the blossoming beans.

"Day and night at midsummer, hardly the priests have their rattles out of their hands. You hear them calling from the house-tops, and the beat of bare feet on the dancing places. But the summer after Father Letrado built his chapel of the Immaculate Virgin at Halona and the chapel and parish house of the Immaculate Conception at Hawikuh, he set his face against the Rain Dance, and especially against the Priests of the Rain. Witchcraft and sorcery he called it, and in Zuñi to be accused of witchcraft is death.

"The people did not know what to do. They prayed secretly where they could. The Priests of the Rain went on with their preparations, and the soldiers of Father Letrado—for he had a small detachment with him—broke up the dance and profaned the sacred places. Those were hard days for Ho-tai the Two-Hearted. The gods of the strangers were strong gods, he said, let the people wait and see what they could do. The white men had strong Medicine in their guns and their iron shirts and their long-tailed, smoke-breathing beasts. They did not work as other gods. Even if there was no rain, the white gods might have another way to save the people.

"These were the things Father Letrado taught him to say, and the daughter of the Chief Priests of the Bow feared that his heart would be quite pulled away from the people of Zuñi. Then she went to her father the Chief Priest, who was also the keeper of the secret of the Holy Places of the Sun, and neared the dividing of the ways of life.

"'Let Ho-tai be chosen Keeper in your place,' she said, 'so all shall be bound together, the Medicine of the white man and the brown.'

"'Be it well,' said the Priest of the Bow, for he was old, and had respect for his daughter's wisdom. Feeling his feet go from him toward the Spirit Road, he called together the Priests of the Bow, and announced to them that Ho-tai would be Keeper in his stead.

"Though Two-Hearted was young for the honor, they did not question it, for, like his wife, they were jealous of the part of him that was white—which, for her, there was no becoming—and they thought of this as a binding together. They were not altogether sure yet that the Spaniards were not gods, or at the least Surpassing Beings.

"But as the rain did not come and the winter set in cold with a shortage of corn, more and more they neglected the bowings and the reverences and the service of the mass. Nights Father Letrado would hear the muffled beat of the drums in the kivas where the old religion was being observed, and because it was the only heart open to him, he twisted the heart of Ho-tai to see if there was not some secret evil, some seed of witchcraft at the bottom of it which he could pluck out."

"That was great foolishness," said the Road-Runner; "no white man yet ever got to the bottom of the heart of an Indian."

"True," said the Condor, "but Ho-tai was half white, and the white part of him answered to the Padre's hand. He was very miserable, and in fact, nobody was very happy in those days in Hawikuh. Father Martin who passed there in the moon of the Sun Returning, on his way to establish a mission among the People of the Coarse Hanging Hair, reported to his superior that Father Letrado was ripe for martyrdom.

"It came the following Sunday, when only Ho-tai and a few old women came to mass. Sick at the sound of his own voice echoing in the empty chapel, the Padre went out to the plaza of the town to scold the people into services. He was met by the Priests of the Rain with their bows. Being neither a coward nor a fool, he saw what was before him. Kneeling, he clasped his arms, still holding the crucifix across his bosom, and they transfixed him with their arrows.

"They went into the church after that and broke up the altar, and burned the chapel. A party of bowmen followed the trail of Father Martin, coming up with him after five days. That night with the help of some of his own converts, they fell upon and killed him. There was a half-breed among them, both whose hearts were black. He cut off the good Padre's hand and scalped him."

"Oh," said Oliver, "I think he ought not to have done that!"

The Condor was thoughtful.

"The hand, no. It had been stretched forth only in kindness. But I think white men do not understand about scalping. I have heard them talk sometimes, and I know they do not understand. The scalp was taken in order that they might have the scalp dance. The dance is to pacify the spirit of the slain. It adopts and initiates him into the tribe of the dead, and makes him one with them, so that he will not return as a spirit and work harm on his slayers. Also it is a notice to the gods of the enemy that theirs is the stronger god, and to beware. The scalp dance is a protection to the tribe of the slayer; to omit one of its observances is to put the tribe in peril of the dead. Thus I have heard; thus the Old Ones have said. Even Two-Hearted, though he was sad for the killing, danced for the scalp of Father Martin.

"Immediately it was all over, the Hawikuhkwe began to be afraid. They gathered up their goods and fled to K'iakime, the Place of the Eagles, on Thunder Mountain, where they had a stronghold. There were Iron Shirts at Santa Fé and whole cities of them in the direction of the Salt Containing

Waters. Who knew what vengeance they might take for the killing of the Padres? The Hawikuhkwe entrenched themselves, and for nearly two years they waited and practiced their own religion in their own way.

"Only two of them were unhappy. These were Ho-tai of the two hearts, and his wife, who had been called Flower-of-the-Maguey. But her unhappiness was not because the Padres had been killed. She had had her hand in that business, though only among the women, dropping a word here and there quietly, as one drops a stone into a deep well. She was unhappy because she saw that the dead hand of Father Letrado was still heavy on her husband's heart.

"Not that Ho-tai feared what the soldiers from Santa Fé might do to the slayer, but what the god of the Padre might do to the whole people. For Padre Letrado had taught him to read in the Sacred Books, and he knew that whole cities were burned with fire for their sins. He saw doom hanging over K'iakime, and his wife could not comfort him. After awhile it came into his mind that it was his own sin for which the people would be punished, for the one thing he had kept from the Padre was the secret of the gold.

"It is true," said the Condor, "that after the Indians had forgotten them, white men rediscovered many of their sacred places, and many others that were not known even to the Zuñis. But there is one place on Thunder Mountain still where gold lies in the ground in lumps like pine nuts. If Father Letrado could have found it, he would have hammered it into cups for his altar, and immediately the land would have been overrun with the Spaniards. And the more Ho-tai thought of it, the more convinced he was that he should have told him.

"Toward the end of two years when it began to be rumored that soldiers and new Padres were coming to K'iakime to deal with the killing of Father Letrado, Ho-tai began to sleep more quietly at night. Then his wife knew that he had made up his mind to tell, if it seemed necessary to reconcile the Spaniards to his people, and it was a knife in her heart.

"It was her husband's honor, and the honor of her father, Chief Priest of the Bow; and besides, she knew very well that if Ho-tai told, the Priests of the Bow would kill him. She said to herself that her husband was sick with the enchantments of the Padres, and she must do what she could for him. She gave him seeds of forgetfulness."

"Was that a secret too?" asked Dorcas, for the Condor seemed not to remember that the children were new to that country.

"It was *peyote*. Many know of it now, but in the days of Our Ancients it was known only to a few Medicine men and women. It is a seed that when eaten wipes out the past from a man's mind and gives him visions. In time its influence will wear away, and it must be eaten anew, but if eaten too often it steals a man's courage and his strength as well as his memory.

"When she had given her husband a little in his food, Flower-of-the-Maguey found that he was like a child in her hands.

"'Sleep,' she would say, 'and dream thus, and so,' and that is the way it would be with him. She wished him to forget both the secret of the gold in the ground and the fear of the Padres.

"From the time that she heard that the Spaniards were on their way to K'iakime, she fed him a little *peyote* every day. To the others it seemed that his mind walked with Those Above, and they were respectful of him. That is how Zuñis think of any kind of madness. They were not sure that the madness had not been sent for just this occasion when they had need of the gods, and so, as it seemed to them, it proved.

"The Spaniards asked for parley, and the Caciques permitted the Padres to come up into the council chambers, for they knew that the long gowns covered no weapons. The Spaniards had learned wisdom, perhaps, and perhaps they thought Father Letrado somewhat to blame. They asked nothing but permission to reëstablish their missions, and to have the man who had scalped Father Martin handed over to them for Spanish justice.

"They sat around the wall of the kiva, with Ho-tai in his place, hearing and seeing very little. But the parley was long, and, little by little, the vision of his own gods which the *peyote* had given him began to wear away. One of the Padres rose in his place and began a long speech about the sin of killing, and especially of killing priests. He quoted his Sacred Books and talked of the sin in their hearts, and, little by little, the talk laid hold on the wandering mind of Ho-tai. 'Thus, in this killing, has the secret evil of your hearts come forth,' said the Padre, and 'True, He speaks true,' said Ho-tai, upon which the Priests of the Hawikuhkwe were astonished. They thought their gods spoke through his madness.

"Then the Padre began to exhort them to give up this evil man in their midst and rid themselves of the consequences of sin, which he assured them were most certain and as terrible as they were sure. Then the white heart of Ho-tai remembered his own anguish, and spoke thickly, as a man drunk with *peyote* speaks.

"'He must be given up,' he said. It seemed to them that his voice came from the under world.

"But there was a great difficulty. The half-breed who had done the scalping had, at the first rumor of the soldiers coming, taken himself away. If the Hawikuhkwe said this to the Spaniards, they knew very well they would not be believed. But the mind of Ho-tai had begun to come back to him, feebly as from a far journey.

"He remembered that he had done something displeasing to the Padre, though he did not remember what, and on account of it there was doom over the valley of the Shiwina. He rose staggering in his place.

"'Evil has been done, and the evil man must be cast out,' he said, and for the first time the Padre noticed that he was half white. Not one of them had ever seen the man who scalped Father Letrado, but it was known that his father had been a soldier. This man was altogether such a one as they expected. His cheeks were drawn, his hair hung matted over his reddened eyes, as a man's might, tormented of the spirit. 'I am that man,' said Ho-tai of the Two Hearts, and the Caciques put their hands over their mouths with astonishment."

"But they never," cried Oliver,—"they never let him be taken?"

"A life for a life," said the Condor, "that is the law. It was necessary that the Spaniards be pacified, and the slayer could not be found. Besides, the people of Hawikuh thought Ho-tai's offer to go in his place was from the gods. It agrees with all religions that a man may lay down his life for his people."

"Couldn't his wife do anything?"

"What could she? He went of his own will and by consent of the Caciques. But she tried what she could. She could give him *peyote* enough so that he should remember nothing and feel nothing of what the Spaniards should do to him. But to do that she had to make friends with one of the soldiers. She chose one Lujan, who had written his name on the Rock on the way to K'iakime. By him she sent a cake to Ho-tai, and promised to meet Lujan when she could slip away from the village unnoticed.

"Between here and Acoma," said the Condor, "is a short cut which may be traveled on foot, but not on horseback. Returning with Ho-tai, manacled and fast between two soldiers, the Spaniards meant to take that trail, and it was there the wife of Ho-tai promised to meet Lujan at the end of the second day's travel.

"She came in the twilight, hurrying as a puma, for her woman's heart was too sore to endure her woman's body. Lujan had walked apart from the camp to wait for her; smiling, he waited. She was still very beautiful, and he thought she was in love with him. Therefore, when he saw the long, hurrying stride of a puma in the trail, he thought it a pity so beautiful a woman should be frightened. The arrow that he sped from his cross-bow struck in the yellow flanks. 'Well shot,' said Lujan cheerfully, but his voice was drowned by a scream that was strangely like a woman's. He remembered it afterward in telling of the extraordinary thing that had happened to him, for when he went to look, where the great beast had leaped in air and fallen, there was nothing to be found there. Nothing.

"If she had been in her form as a woman when he shot her," said the Condor, "that is what he would have found. But she was a Passing Being, not taking form from without as we do, of the outward touchings of things, and her shape of a puma was as mist which vanishes in death as mist does in the sun. Thus shortens my story."

"Come," said the Road-Runner, understanding that there would be no more to the Telling. "The Seven Persons are out, and the trail is darkling."

The children looked up and saw the constellation which they knew as the Dipper, shining in a deep blue heaven. The glow was gone from the high cliffs of El Morro, and the junipers seemed to draw secretly together. Without a word they took hands and began to run along the trail after the Road-Runner.

❖ ❖ ❖

One-Smoke Stories

One-Smoke Stories (1934) is a collection of Native American and folk stories. In her introduction, Austin presents a succinct description of the stories' form. Each is told, ritually, in the time it takes its teller's cigarette to burn, remaining brief and allusive, "located somewhere in the inner sense of the audience, unencumbered by . . . background" (xiii). The form is determined by the oral tradition:

> Your true desert-dweller travels light. He makes even of his experience a handy package with the finished neatness that distinguishes his artifacts. How else could they be passed intact from tribe to tribe, from generation to generation? Just before the end, like the rattle that warns that the story is about to strike, comes the fang of the experience, most often in the shape of a wise saying. Then the speaker resumes the soul-consoling smoke, while another takes up the dropped stitch of narrative and weaves it into the pattern of the talk (xiii).

Austin felt such stories were the basis for culture, expressing the shared experience of humankind.

Most of the stories are about everyday affairs in Indian tribes, about the subjects Austin claimed in *Lost Borders* interested Indian women—and all women: relations between men and women, mothers and children, Indians and whites. Austin had been collecting the stories for years, influenced by advice given her in 1899 by "Dr. Frederick Webb Hodge, the Indian specialist, who told her the thing she wanted most to know, the way of collecting and recording Indian affairs, the thing she wouldn't have thought of questioning. 'Let be,' he said, 'the strange and unusual; fix on the usual, the thing that is always done, the way of the tribe; the way of the average; the way and the why of it'" (*Earth Horizon*, 291). Several of the stories are told by dramatized Indian storytellers; "The Way of a Woman," for instance, is a retelling of Austin's earlier story, "The Divorcing of Sina," from the father's point of view. Although contemporary Native

Americans would no doubt challenge many of Austin's perceptions about their people, she was a sympathetic transcriber of the stories she heard. She knew she wrote for a white audience, and she tried to give that audience a richer understanding of Indian life.

Although some of the tales from *One-Smoke Stories* had been published in periodicals, Austin had had trouble placing them. Like many western writers of her own time and today, she believed the eastern literary establishment was prejudiced against western material. Chiefly "because my folk tales were Western, Indian, and Mexican," she said, "there was no demand for them until five or six years ago when Mr. Mencken published half a dozen of them [in *American Mercury*] so successfully that other westerners took heart . . . and the folk tale found a more general acceptance" (*Earth Horizon,* 336). Like Austin, Mencken had faith in the American grain, in native traditions. One has to wonder if Austin is so little known today because she wrote western literature about Indians, Mexicans, and women.

❖ ❖ ❖

The Man Who Lied About a Woman

*"The Man Who Lied About a Woman"
was one of the stories Mencken published
in* American Mercury. *Along with "The
Way of a Woman," the retelling of "The
Divorcing of Sina" (which appears later
in this volume), and "Papago Wedding,"*
*it was printed under the title, "American
Marriage." In this ironic story about the
lies between men and women, Austin suggests that bragging about sexual exploits
sometimes backfires.*

Everybody knew that the girl who passed for the daughter of Tizessína was neither her daughter nor a Jicarilla Apache. Tizessína, being childless, had bought her, squalling, from a Navajo whose wife had died in giving birth, and she loved her inordinately. She was called Tall Flower after the hundred-belled white yucca, and carried herself always with the consciousness of superior blood. None of the Jicarilla youths, it seemed, were good enough for her. When Tizessína, who was as anxious as any real mother to see the girl well settled, asked her what she wanted, 'I shall know when I see it,' said Tall Flower, and continued to give the young men who walked with her the squashes. For she was the sort that every man desired and herself desired nothing. She laughed and went her way, and whatever she did Tizessína approved.

Nevertheless, she was disappointed when the girl hunched her shoulder to Natáldin, who, besides being the richest young man of the Apaches, was much sought after and would require careful handling. 'But, my mother,' laughed Tall Flower, 'I shall handle him not at all.'

This being her way with him, Natáldin, who was used to having mar-riageable girls go to a great deal of trouble on his account, was hurt in his self-esteem. To keep the other young men from finding out that with the daughter of Tizessína he had to take all the trouble himself, he took the manner when he walked with her of a lover who is already successful. He stuck a flower in his hat and swung his blanket from his shoulder until Tizessína herself began to nod and wink when the other women hinted.

Then suddenly Tall Flower went off overnight with her mother and two or three other women to Taos Pueblo to gather wild plums for drying. She went without letting Natáldin know, and, when the young men of Jicarilla found this out, they laughed and presented him with a large ripe squash. Nothing like this having happened to the young man before, he stiffened his lip and swung his shoulder. 'And if I did not get the young woman,' he said, 'I got as much as I wanted of her.'

No one liked to ask him what he meant by this, for to the others the girl had been as straight and as aloof as her name flower, and to take away a maiden's honor is a serious matter among the Jicarilla Apaches. But Natáldin, for the very reason that he had had not so much from Tall Flower as the touching of her littlest finger, salved his pride with looks and shrugs and by changing the subject when her name was mentioned. The truth was that he was afraid to talk of her, not for fear he might tell more than was seemly, but for fear somebody might find out what he had lately discovered, that if he did not have the daughter of Tizessína to be his wife, his life would be as a wild gourd, smooth without, but within a mouthful of bitter ashes.

The girl and her mother went not only to Taos Pueblo where the plum branches are bent over with bright fruit, but to Taos town, where a white man persuaded Tall Flower to be painted among the plum branches. Then they gathered *osha* in the hills toward Yellow Earth, where Tizessína, who was Government School taught, stayed for a month to cook for a camp of Government surveyors. In the month of the Cold Touching Mildly, they came to Jicarilla again.

Natáldin, who found Tall Flower more to be desired than ever, was in two minds how he should punish her, but unfortunately what was in his mind turned out to be so much less than what was in his heart that he ended by thinking only how he could persuade her to be his wife. Tizessína, he saw, was wholly on his side, but some strange fear of her daughter kept her silent. Natáldin would catch her looking at him as though she wished him to know something that she feared to tell. At other times Tizessína looked at Natáldin from behind a fold of her blanket as a wild thing watches a hunter from the rocks, while Tall Flower looked over and beyond them both. There was a dream in her eyes, and now and then it flowered around her mouth.

Presently there began to be other looks: matrons watching Tall Flower out of the tails of their eyes, young girls walking in the twilight with their arms about one another, looking the other way as she passed; young men lookly slyly at Natáldin, with laughs and nudges. Natáldin, who was sick to think that another had possessed her, where he had got the squash, denied nothing. If he remembered the punishment that is due to a man who lies about a woman, he reflected that a woman who has given herself to one lover is in no position to deny that she has given herself to two. But in fact he reflected very little. He was a man jabbing at an aching tooth in the hope of driving out one pain with another. It had been midsummer when Tizessína had taken her daughter to gather plums, and in the month of Snow Water, Tall Flower being far gone with child, the two women talked together in their house.

'I have heard,' said Tizessína, 'that Natáldin tells it about camp that he is the father of your child.'

'Since how long?' said Tall Flower.

'Since before we had come to Taos town,' said the mother, and repeated all she had heard.

'Then he has twice lied,' said the girl.

'He is the richest man in Jicarilla, as well as a liar,' said Tizessína, 'and you will not get a husband very easily after this. I shall bring it to Council.'

'What he does to another, that to him also,' said the girl, which is a saying of the Apaches. 'By all means take it to Council. But I shall not appear.'

When Natáldin saw the *algucil* coming to call him before the Council, he was half glad, for now his tooth was about to come out. But he was sick when he saw that the girl was not there; only Tizessína, who stood up and said, 'O my fathers! You know that my daughter is with child, and this one says that he is the father of it. This is established by many witnesses. Therefore, if he is the father, let him take my daughter to his house. But if he has lied, then let him be punished as is the custom for a man who has lied about a woman.'

Said the Council, 'Have you lied?' and Natáldin saw that he was between the bow and the bowstring.

'Only Tall Flowers knows if I have lied,' he said, 'and she does not appear against me. But I am willing to take her to my house, and the child also.'

'So let it be,' said the Council; and the young man's tooth was stopped, waiting to see whether it would come out or not.

But Tall Flower, when the judgment was reported to her, made conditions. 'I will come to his house and cook for him and mend,' she said, 'but until after the child is born I will not come to his bed.' And Natáldin, to whom nothing mattered except that now Tall Flower should be his wife, consented. Although he was tormented at times by the thought of that other who had had all his desire of her where Natáldin himself had got the squash, the young man salved his torment by thinking that, now the girl was his wife, nobody would be able to say that he had not also been her lover. He thought that when he told the daughter of Tizessína that he had lied to save her shame, she would never shame him by telling that he had lied. What nobody knows, nobody doubts; which is also a saying of the Jicarilla Apaches. Therefore, when he walked abroad with his young wife, Natáldin carried himself as a man who has done all that can be expected of him. As for Tizessína, she walked like the mother-in-law of the richest young man in Jicarilla, and Tall Flower walked between them, dreaming.

In due time, as he worked in his field Natáldin saw Tizessína and the neighbor women hurrying to his house, after which he worked scarcely at all, but leaned upon his hoe until the sun was a bowshot from its going down, and listened to the shaking of his own heart. As he came up the trail to his house at last, he saw his wife lying under the *ramada,* and beside her Tizessína with something wrapped in a blanket. 'Let me see my son,' he said, and wondered why the neighbor women rose and hurried away with their blankets over their faces, for with the first-born there should be compliments and present-giving. But when Tizessína turned back the blanket and showed him the child's face, he knew that after all he should not escape the punishment of a man who has lied about a woman. For the child was white!

❖ ❖ ❖

The Medicine of Bow-Returning

Although Austin sometimes—not al-
ways—used the generic "man" herself, she
often complained that women's needs were
swallowed up in the dominance of the
male point of view. "The Medicine of
Bow-Returning" reveals the invisibility
of women, the way they are taken for
granted by men. Although the comparison
seems unlikely at first, this story may well
be Austin's retelling of a story by one of
her favorite writers, Henry James's "Beast
in the Jungle."

There was a man of the Plains whose mother named him Taku-Wakin, which means Something Wonderful. She felt in her heart that he would do some great thing and to that mind she reared him.

When the time came, according to custom, she sent him into the hills to fast and find his medicine. This is the way it happens when a youth is of age to become a tribesman; he walks apart, keeping holy silence, seeking. During his search he eats nothing, drinks a little water, sees no one, visits the holy places. After two or three days the One-Who-Walks-in-the-Sky is revealed to him in the form of a bird or an animal, or it may be as the small grass or the rainbow. Whatever thing appears, that becomes his medicine. Through it he reaches up to the All-ness, he becomes part of the All-ness and receives much *wakonda,* that is to say, strength of spirit. According to the strength of his spirit a man prospers.

So Taku-Wakin, who was afterward called Bow-Returning, went toward the mountain called Going-to-the-Sun for his fast, and as he went he felt the thoughts of his mother push him. He went far, climbed the high mountains and bathed in the sacred lakes, keeping holy silence. On the mountain, when by fasting he was removed from himself, his eyes were opened. He saw all the earth and the sky as One Thing, even as the bow is one thing and the cord of the bow which draws it. Even so he saw the thoughts of men pulling at the corners of the world as the cord pulls at the bow, and the bow bending and returning. In the silence he heard in his heart the One-Who-Walks-in-the-Sky talking.

'This is true medicine, Taku-Wakin. All things are one, man and the mire, the small grass and the mountain, the deer and the hunter pursuing, the thing that is made and the maker, even as the bow and the cord are one thing. As the bow bends to the cord, so all things bend and return, and are opposed and together. The meaning of the medicine is that man can hurt nothing without also hurting himself.' Thus said the One-Who-Walks-in-the-Sky to Taku-Wakin.

Taku-Wakin ate and drank and went down the mountain, walking carefully that he might hurt nothing. To his mother he said, 'It is my medicine to know that man can hurt nothing without hurting himself also.' And to the tribesmen he said that from this time forth he should be called Bow-Returning. From that time also he was much respected because of his strong medicine. Meat he ate according to the law of food-taking, but there was no man who could say he had hurt of any sort at the hands of Bow-Returning.

In the counsel of time it came into the heart of Bow-Returning that he ought to go about among his tribes teaching the medicine of the Bow-Returning. Then he said there will be no man hurting another. This he said to his wife, for by this time he had a wife, and, though she was sad to think of his leaving her, she began at once to make him moccasins. From tribe to tribe, strong in his medicine, went Bow-Returning with a great following. But as he went, his *wakonda* began to go from him. When his medicine would no longer work, then men refused to believe him, and one by one his following fell away from him. Troubled in heart, as Taku-Wakin he returned to his home camp. But his tent was not among the others, for his wife had died of grieving and his son had been given to another. Bow-Returning purged himself in the sweat lodges, with smoke of sweet grass he sanctified himself, and went again on the mountain, keeping holy silence.

After long seeking he heard the voice of the Sky-Walker. Then said Bow-Returning: 'This is my medicine, that everything is One Thing, and in this fashion I have kept it. Meat I have taken for my needs according to the law of food-taking, but I have hurt no man. Neither the flower in the field have I crushed, nor trodden on the ant in my pathway. How is it, then, that my wife is dead, my son given to another, and my medicine is gone from me?'

Then said the One-Who-Walks-in-the-Sky to Bow-Returning, 'Did I not also make woman?'

❖ ❖ ❖

Stewed Beans

Like many feminists, Austin was often accused of lacking a sense of humor, but many of her stories are quite funny. In her introduction to One-Smoke Stories, *she says that she has chosen not to tell some Indian stories, often the wittiest, because of "the taboos of [her] own tribe." "But," she adds, "lest you imagine that the untellables are of a sliminess that characterizes our own untellables, I have included 'Stewed Beans'" (xv).*

Though Austin's white audience might have assumed that "primitive" people solve their problems violently, Spotted Horse comes up with a sure-fire nonviolent solution.

Now I tellin' you thiss stewed beans story. Thass Apache story. Iss very fonny. You savvy stewed beans; how they make everybody go in his insides *r-r-r-ru, phutt-phutt!* Only if you not cook him right; if you pour the water off while they cooking two-three times, they not make. But if water is not poured off, then they make *phutt-phutt!* Well, I tellin' you.

There iss man in Apache Village in the Chirricahua Mountains, and his wife she not likin' him any more. She likin' 'nother man, only she don' tell him that, 'cause he don' live in her village. There iss three villages that make the same talk an' have one council, an' thiss man an' her husband they both bein' members of that council. So when thiss man from Lone Spring Village come over to Chirricahua Council, he visitin' that woman, an' some other times when he come on business. Thiss man is name Two-Comes-Over-the-Hill, an' thiss woman's husband is named Spotted Horse. Spotted Horse he think maybe Two-Comes-Over-the-Hill is comin' to see his wife, only he not sure. He never catch him; an' maybe he no like to catch him; only to make so that man don' think he not knowin'. He don' want to lose hees wife; only to make so that everybody been laughin' at thiss man an' not at Spotted Horse.

So then there is a Council, an' Spotted Horse think maybe so Two-Comes-Over-the-Hill will be visitin' hees wife. He watch an' he seein' hees wife makin' big supper, like when company comin', an' he stay 'roun' the house all afternoon. Hees wife she cookin' stewed beans; an' she want to go out an' pick some greens; so she say, 'I go pickin' greens, you watch those beans, an' make sure you pour the water off two-three times.'

So that man say, 'All right.' Well, he stayin' there while his wife pickin' greens, an' he don' pour that water off those beans, not one time. But when his wife come askin' him, he say, 'Yes, the water is pour off, two times.' So she fixin' the beans good; meat an' everything; an' when supper ready, he say he feel sorta sick an' he not carin' to eat any beans. Then he go to that Council, and when men sayin', 'How come you so early?' he sayin', 'Well, I didden' eat much supper tonight 'cause my wife left me to pour the water off the beans an' I forgot, so I not eatin' any beans,' an' everybody laugh an' make jokes with him 'bout those beans.

So it gettin' dark an' the Council wait until those mans from Lone Spring Village come, an' by an' by Two-Comes-Over-the-Hill come along an' sit in the Council. An' he sayin', 'You gotta excuse me 'cause I was eatin' supper with beans with meat an' greens,' so of course they excused him. Iss not polite for mans invited to supper to eat too fast an' not eat a lot. So Spotted Horse say, 'I was goin' to ask you to supper at my house, but my wife left me to pour the water off the beans an' I forgot. You are a lot better off.' So they went on with the Council, an' by an' by the beans began to *r-r-r-ru* in Two-Comes-Over-the-Hill's insides an' pretty soon he begins to go *phutt-phutt!* An' Spotted Horse he kinda laughin' an' he say, 'Sounds like you been eatin' some of my wife's beans,' an' Two-Comes-Over-the-Hill he sayin', 'Oh, no, no, not at all.' An' the beans go *phutt-phutt!* An' pretty soon *phutt-phutt-phutt—phu—utt!* An' everybody begin sort of laughin', so when the Governor of the Council calls for a vote, the beans goin' *r-r-r-ru, phutt!* An' somebody say, 'The beans don' got no vote.' Which make everybody laugh. An' Two-Comes-Over-the-Hill say, 'You gotta excuse me; I ain't feelin' so well.' An' Spotted Horse say, 'I gotta see my wife about this'; an' all the Council is laughin'. Every time Two-Comes-Over-the-Hill goes *phutt-phutt!* they laugh, an' Spotted Horse say, 'If you told me you were comin' to my house to supper, I would have poured the water off.' An' he act sorry like, so they all laugh an' laugh. So the Headman he say, 'You are excuse from this Council,' 'cause he don' like they all laughin' all the time.

So Two-Comes-Over-the-Hill he gathers up hees blanket an' he goes away from there. They watch an' see that he goes in the direction of Spotted Horse's house, an' go 'way from it in a few minutes. An' Spotted Horse when he get home see that his wife has been cryin'. 'Iss not your fault,' he say. 'I forgot to pour the water off. Next time old *Phutt-Phutt* is comin', I think you better tell me.' She say, 'There ain't goin' to be no next time. That Two-Comes-Over-the-Hill, he iss got no highness.' Sure 'nough, he is not comin' there again where he is call' *Phutt-Phutt,* an' somebody always ask him if he would like some stewed beans. That's very fonny story.

❖   ❖   ❖

White Wisdom

"White Wisdom" is a story about racial identity, as the narrator makes clear. Dan Kearny, like many other American "half-breeds," is at war with himself, and he becomes a "two-talker." "Whiteness had shone upon him," yet, we discover, "he is the worse for it." The narrator's "Telling" is a lesson to his audience not to "covet the wisdom of the whites for your children,"

for the "wisdom of the whites is such that even the whites are sick of it."

An interesting subtext to "White Wisdom" concerns the relationship between the storyteller and his mother, a chisera. His portrayal of her and her power tells us much about the status of women in the Ute tribe.

My friends: Touching the matter of the horses of my brother's widow which have strayed in your reservation, all is made beautiful between us. Therefore, going, I leave a Telling with you as a gift in return for your gift of kindness while I have been in your hogans. For I see that you Navahos, though you be called horse-thieves and cattle-stealers, are sound men and honorable; and as for the grass which my brother's horses have eaten, I hold it but witness to the goodness of your country, for in no other could so few horses have eaten so much. It shall be paid for according to the writing which is between us. In beauty it is finished. But seeing you are troubled, coveting the Wisdom of the Whites for your children, so that you pray Washington to build schools for them with the money your elders saved for brood cattle, I leave this Telling with you as a seed which may grow to a tree of protection. Many times while I am among you, you have inquired of me as to Twice-Bitten, the Gray-Eyed Ute, who is in power among us, in whom White Wisdom is a shield under which the tribal use flourishes, and a thorn in the side of the Agency which they can in no wise pluck out. To this I have answered as Elders of the tribes to strangers. But now, as one tribesman to another, I tell you that the thorn is in the side of Twice-Bitten so deep that he dare not pluck at it, lest his life come out with it. This is the Telling:

When I was but just come to be a man, there was great scarcity of rain in the Ute country, and of food also, so that my mother's sister, being widowed, but strong and well-thinking, said to me that we two should go into the mining country, where we had heard there were jobs with wages, so that we might be fed, and perhaps send back a present of money. So in five days' walking we came to the edge of the gold country at Dripping Spring, where there was a White man had made the beginning of a ranch. There, his wife being sick, he hired my mother's sister to stay with her; I going on to the mines, where I had good wages. But after a year and more, hearing there was rain in my own country, I returned to it, by way of Dripping Spring. There I found a stranger who had bought the ranch from Dan Kearny after his wife had died, himself having gone toward Tonapah, taking with him the Ute woman, my aunt, who had kept his house, and her young child. Therefore I returned to my mother's house, and of her sister we heard from time to time, as other of our people came and went among the mines, that she lived well with Dan Kearny and that the child was called openly by his name, which we took to be a good sign.

So no more until the child would have been about eight years of age, when my mother had word from her sister that, Dan Kearny being dead, she had come with the boy, who was also called Dan Kearny, as far as the Bellows Ranch, which was at the north side of the Agency going toward Red Rock. There she had work on account of a child of the ranchman, which was sick in the back, so that it must be lifted and turned in the bed. There my mother and I visited her, partly because she prayed us, and partly because Mr. Malone, the Agent, having heard of the boy, Dan Kearny, had demanded that he be sent back to the Reservation to be numbered with the school census. But because my mother's sister would not be parted from him, nor the sick child from her, Bellows arranged with Malone that, while the boy should be numbered with the Agency children, he should attend district school with the Bellows children, with whom he was as another. He was in truth more White than Ute, to look at, and his eyes were gray. Nevertheless, I, being the head of my family and having only daughters, saw to it that Dan Kearny lacked nothing of the Wisdom of the Utes. After he was twelve years old, he would come out of his bed at night with eyes shining, like an eagle's, to meet me among the willows by the *acequia*, and there I would instruct him. This I did out of my own heart, and at the urging of my mother who was a *chisera*, and foreknowing. 'For,' she said, 'though he seems now all White to himself, yet in time both he and his White friends will remember that he is a Ute, and the game goes to him who remembers first.'

So, until the end of other eight years: then came a runner in the night to my mother, for there was a killing sickness abroad that winter and my aunt died of it. Something passed between her and my mother, but what, at the time, I knew not; and something more between her and Mr. Bellows. There was money, which my aunt had hidden, which the boy's father had left him, and letters to his kin in the East which she had kept secret, not being willing to part with the child; but now, dying, desirous that his father's wish should be fulfilled for him, and that he should be brought up altogether White. This being promised and agreed to among all of us, yet the lad was two-minded, all of us talking together in the council room of the Bellows house. 'What string is this,' said I, 'that ties you 'gainst the wish of your father?'

'The string,' said he, looking around miserably, 'of a strong-tied affection. And yet,' he said, 'I am deep-bitten with the desire of White Wisdom, even as my father wished it.'

'That,' said my mother, 'is a desire that, once it has bitten its way to the heart, turns often and bites its way out again. Make sure that you are not twice-bitten!'

This angered me somewhat, but for that it was my mother I said nothing; my mother was a *chisera,* and I myself am somewhat foreknowing. But there was a girl of the Bellows, about my cousin's age, who was as a sister to him, whom he had named Morning Light. At first, when she heard he was to leave, she wept; but now, when all was explained, she clapped her hands. 'Oh, Dan,' she said, 'you shall go and learn all that is known to White people, and then you shall come back and be a leader and a great teacher among the Utes.' This was a ripe nut to Mrs. Bellows which she put up her hands like a squirrel's to reach, crying, 'Surely this is the word of the Lord!' She had been a teacher at the Mission to the Uncompaghres before Bellows married her, and it is the way of such to find the word of the Lord in whatever they approve. For that time her husband, her daughter, and my cousin, Dan Kearny, agreed with her.

In seven years more, when he who was elected Teacher of the Utes returned to us, it was to be seen that Whiteness had shone upon him. On his face, on the skin of his body, on his clothes, he was as one painted with Whiteness for the dance of the Sun Returning, and the Whites saw it. At the trading post men called him Mr. Kearny, and the Bellows had him to table with them. Where he rode about the Reservation, thinking what he would do in it for his mother's people, the girl who was called by all the Utes Morning Light rode with him. For she was rosy of skin and turquoise-eyed and her hair was long and bright like the rays of the sun rising. And my cousin, for all his Whiteness, was flat in the back as the Utes are, and had a chief's way with him. So the Agent made him a choice allotment where a ranch was to be made in every way according to the Whites, and a house with windows. Presently as he rode, if the girl were not with him, there would be one of our young men, and another, and another. When there was anything to be asked at the Agency, they would sit around him in a ring, as of old around a war-chief, and my cousin was pleased with himself. Even the old men would sometimes say that if his eyes were gray, so also were the eyes of eagles! He had a White man's way of laughing as he talked, and when the Agent would not agree with him he would say, 'Now, Mr. Malone, as one Irishman to another'; but when the Elders were to be persuaded he said, 'We Utes.' So he got what he wanted.

I, being troubled by this two-talking, would question my mother, who watched him always, trying if I could get a foreknowing out of her, for my mother was a *chisera*, and it was in my mind that there was more in hers than she would give tongue to. 'By the ghost of my grandmother,' said I, 'is this one a Ute, or otherwise?' 'He is a very young man,' said my mother, 'and the sun has shone on him. Let him lie in the shade of the arrows awhile, and color will come out in him.' But it was in my mind that not the smallest feather shade of grief would ever fall on him.

My friends, it is no new thing to you that Washington will have all Indians to live wholly in the White way except for the one thing of living according to their heart's need of living. Especially will they have it that religious freedom is freedom to choose among the White man's religions, forsaking the religion of our fathers, and to have no dance but their dance. This is a hard thing to us, for the White men dance only one dance, the man-woman dance, which is a scandal to our Elders. And to theirs, too, sometimes, I have heard, for it is their custom to deny that their dance is a man-woman dance, and to take offense when it is so danced that this is made plain to them. With us this is not so, for, though we Utes have a man-woman dance, we know what it is—how else could it be danced fruit-fully?—but also we dance to the Earth and the Sun and the Rain. We dance against sickness, and for the corn, that it grow tall, and for the beasts that they make food for us, and to Our Ancients, even as you, O Diné! And since all these things are an abomination to the Whites, for politeness we go apart in the hills where none may see us, which to some is even more of an offense. For it is in their minds that we shall be dancing the man-woman dance, knowing and doing according as Our Ancients appointed, which, since they cannot bear to do knowingly themselves, they sicken at knowing about.

Now this summer that my cousin Dan Kearny came back to be a Teacher of White Wisdom and a leader among the young Utes, was the season of the greatest of all our dances, not only the man-woman dance for the younger who had not yet learned it, but the Dance of the Dead Returning, which we do but once in three years. Therefore, we had planned to move the campody, such as were neither too young nor too old, to Big Meadows, where the odor of offense might not track us. And the Agent and the Bellows had persuaded Dan Kearny, who had not yet danced any dance of our people, that he should set himself against it. Said he to his following, of which nearly all were young men:

'This is a foolishness that keeps you forever under the thumb of the Whites, that you do after the fashion of the Ancients rather than after the fashion of the day you live in. Will you then also dress in skins and eat raw meat as did Our Ancients, since you must dance like them? As for dancing, it is nothing to me that you dance buffalo trot or fox trot; if you do one step or deer step, or nothing. But if you dance, saying to the rain or to the corn, obey me, that is the talk of savages. As for the increase of men and cattle, that is a law, even as the increase of earthworms and lice is a law, and your dancing alters neither. Why, then, do you make yourselves a mock, O you skin-deep moderns. Not with your feet, young men of the Utes, will you make yourselves respected against the Whites, but with your heads, if you use them.'

At that there was much stir among the youngers, and even among the elders who had not been able to stand before the Whites, but must come and go even as Washington ordered.

Then said Dan Kearny: 'O young men, kinsmen, I have read in the books of the Whites that once their Ancients thought as you do, but they put off such thinking as only fit for savages, and became our conquerors. So I say to you, put away such thoughts and become men among other men.'

This also agreed to the thoughts of such others of our young men as had been to Board School and washed themselves in dishes like women. But there was one, White Horse Charlie, who had thought to be a leader among them himself, who spoke, not loud but cunningly.

'Yea,' he said, 'men among other men, even as you are Mr. Kearny among White people who will eat with you, talk with you, trade with you. But will they marry with you? Will they bear children to you, O Gray-eyed Ute?'

This, whispered from ear to ear like wind in the corn, bred question and a little laughter. For as many of them as had seen Dan Kearny riding with the girl he called Morning Light, and Turquoise-Eyed, and Rose-of-Spring, knew well that he was deep bitten of desire for more than the outward ways of the Whites. All the days that they were pulling this way and that over the dance at Big Meadows, it was in the minds of the cam-pody that, if it could be proved that the Wisdom of the Whites would bring Dan Kearny a White wife, it would be proved more powerful than the medicine of any dance. This it was that colored their thought like frost in the aspens, and at last it was plain to Dan Kearny.

I being his elder kinsman would have opened the matter to him, but I waited for my mother to come back from Rock Creek where she had gone with other women to gather wild plums for drying, my mother being, as I have said, a wise woman. So, then, the roof of his house being finished and the floors laid, my cousin spoke of it himself, we riding at the time, the borders of his field toward the *acequia*.

Said I, 'Will you have the house-building ceremony after the fashion of our fathers?' Said he, 'Should there not be first a woman at the hearth?'—and more to that purpose. Said I, 'If she marries you, will she marry an Irishman or a Ute?' 'She will marry a man,' said Dan Kearny. 'Think you I would take a wife to one half of me?' After that he talked much, too much. Was it not she who had first put it to him that the White half of him owed it a duty to his Ute half that he should bring wisdom from one to the other? Had he any thought that he had not first from her? Was his house builded other than as she had described it? Was not he himself a man of her making? 'Is she not the wife of my thought and the mother of my deed?' he inquired of me. Altogether he was like one singing at night. 'Ask her then,' I said, 'for if she goes unasked much longer, then are your thoughts and your deeds but a last year's nest to the younger of the Utes.'

'O cousin,' he said, 'if she will not have me, then am I a stalk which the seed-gatherers left standing. Now I will ask her, walking in her mother's garden. But come with me, kinsman, stand close in the bushes, but not too close, so that I may feel your medicine work for me, for what am I that one of the Surpassing Ones should marry me!'

This being arranged, I came up behind them among the bushes at the end of the garden, and saw them walking in the yellow light. I not hearing, but seeing the girl stop and stiffen, holding by a branch of the rose, even as a doe stiffens when she scents the hunter up the wind. So she stood, fear growing in her as though the hunter might have been not man the blunderer, but that cunning one, my lord puma. Dan Kearny's back was to me, but I saw him move toward her, spreading out his arms, and the girl, stretching out her throat as a frightened fawn, go running. Close by the house her mother came suddenly out of the door to take her. So I, thinking my kinsman had need of me, drew closer and heard the missionary woman spitting venom. 'So, *this* is what you were after! This! *Your* wife! Your squaw! After all we have done for you. Like one of our own children almost—as though you were White—' The girl sickened, crying, "Oh, Mother, Mother, don't let him touch me!' . . . The two clung together shaking like aspens the wind had tangled. Bellows came in from the field and heard them . . . Said he, 'You damned half-breed.'

I took my cousin by the arm and led him, he as one sleep-walking. Then he began to swear as a White man, long and steadily. Then, being still, he began to run drunkenly. He got upon his horse, he was altogether as one whom Uniputs have taken.

Three days later, when my mother came back from Rock Creek, the campody had moved almost wholly to Big Meadows. Like a dog who has stolen the children's meat, my mother berated me. 'Bring him, you fool, bring him.' But not until the fifth day could word be had of Dan Kearny, who had ridden from me, as one whose mouth being opened with astonishment, the Uniputs had jumped down it. The word was that he could be found dancing at Big Meadows. 'Oh,' said my mother, 'that I should have brought forth such a mud-head! Take me to him!'

Two days, as we rode, we heard the drums like the heart of the mountain beating, and by times singing. By the crossing into the Meadows we met a crowd of young people, riding with much laughter. And had it not been for his gray eyes, how should we know who led them? Feathers tied in his hair, also the clan sign painted across his face, and from lip to chin the three blue lines, and around his neck blue beads, as thick as a man's wrist, and silver squash blossoms. 'Ho, Mother,' he said when he saw us, 'you come late to my wedding.' For already we had seen the girl, White Horse Charlie's sister, riding behind him all vermilion-streaked as a bride should be. 'There has been a marriage, Mother,' said he, 'and a name-giving and a blood-letting, for of the blood of Dan Kearny there is little left, Mother, and what is left is the blood of Twice-Bitten, the Gray-Eyed Ute'—for he remembered what she had said to him how the desire of the White Wisdom, when it had reached his heart, would bite its way out again. 'Come, cousin,' he said, 'and dance on my new floor at my house with Twice-Bitten and his squaw'—and he laughed drunkenly. After they had passed, my mother lay on the grass face downward a long time before she would talk with me.

Thus it happened, my friends, that Twice-Bitten, from being a teacher of White Wisdom, became a defender of the tribe against it so that young men and old follow him and are unruly until Malone the Agent is half-crazy because of the cunning of the White Wisdom turned against him. Therefore I speak warnings. But it is not because of what my kinsman, the Gray-Eyed Ute, has declared against it, but for what he has shown, unknowing. For this my mother told me after she had mourned face downward, for an hour, on the grass at Big Meadow; that there is of Ute blood in him who was called Dan Kearny not a drop. For he was born to the White wife of Dan Kearny at Dripping Spring, who died bearing; and after he was given to the care of my mother's sister, who loved him with exceeding affection. This she told my mother at the ranch-house where she lay in her last sickness, and that my mother should keep it from him so that he might feel for his Ute nurse the love of a child for his mother. For she thought then, and my mother thought, that he would never come back to the Reservation. And my mother would have told him, had she known of his love of the girl called Morning Light, and of her despising. But after he had married the sister of White Horse Charlie, what then? Also the Utes loved him, and the old customs flourish, so that if every man of them knew this none would tell him. But this I say, this is my Telling, that the Wisdom of the Whites is such that even the Whites are sick with it; so that it eats them; even as it ate Twice-Bitten. Shall you be eaten then, O Diné? For now your hearts are good, your blood is pure, your thoughts leave not the straight path. Be it far from you. So ties my story.

The Man Who Was Loved by Women

Austin wrote often about women's need for monogamous relationships, but in "The Man Who Was Loved by Women" she creates an early "open marriage" initiated by a woman, who "has taken all women for her sisters." Dysildji's motives for her marriage remain suggestively am-

biguous. Like "The Man Who Lied About a Woman," this story shows the role of the tribal elders in marriages and sexual relationships, yet like many other selections from One-Smoke Stories, it suggests that Indian women have a good deal of control over their sexuality and their lives.

There was a man of the Navajo who, without deserving it, was much loved by women. It was not believed, in the beginning, that he had desired anything of the kind, or that he practiced any medicine to turn their hearts. He was handsome, which, as he said in a song he made about himself, was hardly his fault, and in one way and another was the source of a great deal of trouble to him.

If this Tsaysiki had married the first maiden who fixed her affections upon him, he would have had children and become an excellent tribesman; but before he had collected the proper number of horses for her dowry, he went with his father to the place of the Four Smokes to trade. There he met a Comanche woman, somewhat older than himself, who had a way of talking to men so that they believed her. She told Tsaysiki that it was a mistake for him to fasten a pack-strap to his back before he had proved himself against tribes other than his own. When a man has lived always among his own kin, who can say how much of what happens to him is pure kindness? So Tsaysiki sent a present to his girl at Peach Springs, and went North with the Comanche woman for the space of four moons, returning by way of Taos and the Tewa pueblos.

At first, being young and without experience, he told the women he met that he was betrothed to a girl at home, and got so much credit with them for his honesty that the way was opened for him to take what was offered without giving more than his pleasure in return. This is a mistake, for with women, no matter how free the giving, there is always something to pay for it in the end, and it is easiest paid where it is owed. The women of Taos were handsome, and proud givers, not asking for anything that is not bestowed, but the men of Taos are proud also, and though not so light on their feet, heavier than the Navajos. So Tsaysiki returned by way of Tesuque and the Keres towns, to his home camp under Carizal, to find that the girl he left had been married to somebody else in his absence.

Though he had forgotten her many times in the course of his journey, Tsaysiki felt himself injured. For his hurt's sake he had to make her sorry for herself by showing her how many other women cared for him. This he did so successfully that the Elders advised him that unless he felt disposed to marry one of them and devote himself to his duties as the father of a family, he would do better to join the remnant of his clan at Horizontal Water. But lest he should find himself in danger of again being pressed to take a wife, when he arrived there, Tsaysiki sought comfort from the women already married. He was always able to find one or two who believed him when he said he could not help what happened to him on account of women. But their husbands, on whom no doubt they had proved it, were even less kind than the fathers at Peach Springs, and in the end Tsaysiki found it more convenient to join an unimportant band that moved about a great deal in the neighborhood of Pelado Peak, and was dominated, not by a Head Man, but by a woman called Dysildji. There, in the course of a few weeks, he fell into serious trouble over a girl who had taken the Jesus Road by the advice of the missionaries, and, when she found herself with child, ate wild parsnip root and died of it.

This was hard on Tsaysiki, for she was a plain and simple girl to whom he had been kind merely from habit. Nevertheless, he was called before the Elders, for the band was a small one, and the death of a young and healthy woman was rated far more than twenty head of cattle. Besides, there were the missionaries who, notwithstanding they had put the idea into the girl's head that an unfathered child was a thing to eat wild parsnip over, would have laid her death to the Navajos. Before putting anything in execution against Tsaysiki, however, the Elders waited for Dysildji, who had gone down to Kayenta to oversee the shearing of her sheep of which she had three bands, as well as cattle and many horses which she had from her father. Dysildji was not altogether young, but well looking and of so free a fancy that, though she had tried several, she had not yet found a husband to suit her. But because she had always been constant to the rights of other women, and because of her great possessions, she was left unrebuked, and much respected.

Dysildji came in from her shearing with the red sun behind her and looked the young man over. She saw that he was handsome, and had a way with women which he did not hesitate to use with Dysildji as soon as he found her looking at him. For some reason this pleased her. Other men had been too much in fear of her sharp mind and her great wealth to play upon her, and that may have been what she wanted. But it must also be remembered that she has taken all women for her sisters, and the account of Tsaysiki's loves had followed him. She heard what the Elders said, and how Tsaysiki answered them, with his eye sidewise toward the Head Woman—how he was the sort of man who could not help what happened to him on account of women.

'Leave him to me,' said the Head Woman, and the Elders were well satisfied to have it so. Dysildji took the young man to her house and explained that they should be married. 'For we will make a handsome couple,' she said, 'and I mean to have several children. Also, since we are both the sort of people that other people cannot help falling in love with, we will understand that, when that happens, there will be no offense taken on either side.'

Tsaysiki was as pleased as a stallion, for to be the husband of the richest woman of the Navajos and at the same time free in his affections was more than even a favorite of the Yei had a right to expect from them. Dysildji gave him a silver belt having conchos of a hand's breadth, necklaces set with great lumps of turquoise, and a different blanket for every occasion, so that when they walked abroad together they clinked pleasantly of silver, and were noticed by everybody. Dysildji introduced her husband to all her women friends explaining that there was an understanding between them that anybody who fell in love with either of them was to expect nothing but highness from the other. Then she asked him to sing the song he had made about himself some years earlier, and which ran thus:

> Blame not me but the Yei
> Who have brought handsomeness upon me,
> How can I help it if women love me?

At this the other women, instead of looking sympathetically as they had used, looked every other way, and even occasionally snickered.

If, however, Tsaysiki did not know it before, he found out very quickly that, though women will fight for a man they have marked for their own, they will not take him as a gift from another woman. He also discovered that, no matter what agreement he has made with her, a man who is openly neglected by his wife for the head of the Four-Feather Band is made to seem ridiculous. But by the time he discovered how ridiculous it was, it was too late for him to do anything about it, either when the men complimented him on his forbearance or the other women consoled him. And a Navajo may not divorce his wife for conduct he has once tolerated.

In the course of time Dysildji's flocks increased, so that she brought up a young man of the Yaquis, whom she had met at the *fiesta* of San Carlos, to be head herder to them. He was a personable man, and knew how to make himself secure with his employer. It is told that the first time Dysildji brought him to the hogan, Tsaysiki came out to meet them.

'This is only my husband,' she told the herder. 'You need not pay any attention to what he thinks, and he will not say anything, because we have an agreement,' and she gave him the horses to hold. Half an hour later the Yaqui, looking out of the window and seeing the husband still there, became a little uneasy, for the Yaquis are strict with their women. 'You needn't be,' Dysildji assured him. 'My husband is the sort of man who cannot help what happens to him on account of a woman.' And out of consideration for the Yaqui, she said it aloud so that Tsaysiki, holding the two horses, heard her.

❖ ❖ ❖

Papago Wedding

Along with the next story, "The Last An-
telope," "Papago Wedding" is one of Aus-
tin's most anthologized stories. Originally
appearing in American Mercury *in 1925,*
it won the O. Henry Prize of 1925 for the
best short-short story of the year. It later
appeared in such collections as Great
American Short Stories *and* Great
Stories of All Nations; *recently it ap-*
peared in The Other Woman: Stories
of Two Women and a Man, *edited by*
Susan Koppelman.[1]

As Koppelman points out in her intro-
duction, some editors probably saw it as an
amusing race story, and it does have an
O. Henry-like ironic twist. Yet the story,
like many others in One-Smoke Stories,
presents a disturbing feminist analysis of
relations between men and women, not so
hidden beneath its light, ironic tone and
treatment of cultural differences.

There was a Papago woman out of Panták who had a marriage paper
from a white man after she had borne him five children, and the man
himself was in love with another woman. This Shuler was the first to raise
cotton for selling in the Gila Valley—but the Pimas and Papagos had raised
it long before that—and the girl went with him willingly. As to the writing
of marriage, it was not then understood that the white man is not master
of his heart, but is mastered by it, so that if it is not fixed in writing it
becomes unstable like water and is puddled in the lowest place. The Sisters
of San Xavier del Bac had taught her to clean and cook. Shuler called her
Susie, which was nearest to her Papago name, and was fond of the children. He sent them to school as they came along, and had carpets in the
house.

In all things Susie was a good wife to him, though she had no writing of
marriage and she never wore a hat. This was a mistake which she learned
from the Sisters. They, being holy women, had no notion of the *brujería*

1. (Old Westbury, N.Y.: The Feminist Press, 1984).

which is worked in the heart of the white man by a hat. Into the presence of their God also, without that which passes for a hat they do not go. Even after her children were old enough to notice it, Susie went about the country with a handkerchief tied over her hair, which was long and smooth on either side of her face, like the shut wings of a raven.

By the time Susie's children were as tall as their mother, there were many white ranchers in the Gila country, with their white wives, who are like Papago women in this, that, if they see a man upstanding and prosperous, they think only that he might make some woman happy, and if they have a cousin or a friend, that she should be the woman. Also the white ones think it so shameful for a man to take a woman to his house without a writing that they have no scruple to take him away from her. At Rinconada there was a woman with large breasts, surpassing well-looking, and with many hats. She had no husband, and was new to the country, and when Shuler drove her about to look at it, she wore each time a different hat.

This the Papagos observed, and, not having visited Susie when she was happy with her man, they went now in numbers, and by this Susie understood that it was in their hearts that she might have need of them. For it was well known that the white woman had told Shuler that it was a shame for him to have his children going about with a Papago woman who had only a handkerchief to cover her head. She said it was keeping Shuler back from being the principal man among the cotton-growers of Gila Valley, to have in his house a woman who would come there without a writing. And when the other white women heard that she had said that, they said the same thing. Shuler said, 'My God, this is the truth, I know it,' and the woman said that she would go to Susie and tell her that she ought to go back to her own people and not be a shame to her children and Shuler. There was a man of Panták on the road, who saw them go, and turned in his tracks and went back in case Susie should need him, for the Papagos, when it is their kin against whom there is *brujería* made, have in-knowing hearts. Susie sat in the best room with the woman and was polite. 'If you want Shuler,' she said, 'you can have him, but I stay with my children.' The white woman grew red in the face and went out to Shuler in the field where he was pretending to look after something, and they went away together.

After that Shuler would not go to the ranch except of necessity. He went around talking to his white friends. 'My God,' he kept saying, 'what can I do, with my children in the hands of that Papago?' Then he sent a lawyer to

Susie to say that if she would go away and not shame his children with a mother who had no marriage writing and no hat, he would give her money, so much every month. But the children all came in the room and stood by her, and Susie said, 'What I want with money when I got my children and this good ranch?' Then Shuler said, 'My God!' again, and, 'What can I do?'

The lawyer said he could tell the Judge that Susie was not a proper person to have care of his children, and the Judge would take them away from Susie and give them to Shuler. But when the day came for Susie to come into court, it was seen that, though she had a handkerchief on her hair, her dress was good, and the fringe of her shawl was long and fine. All the five children came also, with new clothes, well-looking. 'My God!' said Shuler, 'I must get those kids away from that Papago and into the hands of a white woman.' But the white people who had come to see the children taken away saw that, although the five looked like Shuler, they had their mouths shut like Papagos; so they waited to see how things turned out.

Shuler's lawyer makes a long speech about how Shuler loves his children, and how sorry he is in his heart to see them growing up like Papagos, and water is coming out of Shuler's eyes. Then the Judge asks Susie if she has anything to say why her children shall not be taken away.

'You want to take thees children away and giff them to Shuler?' Susie asked him. 'What for you giff them to Shuler?' says Susie, and the white people listening. She says, 'Shuler's not the father of them. Thees children all got different fathers,' says Susie. 'Shuler—'

Then she makes a sign with her hand. I tell you if a woman makes that sign to a Papago he could laugh himself dead, but he would not laugh off that. Some of the white people who have been in the country a long time know that sign and they begin to laugh.

Shuler's lawyer jumps up . . . 'Your Honor, I object—'

The Judge waves his hand. 'I warn you the court cannot go behind the testimony of the mother in such a case . . .'

By this time everybody is laughing, so that they do not hear what the lawyer says. Shuler is trying to get out of the side door, and the Judge is shaking hands with Susie.

'You tell Shuler,' she says, 'if he wants people to think hees the father of thees children he better giff me a writing. Then maybe I think so myself.'

'I *will*,' said the Judge, and maybe two-three days after that he takes Shuler out to the ranch and makes the marriage writing.

Then all the children come around Susie and say, 'Now, Mother, you will have to wear a hat.'

Susie, she says, 'Go, children, and ask your father.'

But it is not known to the Papagos what happened after that.

❖ ❖ ❖

The Last Antelope

"The Last Antelope," which originally appeared in Lost Borders, *must have been a favorite of Austin's because she reprinted it in* One-Smoke Stories. *The story does not fit particularly well in either collection; its subject matter is most closely integrated with Austin's early work on sheepherding in California,* The Flock. *In* The Flock, *as in "The Last Antelope" and* The Ford, *Austin sympathetically explores male experience in the West. Perhaps she reprinted "The Last Antelope" because she saw it as her best native folk story about the lone male in the wilderness:*

> *At Tejon [I] had already picked up a number of animal stories such as men seldom think of telling to women, not because they are untellable, but because*

they seem perhaps to belong so exclusively to the male life, such tales as "The Last Antelope," which could only have happened in America, and in America only in the Southwest (Earth Horizon, 215).

Though perhaps too sentimental for modern tastes, "The Last Antelope" is a powerful ecological statement about one of the themes Austin explored most faithfully throughout her long career: the human response to nature, which nourishes the lonely soul and expands the consciousness. It also presents her despairing awareness of the inevitability of change, the contrast between the time when humans lived in harmony with nature and the destruction "that defines the frontier of men."

There were seven notches in the juniper by the Lone Tree Spring for the seven seasons that Little Pete had summered there, feeding his flocks in the hollow of the Carrizal. The first time of coming he had struck his axe into the trunk, meaning to make firewood, but thought better of it, and thereafter chipped it in sheer friendliness, as one claps an old acquaintance, for, by the time the flock had worked up the treeless windy stretch from the Little Antelope to the Carrizal, even a lone juniper has a friendly look. And Little Pete was a friendly man, though shy of demeanor, so that, with the best will in the world for wagging his tongue, he could scarcely pass the time of day with good countenance; the soul of a jolly companion with the front and bearing of one of his own sheep.

He loved his dogs as brothers; he was near akin to the wild things. He knew his sheep by name, and had respect to signs and seasons; his lips moved softly as he walked, making no sound. Well—what would you?—a man must have fellowship in some sort. Where he went about sheep camps and shearings, there was sly laughter and tappings of foreheads, but those who kept the tale of his flocks spoke well of him and increased his wage.

Little Pete kept to the same round year by year, breaking away from La Liebre after the spring shearing, south around the foot of Piños, swinging out to the desert in the wake of the quick, strong rains, thence to Little Antelope in July to drink a bottle for *La Quatorze,* and so to the Carrizal by the time the poppy fires were burned quite out and the quail trooped at noon about the tepid pools. The Carrizal is not properly mesa nor valley, but a long-healed crater miles wide, rimmed about with the jagged edge of the old cone. It rises steeply from the tilted mesa, overlooked by Black Mountain, darkly red as the red cattle that graze among the honey-colored hills. These are blunt and rounded, tumbling all down from the great crater and the mesa edge toward the long, dim valley of Little Antelope. Its outward slope is confused with the outlines of the hills, tumuli of blind cones, and the old lava flow that breaks away from it by the west gap and the ravine of the spring; within, its walls are deeply guttered by the torrent of winter rains. In its cuplike hollow, the sink of its waters, salt and bitter as all pools without an outlet, waxes and wanes within a wide margin of bleaching reeds. Nothing taller shows in all the Carrizal, and the wind among them fills all the hollow with an eerie whispering. One spring rills down by the gorge of an old flow on the side toward Little Antelope, and, but for the lone juniper that stood by it, there is never a tree until you come to the foot of Black Mountain.

The flock of Little Pete, a maverick strayed from some rodeo, a prospector going up to Black Mountain, and a solitary antelope were all that passed through the Carrizal at any time. The antelope had the best right. He came as of old habit; he had come when the lightfoot herds ranged from here to the sweet, mist-watered cañons of the Coast Range, and the bucks went up to the windy mesas what time the young ran with their mothers nose to flank. They had ceased before the keen edge of slaughter that defines the frontier of men.

All that a tardy law had saved to the district of Little Antelope was the buck that came up the ravine of the Lone Tree Spring at the set time of the year when Little Pete fed his flock in the Carrizal, and Pete averred that they were glad to see one another. True enough, they were the friendliest thing that either found there, for though the law ran as far as the antelope ranged, there were hill dwellers who took no account of it, namely, the coyotes. They hunted the buck in season and out, bayed him down from the feeding-grounds, fended him from the pool, pursued him by relay races, ambushed him in the pitfalls of the black rock.

There were seven coyotes ranging the east side of the Carrizal at the time when Little Pete first struck his axe into the juniper tree, slinking, sly-footed, and evil-eyed. Many an evening the shepherd watched them running lightly in the hollow of the crater, the flash-flash of the antelope's white rump signaling the progress of the chase. But always the buck outran or outwitted them, taking to the high broken ridges where no split foot could follow his seven-leagued bounds. Many a morning Little Pete, tending his cooking-pot by a quavering sagebrush fire, saw the antelope feeding down toward the Lone Tree Spring, and looked his sentiments. The coyotes had spoken theirs all in the night with derisive voices; never was there any love lost between a shepherd and a coyote. The pronghorn's chief recommendation to an acquaintance was that he could outdo them.

After the third summer, Pete began to perceive a reciprocal friendliness in the antelope. Early mornings the shepherd saw him rising from his lair, or came often upon the warm pressed hollow where he had lain within cry of his coyote-scaring fire. When it was midday in the misty hollow and the shadows drawn close, stuck tight under the juniper and the sage, they went each to his nooning in his own fashion, but in the half-light they drew near together.

Since the beginning of the law the antelope had half-forgotten his fear of man. He looked upon the shepherd with steadfastness; he smelled the smell of his garments which was the smell of sheep and the unhandled earth, and the smell of wood smoke was in his hair. They had companionship without speech; they conferred favors silently after the manner of those who understand one another. The antelope led to the best feeding-grounds, and Pete kept the sheep from muddying the spring until the buck had drunk. When the coyotes skulked in the scrub by night to deride him, the shepherd mocked them in his own tongue, and promised them the best of his lambs for the killing; but to hear afar off their hunting howl stirred him out of sleep to curse with great heartiness. At such times he thought of the antelope and wished him well.

Beginning with the west gap opposite the Lone Tree Spring about the first of August, Pete would feed all around the broken rim of the crater, up the gullies and down, and clean through the hollow of it in a matter of two months, or, if the winter had been a wet one, a little longer, and in seven years the man and the antelope grew to know each other very well. Where the flock fed, the buck fed, keeping farthest from the dogs, and at last he came to lie down with it.

That was after a season of scant rains, when the food was poor and the antelope's flank grew thin; the rabbits had trooped down to the irrigated lands, and the coyotes, made more keen by hunger, pressed him hard. One of those smoky, yawning days, when the sky hugged the earth, and all sound fell back from a woolly atmosphere and broke dully in the scrub, about the usual hour of their running between twilight and mid-afternoon, the coyotes drove the tall buck, winded, desperate, and fore-done, to refuge among the silly sheep, where for fear of the dogs and the man the howlers dared not come. He stood at bay there, fronting the shepherd, brought up against a crisis greatly needing the help of speech.

Well—he had nearly as much gift in that matter as Little Pete. Those two silent ones understood each other; some assurance, the warrant of a free-given faith, passed between them. The buck lowered his head and eased the sharp throbbing of his ribs; the dogs drew in the scattered flocks; they moved, keeping a little cleared space nearest the buck; he moved with them; he began to feed. Thereafter the heart of Little Pete warmed humanly toward the antelope, and the coyotes began to be very personal in their abuse. That same night they drew off the shepherd's dogs by a ruse and stole two of his sheep.

In seven years a coyote may learn somewhat. Those of the Carrizal learned the ways of Little Pete and the antelope. Trust them to have noted, as the years moved, that the buck's flanks were lean and his step less free. Put it that the antelope was old and that he made truce with the shepherd to hide the failing of his powers; then, if he came earlier or stayed later than the flock, it would go hard with him. But as if he knew their mind in the matter, the antelope delayed his coming till the salt pool shrank to its innermost ring of reeds and the sun-cured grasses crisped along the slope. It seemed the brute sense waked between him and the man to make each aware of the other's nearness. Often, as Little Pete drove in by the west gap, he would sight the prongs of the buck rising over the barrier of black rocks at the head of the ravine. Together they passed out of the crater, keeping fellowship as far as the frontier of evergreen oaks. Here Little Pete turned in by the cattle fences to come at La Liebre from the north, and the antelope, avoiding all man-trails, growing daily more remote, passed into the wooded hills on unguessed errands of his own. Twice the solitary homesteader, who had built him a house at the foot of the Carrizal, saw the antelope go up to it at that set time of the year. The third summer, when he sighted him, a whitish speck moving steadily against the fawn-colored background of the hills, the homesteader took down his rifle and made haste into the crater. At that time his cabin stood on the remotest edge of settlement, and the grip of the law was loosened in so long a reach. 'In the end the coyotes will get him. Better that he fall to me,' said the homesteader.

The coyote that kept the watch at the head of the ravine saw him come, and lifted up his voice in the long-drawn, dolorous whine that warned the other watchers in their unseen stations in the scrub. The homesteader heard also, and let a curse softly under his breath, for, besides that they might scare his quarry, he coveted the howlers' ears, in which the law upheld him. Never a tip nor a tail of one showed above the sage when he had come up into the Carrizal.

The afternoon wore on; the homesteader hid in the reeds, and the coyotes had forgotten him. Away to the west in a windless blur of dust the sheep of Little Pete trailed up toward the crater's brim. The leader, watching by the spring, caught a jack-rabbit and was eating it quietly behind the black rock.

In the meantime, the last antelope came lightly and securely by the gully, by the black rock, and the lone juniper into the Carrizal. The friendliness of the antelope for Little Pete betrayed him. He came with some sense of home, expecting the flock and the protection of man-presence. He strayed witlessly into the open, his ears set to catch the jangle of the bells. What he heard was the snick of the breech bolt as the homesteader threw up the sight of his rifle, and a small demoniac cry that ran from gutter to gutter of the crater rim, impossible to gauge for numbers or distance.

At that moment Little Pete worried the flock up the outward slope where the ruin of the old lava flows gave sharply back the wrangle of the bells. Three weeks he had won up from the Little Antelope and three by way of the Sand Flat, where there was a great scarcity of water, and in all of that time none of his kind had hailed him. His heart warmed toward the juniper tree and the antelope whose hoof-prints he found in the white dust of the mesa trail. Men had small respect by Little Pete, women he had no time for: the antelope was the noblest thing he had ever loved. The sheep poured through the gap and spread fanwise down the gully; behind them Little Pete twirled his staff and made merry wordless noises in his throat in anticipation of friendliness. 'Ehu!' he cried when he heard the hunting howl, 'but they are at their tricks again'—and then in English he voiced a volley of broken, inconsequential oaths, for he saw what the howlers were about. It was so they plotted the antelope's last running in the Carrizal: two to start the chase from the black rock toward the red scar of a winter torrent; two to leave the mouth of the wash when the first were winded, one to fend the ravine that led up to the broken ridges, one to start out of the scrub at the base of a smooth upward sweep, and, running parallel to it, keep the buck well into the open; all these, when their first spurt was done, to cross leisurely to new stations to take up another turn. Round they went in the hollow of the crater, velvet-footed and sly even in full chase, and biding their time. It was a good running, but it was almost done when, away by the west gap, the buck heard the voice of Little Pete raised in adjuration and the friendly blether of the sheep. Thin spirals of dust flared upward from the moving flocks and signaled truce to chase. The antelope broke for it with wide, panting bounds and many a missed step picked up with incredible eagerness, the thin rim of his nostrils oozing blood. The coyotes saw and closed in about him, chopping quick and hard. Sharp ears and sharp muzzles cast up at his throat, and were whelmed in a press of gray flanks. One yelped, one went limping from a kick, and one went past him, returning with a spring upon the heaving shoulder, and the man in the reeds beside the bitter water rose up and fired.

All the luck of that day's hunting went to the homesteader, for he had killed an antelope and a coyote with one shot, and, though he had a bad quarter of an hour with a wild and loathly shepherd, who he feared might denounce him to the law, in the end he made off with the last antelope, swung limp and graceless across his shoulder. The coyotes came back to the killing ground when they had watched him safely down the ravine, and were consoled with what they found. As they pulled the body of the dead leader about before they began upon it, they noticed that the homesteader had taken the ears of that also.

Little Pete lay in the grass and wept simply; the tears made pallid traces in the season's grime. He suffered the torture, the question extraordinary of bereavement. If he had not lingered so long in the meadow of Los Robles, if he had moved faster on the Sand Flat trail—but, in fact, he had been breathed upon by that spirit which goes before cities like an exhalation and dries up the gossamer and the dew.

From that day the heart had gone out of the Carrizal. It was a desolate hollow, reddish-hued and dim, with brackish waters, and moreover the feed was poor. His eyes could not forget their trick of roving the valley at all hours; he looked by the rill of the spring for hoof-prints that were not there.

After three weeks he passed out on the other side and came that way no more. The juniper tree stood greenly by the spring until the homesteader cut it down for firewood. Nothing taller than the rattling reeds stirs in all the hollow of the Carrizal.

❖ ❖ ❖

Mother of Felipe and Other Early Stories

THE LOST MINE OF FISHERMAN'S PEAK

In 1950, Franklin Walker put together a collection of early Austin stories, those published in the *Overland Monthly* and Charles Lummis's journal *Outwest* (first titled *Land of Sunshine*). "The Lost Mine of Fisherman's Peak," originally published in *Outwest* in November 1903, is one of these stories.

"The Lost Mine of Fisherman's Peak" is typical of Austin's early stories in a number of ways. It presents racial stereotypes, particularly in the portrayal of Guadalupe and Tom-Jim, though other characters are types as well. Many early stories are about the search for a lost mine, though this is the only one in which a woman is the seeker. Austin's male characters usually search for the sake of searching; Guadalupe wants money to rejoin her lover. Like most of Austin's first stories, this one is based on personal experience. In *Earth Horizon,* she described a woman she knew well, a half-Indian woman raised by a religious white woman. Lupe married a "Bret Harte-type," a gambler. Although Austin uses a characteristic technique in "The Lost Mine" when she claims not to know the whole story in order to give it a legendary air, she met Lupe in later life, a "young matron" with a little boy (238). The changes Austin made in Lupe's story reveal her early interest in melodrama.

One character from "The Lost Mine of Fisherman's Peak" would reappear often in later Austin stories: the hard good woman who judges other women.

❖   ❖   ❖

_____

The Lost Mine of Fisherman's Peak

Fisherman's Peak lies southward and solitary from the high Sierras, a noble dome of granite above a little, old, weazened remnant of hills, looking well over the brown shoulders of Panamint and the valley of the Bitter Lake. It looks east and south over a great waste of sand and scrub, over the white road where the ore wagons creak through crawling heaps of dust, over the dim purple barrows that fence that quarter of the western world. Near by it, under shrunken and impotent foothills, huddles the sometime busy village of Three Pines, where, as in a pool of slack water, harbors the drift of that wild tide of mining life that eddies fitfully yet in the borders of the Coso Hills.

Here, when the days are long, and no one is passing in the street, when there is no sound louder than the squawking of the village hens or the dropping of ripe fruit in the orchards round about, and nothing more insistent than the gurgle of the hydrant where it runs into the horse-trough at the end of the village street—here, from dropt hints of talk, reminiscence and speculation, one gathers the gist of more tales, and better, than are written.

The nature of a land determines in some wise the manner of the life there. This is a large country, with few and far-between oases of richness and greenness. One may take days' journeys in it and not come by any place or occasion whereby men might live; and other days stumble upon the wealth of dreams. Weeks on end the traveler finds no towns nor places where towns could be, and then drops suddenly into close hives of men, digging, jostling, fighting, drinking, lusting and rejoicing. Every story of that country is colored by the fashion of the life there; breaking up in swift, passionate intervals between long, dun stretches, like the land that out of hot sinks of desolation heaves up great bulks of granite ranges with opal shadows playing in their shining, snow-piled curves.

It is so far from the common ways of men by distance, and the manner of living, that nothing disturbs it not native to the soil. Doctrines, schisms, wars, politics, the trumpets of reform never reach it; only the hankering for gold and the coveting of women—with the rages, sacrifices, hatreds, jealousies and retributions that play about these—quicken the blood at Three Pines. No man was ever known to die out of his bed in that country, except some woman or some mine was at the bottom of it; and no ghost walks there that has not like cause for his unease. And no mine has so much laid to it of the killing of men and the love of women as the lost mine of Fisherman's Peak.

The first that was known of the mine was in the time when there rioted through that country a great body of mining men drawn off from the dwindling diggings of California and Nevada, and to that quarter, by the report of the marvelous strikes of Panamint and the Cerro Gordo. They raged up and down the passes of the hills, man-hunting and mine-hunting with equal good will, and poured into Three Pines for drinking and gaming what time their means allowed. According to the notion of the time, the times were good. Flour was twenty dollars a sack, and eggs two dollars a dozen, hard to come by at that; and no man when he had put down a coin asked for change. There were five saloons in Three Pines, all going at a roaring blast, when on the bar of one of them appeared one morning, among the glasses and the dice, a spar of rotten white quartz shot through with lumps and streaks of gold. At that time the characteristic ore of each of the large mines was as well known to every miner as his neighbor's face, and this was like no other. The news spread; deputations arrived from the other saloons to see and handle the wonder, and question the barkeeper, who kept a discreet, unwinking silence. But it was no such mystery by noon the next day, when a drunken Indian was observed trying to barter a handful of precious specimens for a sack of flour. An Indian mine! Possible riches, probable tragedy—and Romance! All Three Pines lost its head.

The Indians in the campoodie back of the town—Paiutes, still savage and embittered—were made more comfortable in the next three days, by gifts of blankets and canned stuff, than they had expected to be this side the Happy Hunting Ground; and were much too drunk for several days to give any intelligent account of themselves. But nothing transpired. Altogether there leaked out, and into the hands of miners, specimens of the gold-shot quartz to the amount of a bucketful, and many false clues; for about that time set out secretly, by night, a dozen or more prospecting parties in divers directions, returning in a week or so, bootless and disgusted.

At that time, also, there was no Indian dared stir out of his tracks but found himself shadowed by a white man. Nevertheless, by some means, bits of the "Indian Mine" quartz continued to circulate in the camp intermittently for the space of two years. During that time never an Indian was brought to the crude justice of a mining camp, that was not proffered better shift if he would discover the place of the ledge. It is probable that very few of the Indians ever knew, but finally it appeared one did. Upon that errand he set out with six miners secretly, and not one of the seven was seen or heard of alive again. This much came to the surface, by way of the campoodie, that they came to their end either by treachery of the guide, or the wrath of the tribesmen, on the slope of Fisherman's Peak. Once after that, Kern River Jim, a scout notably under the protection of the Government, agreed to guide a party of white men, not to the mine but to that vicinity. He went up Fisherman's Peak and all around it in seven days, returning to the point of starting—but no mine.

"The feet of the white men have been over it, but the eyes have not seen," said the Paiute, and quitted them where they stood. Well, you may guess they were back over that trail with the greatest imaginable caution. But to no purpose. So by such hints and helps, and by the glimmering bits that came up from time to time in barter with the Indians, the story of the mine was kept alive until the last pitiful rebellion of the Paiutes ended in the death of the most part of their fighting men. After that time no more of the white quartz came into Three Pines from any source whatever.

Some years later a squaw-man from Darwin way, reporting what his woman had told him for love, organized a party to prospect for a certain forked pine blasted by lightning, which she recalled as a landmark upon journeys from which her people had returned with the crumbling quartz. It is reported that, though the squaw-man found the blasted pine, he got nothing for his pains. It served, however, to keep fresh in the minds of prospectors the hope of the "Indian Mine," until new discoveries further south drew them out of that country, and the affair came up no more (except in talk) for the space of fifteen years.

About the time all Three Pines wagged with excitement over a handful of nuggets and rotten quartz, Hank Sturgess, freighting in from the dim, hot valley of Salt Wells, saw in the blue dawn three coyotes trotting in narrowing circles about a long heap on the sand, lying out about 200 yards from the road. At times it seemed to stir, and then did not. The small wind that creeps along the surface of desert sands blew upon it, and made a flutter as of garments.

"Lord!" said Hank, halting his eighteen mules, and then the sweat broke out on his tanned forehead to hear the morning stillness pierced by a pin-point wail. The woman lay face downward where she had fallen from illness (or drunkenness, perhaps) dead in the smother of her own garments and the sand. On her back, in its basket, the three-months baby waked and cried. Hank knew who she was, well enough—a Paiute woman who had been as wife to a miner down Panamint way. He, when he had worked out his claim, passed on to other diggings, with no thought given to the woman or her child; it was a common fashion of the time. When Sturgess found her, the woman's face was turned towards home.

The teamster carried the body on to the wash of Grapevine, where he buried it, properly bushed and stoned to keep the coyotes from it; the child, for want of a better shift, he carried to the Señora Lopez, washer-woman-at-large for the camp of Three Pines. The Señora, who was fat and indolent and unwholesome, made much of her condescension in mothering the "half-breed brat," whom she named Guadalupe, and used as a means of exacting contributions from soft-hearted miners. The two became in a manner a charge upon the camp.

The child grew up bright and strong and shapely, choosing her own way of life. There were plenty to tell her who she was; the Señora Lopez, for one—who extolled herself at the expense of the child's possible pride, and her mother's people at the campoodie. Guadalupe was much among the wickiups until she was ten years old and the Lopez woman died. Then Mrs. Hacket, of the Front Street Boarding House, adopted her in a purely missionary spirit.

Mrs. Hacket was a New Hampshire woman with convictions, no race prejudice and no tact. She made no odds of the child's being half white, sent her to school and had her taught to play on the melodeon; taught her to work, too, after a fashion, but never came into so much as the border-land of her hot little heart. So by dint of these things Guadalupe got through seventeen plain years in which Three Pines left off being a camp and became a town; and the lost mine of Fisherman's Peak one of its traditions.

Then, for the reason that she was young and beautiful in a dark fashion, and had come to the full power of womanhood, or for no reason at all, she began to love Castleton, the smooth-mannered faro-dealer and professional gambler of those parts. For her, who had known only miners and teamsters, he was, by all the standards she had, the finest gentleman she had known. Before him she paraded her young attractions with the abandon of perfect unsophistication. For all of which "goings on," Mrs. Hacket corrected her with a scourging tongue. It is a pity good women should be so hard; one would think they might afford the larger compassion. Doubly a pity that they should be so often so unwise. It was at the tide of the year when the spring whimpers in young blood, that accusation and recrimination between Mrs. Hacket and Guadalupe reached a point that the girl's nerves, always keyed to the high pitch of expectancy in those days, were not able to bear. So at the last she broke out crying, with great, dry gasps like a hunted creature, not feeling herself at fault, and burst out through the door into the dusk of the spring evening; then, as some reminder of her Sunday teachings came back to her, and timed with the hot impulse of her blood, she stripped off her shoes and flung them back across the threshold, before she ran lightly up the trail. There, an hour afterward, Castleton followed her, having some inkling of the situation, as, in fact, had every gossip in Three Pines. He found her face downward in the long, sweet grass on the edge of the mesa where the trail turns off toward the little leafy huts of the campoodie; and there he comforted her between the blossoms and grass, until the young moon came up and trod softly on the hills.

So—as you understand—Castleton carried the girl away to Portago, where there were better pickings for his particular trade. They came back again in the summer of that year to Three Pines, Guadalupe going unashamed, glorious in sumptuous clothing and the high pulse of young delight.

You will not understand; but *they* understand, who have walked that path, how she trod it with a pure heart. But with whatever heart, one comes very quickly to the end of such treading. It was nearly a year from the time Guadalupe began to be known as "Mrs. Castleton," and the spring came on thick and warm. She sat in the dance-hall of the "Same Old Luck," talking to the pianist there, dressed in the tawny yellows that so became her, laughing as she talked, but half turning, as her habit was, never quite to lose sight of Castleton, who was gaming idly with two Cerro Gordo men. The door was open, to let in the warm spring afternoon and a sweet smell of blossoming vines that mixed with the sickly odors of the saloon.

Suddenly there was a commotion outside, and Guadalupe looked up from her bright reflection in the piano lid to see two strangers alighting from dusty, road-weary horses at the door. Idle curiosity satisfied, she looked back smiling at Castleton, since strangers were his particular good fortune, and was surprised to find him gone. It was no surprise, but a vague unease she felt when he did not come to his room at all that night. Often, when the game was good, he sat on into the small hours. But when those hours were come, she woke out of dreams of him—never again to have sweet sleep, or restful, while she lived. Castleton was there in the room, haggard, hurried, anxious, packing a portmanteau deftly.

Guadalupe was out beside him, helping with never a sound. It was over so soon—the hurried movements—a word of explanation: the two strangers men on his track for a thing done in Calaveras a year before—one kiss—another—ah, never no more, no more!

"I will get down to the bay," he said. "I will send for you when I have money." And so, good-bye.

There were harder things to come after that; the loneliness, the dread, no word; then the sharp need of money, the jeers of the women; worse— the ungenerous proffers of the men. But being too young to unlove quickly, and seeing no other end to her affairs, Guadalupe went back to her mother's people. In a wickiup behind the town lived Chico, great-uncle of hers—all the kin she had. The old man took her in; if he had shaped any thought about her at all, it would have been that she had come to that sooner than he expected.

She began to serve him—to learn the crafts of a tribeswoman—suffering no pang in the re-adjustment keener than the need of her lover, of the sight of him, touch of him, print of his foot in the earth.

Chico was wrinkled as the hills, looked older, and wandered in his wits. He could not always remember whose child she was, nor what she had given him for dinner; but he could recall clearly all the things that happened before she was born, and in the course of time he told her about the lost mine of Fisherman's Peak.

"There were four of us," said Chico; "four men who found the mine and kept it, and never we told another, though many persuaded us. But Red Morning tracked us and held the secret to sell to the white men against his time of need. So when we four heard what he would do, we killed him, and the six who were with him. We followed hard on their trail, even as he had followed us, and killed one man in the night with a long arrow through his body; one each night, never any more."

"When the first died, they said, 'So we expected,' and went cautiously about to cover their trail; at the second, they said, 'So many less to share the mine.' But at the third killing they were afraid, and some were for turning back; also, they held that Red Morning had dealt them treachery; but ever he spake with a double tongue. Well he knew who followed."

"So we killed Red Morning last of all, and that was part kindness—for if he had been caught in the town, the white men would have hung him. Then we four made a vow that each should kill the other who told any white man of the mine; but of Kern River Jim we took no account, for there was nothing certain that he knew. It was that he would have the white men think well of him. After that came the war, and they three died, two at Bitter Lake and one at the Stone Corral. Then I said, 'How shall I go to the mine with none to watch and cover my trail?' for there were none of my own people I could trust. But now I am old—I would lie softly— and the gold is clean gold."

Then he would grow suspicious, mumbling that she was white and not to be trusted; that she was a fool to attend an old man's greater folly. Next day he would forget and begin all over again.

Now Guadalupe had not grown up in a mining town to no purpose, and there were people in Three Pines yet who had in their cabinets specimens of the white quartz of the lost Indian mine. With all this maundering of Chico's, the girl began to think. The smallest part of the treasure, provided it could be found, would take her to Castleton, whose desire for her she rated equal to her own for him.

So she beguiled the old man with food and comfortable words, until he should tell her where the ledge might be found; and, reaching out for such help as she must have, laid hold of Tom-Jim.

Tom-Jim was a Paiute of near her own age; who, if the tribe had been living in the tribal relation, would have stood high. The reason why he happened to be standing in the way when the girl cast about for a staff to prop her enterprise, was that he had fallen in love with Guadalupe. He was afraid of her and her superior white ways, but man enough to persist, and savage enough to wish to have her, willing or unwilling. His processes were as simple as his passions. He would serve her in this matter of the mine, upon which she was so keen, and then take her for his pains. He had very little idea of the real value of the mine, and as for Guadalupe, she was too busy with plans for the bestowal of herself and the treasure to give a thought to his thought. She would have used him just the same if she had known.

Between them they contrived a way to leave the campoodie, unsuspected, along the trail of Fisherman's Peak. It was a devious path, and steep. Chico lacked breath for it; the old knees wavered and old wits wandered more and more. When they came to the bluff of the blasted pine, he was too far gone to be of any use to them. He might come out of that sickness, and he might not; in the meantime, since they were poorly provisioned, they must trust to finding the ledge with the facts they had. The search fell to Tom-Jim; Guadalupe, for her share, watched by the old man under the glooming pines.

The landmark pine stood on the brink of a steep gorge heading there. The mouth of the gorge opened miles away eastward on a river cañon. Somewhere in the gorge, which was called Eagle Rocks, on an open scarp, masked by vines, cropped out a ledge of rotten quartz shot through with gold. Tom-Jim set out to find it. Under the pine, hearing the drone of wild bees above the old man's fluttered breath, Guadalupe comforted her heart against alarms by foolish dreams. Along in the warm afternoon she woke out of a drowse to see Chico lie on his bed of pine boughs with his eyes rolled upward under the dropped lids and no breath coming and going between his parted lips.

Of much that happened after that, the secret is kept by the ravine of Eagle Rocks and the impalpable somewhat that holds the record of human thought—of candles gone out—of fires burned down. There is a belief among miners, very ill expressed or not expressed at all, that the hot essences of greed and hate and lust are absorbed, as it were, by the means that provoke them, and inhere in house, lands or stones to work mischief to the possessor. That is why, though many strangers have looked for it, no miner of Three Pines who knows all this story will prospect for the lost "Indian Mine."

Between her fear of dead Chico, for so she judged him, and desire to get on with the search, Guadalupe hurried down from the blasted pine into the ravine, by no trails, slipping, falling over places where she never could have climbed up, dislodging a rubble of small stones, and at last (savage fear getting the better of savage caution) crying aloud for Tom-Jim. She found him not far from the foot of that bluff where her watch had been, having worked up all that gully from the river and found no likely place where a mine might be. Even now he was hacking and tearing at the vines that mantled all that front of rock. Chico's directions had been tolerably plain. Guadalupe found herself reassured to help him with such homely labors. So at last they found it, a small vein hollowed out a little by reason of its softness between two walls of country rock. They spent a long time over it, eager, laughing, blowing the sand from yellow grains between their fingers, picking out the soft metal from the rotten quartz with the point of a knife—lingered until the sunlight was clean gone up out of the gully of Eagle Rocks. All at dusk there came a great cry that rose and shuddered brokenly between the cañon walls. They looked up and down, and could not tell for the moment from what quarter it came, nor what it might be.

It seems that the old man had waked out of the trance or swoon, or whatever held him in the semblance of death, with that unexpected accession of vitality that comes sometimes before the final spark, and drawn by the last sane impulse of his wandering mind, had come down into the gully by some shorter, secret trail to find those two before him. It is plain that he had forgotten them or repented of his purpose, for it was his cry of fury that rang among the rocks, and his body that shot out from the scarp with the impact of a beast against Tom-Jim's shoulders. The two swayed together for one instant of rage; then Chico's arms slacked and fell away, his body shuddered, sagged downward, fell, with knees crumpled under it, among the crumpled vines. This time he was quite dead.

The dark came on; the body of the old man grew large, and half it seemed to stir. The two young people were alone in the gully. Neither of them had loved Chico much. As for Tom-Jim, he loved only Guadalupe, and he had found the mine. Now his eyes began to burn, and some late-awakened instinct made the girl's flesh to creep. To herself, you will understand, since she had mated with Castleton, she seemed all white.

Now the wind rose up and began to moan among the pines, and they could hear the night tones of the rising stream. Something that was neither wind nor water stirred in the air, and Guadalupe bethought her of the knife that lay where it had dropped among the quartz fragments. She felt for it and hid it under her shawl, moving softly to put the dead man between her and Tom-Jim.

But that would not save her; for when the soft dark was all around them and the night bird called another to the mating, he came upon her to take her in the power of his manhood, as he would have taken a girl of his own clan. And so she killed him with the knife, and he fell, coughing blood, across the other body in the gully of Eagle Rocks.

Three weeks later, a party of hunters in the River Cañon to the east found a young Indian woman wandering crazily in the woods, living on roots and berries, gaunt and wolfish-eyed. In very pity they carried her to Aurora, from which, with the instinct of a homing pigeon, she made her way to Three Pines. There she still lives witlessly in a low, foul hut on the edge of the campoodie, become the prey of creatures more debauched than she. She goes about muttering and seeking on the ground for what she cannot find, and ever as the spring draws to flood-tide, her madness increases; but for the most part she is sodden with drink. About her neck she carries a little leather bag, and in it a splinter of white quartz with a grain or two of gold. And when she is drunken, but not too drunk, she will show you that and with it as much as she remembers—it is not much—of the lost mine of Fisherman's Peak.

❖   ❖   ❖

Uncollected Stories

❖   ❖   ❖

The Castro Baby

First published in the Black Cat in March 1899, "The Castro Baby" presents a slice of western life, the bazaar of a small western town. Maverick, Austin suggests, was once appropriately named, but as the events of her story show, the town is now a place where diverse people come together with compassion for others. Although Austin often criticized the narrowness of religious practices in small towns, the religious revival in Maverick does not seem to have affected the townspeople's sympathy for those with other religions. Although Miss McCracken's comments imply there are cultural divisions in town, the story suggests that Hispanics and whites, Catholics and revivalists, can empathize with each other. Even Miss McCracken learns her lesson.

"The Castro Baby" is the type of story usually described as "sentimental." Perhaps so. But Austin knew how many women lost babies, and she knew how women responded to each others' losses.

The sun climbing to its meridian above Little Long Valley on a certain Fourth of July, saw all the population of Maverick passing between the swinging doors of Sidney McLean's saloon.

The male population of Maverick usually gravitated in that direction in all seasons; in fact, a considerable number of them might be fairly said to live there; but even in its most prosperous days the Spread Eagle had never known such a pervasive air of feminine flutter and fashion, an air that the capacities of mail-order shopping makes possible even in Maverick.

The womenkind of Little Long Valley were not disposed to look favorably on the Spread Eagle. They were even known to view it with open hostility, and to account its inducements to idling and money-spending as only partially compensated for by the personal good qualities of its proprietor. To-day, however, there was in the bustle of coming and going, in the bunting that displayed itself about the front door, in the crescendo buzz of conversation and the rattle of knives and forks that issued from it, evidences that nowhere in the world could be mistaken for anything else than a fancy bazar.

The fact is, Maverick was undergoing a revival of religion. Maverick was accustomed to take its experiences of whatever kind spasmodically. It had lived through two mining excitements and a real-estate boom, and was still very far from learning moderation. The first excitement had given Maverick a definite location and a name, the second had built the Spread Eagle, which was originally a dance hall, and the land boom had built the railroad to within four miles of the town, where it had become discouraged and turned away into the fastnesses of the Nevada hills.

Now the revival of religion was responsible for the fancy bazar in Sidney McLean's saloon, because the Reverend Aaron Frear had decided to include Maverick in his fifty-mile circuit, a church edifice was needed, and the townspeople felt that they must rise to the occasion. The question of ways and means had crystallized around the idea of a bazar, where it had halted for some time in a nebulous state, for want of suitable quarters in which to materialize.

Then it was that Sidney McLean came forward with an offer of the Spread Eagle which, having been built in boom days, was sufficiently capacious. What the Reverend Aaron thought of this is not recorded—he did not hear of it until it was too late.

So the bazar was an accomplished fact, and that nothing might be lacking of its wonted features a traveling photographer, who had set up his tent on the mesa had offered "a dozen cabinets in our very best style" as a prize for the handsomest baby.

So Maverick had also a baby show. The voting was paid for at the rate of five votes for two bits. Maverick had not accustomed itself to smaller change, but it knew how to divide up and distribute the benefits, and the proceeds of the balloting went to swell the building fund.

It was surprising after all how many people could be gathered into Maverick when there was anything to bring them. There were, first of all, the townspeople, who were not any of them wanting, and a good number of farmers from the river bottom. There were owners of mines and the men who worked them; thirteen from the Reward, twenty from the Eclipse mill and smelter, and all the small and solitary mines among the desolate hills poured out their dwellers to make the great American holiday. There was the station agent's family from Lawton, and the weather bureau man from Black Mountain, and a man from Bodie who expected to be the next candidate for sheriff. Last of all there was Miss Mae McCracken. This should have been mentioned first. Miss McCracken was the operator from Lawton; she was a very lively young lady with a fresh complexion such as is not often seen in the rainless, windy West, and spoke

English with what she said was a French accent. Miss McCracken was popularly supposed to be as much of an attraction as the bazar.

There was another woman at Maverick that day who told herself that if she had known of the baby show she would not have come. She was the wife of the owner of the Minnietta, and her husband had sent her down to Maverick for the summer because the doctor had told him if he did not get his wife out of sight of the cliffs of Las Vegas he would soon have no wife. There was a grave at the foot of Las Vegas, a tiny grave that a woman's arm might well cover, dug there because about the Minnietta there was not soil enough to cover the smallest grave. The cliffs of Las Vegas showed white from the mine on the further side of the cañon, and the owner's wife watched them days long with wearying eyes, and could not sleep of nights hearing the coyotes howl and thinking of what lay at the foot of them. When it was moonlight the spectral cliffs were terrible in their loneliness, and when there was no moon the darkness was still more terrible, and one night when her husband had missed her he found her at the foot of Las Vegas covering the grave with her arms. It was then that he sent her to Maverick because she would go no farther. Now she sat and watched the mothers of children, and her heart was very bitter.

The balloting for the prize baby was at its briskest early in the afternoon, with the station agent's plumpest twin in the lead, and a rose-leaf morsel of humanity from the river farm a close second.

The man who expected to be sheriff had distributed his votes impartially among all the candidates and was now trying to tell Miss McCracken that if the prize had only been for the handsomest young lady he could make a close guess at the winner. Miss McCracken had heard something of the same kind a good many times that afternoon and was not particularly attentive.

"Oh, look," she cried; "if there isn't that Castro woman from the Six-Mile house, and she's brought her baby. I do believe she thinks it will take the prize too. Just see the way she has it rigged up. Do look, girls. Did you ever!" The girls looked, everybody within hearing of Miss McCracken's contagious giggle looked, to see the little Mexican mother, sitting shy and bewildered against the bunting-draped wall, clad in the thinnest of black cotton dresses, with the shabby rebozo that preserved a lingering tradition of her race. The baby in her lap was pitifully quiet, its tiny, claw-like hands clinging to the mother's and the black eyes in the wasted little face dull with pain as they uneasily blinked, "For all the world like a little brown owl," said Miss McCracken, "but I suppose she thinks it is perfectly lovely."

The baby had on its best frock, and about its thin throat a string of large blue beads that had been the mother's most cherished ornament for years, and to the front of its dress she had pinned a bunch of limp and formless artificial flowers, a part of her wedding finery, carefully preserved. Nobody knew this—the flowers told their own story.

Then a stronger voice took up the tale. "The woman is a fool," said the bluff doctor, who knew all the secret sorrows of Maverick. "A perfect fool! Walked all the way here in the blazing sun just to show off her kid, when it won't live a week at the outside, and she knows it. They're poor, too; Castro was out of work a long time. I told her there was no chance for it. It beats me what brings her here to-day."

But feminine instinct comprehends even that which is beyond the wisdom of doctors.

"Why, she wanted a picture of it and hadn't the money, and then she heard of the baby show. Of course she thinks it is beautiful—and it is, too—" went on Miss McCracken, incoherently, "that is, it would be if it were not so skinny. Anyway, its eyes are perfectly lovely, and I mean to tell her so."

The sobered girl rose from her seat to carry out her intention, and there was a general movement of the women in the same direction, but the woman from the Minnietta had in the meantime quietly crossed over to the Señora Castro.

"Is it your baby?" she asked. The mother nodded, not daring to speak, lest disappointment should overwhelm her, for till now no one had spoken to her.

"She is very pretty," went on the questioner, "what do you call her?"

A thin smile bubbled up and broke across the mother's face.

"Her name is Mary Carmen Mercedes," she said, "but we call her Chiquita."

"Chiquita? That means 'Little One,' does it not?" And the fairer woman smiled back understandingly, as she lifted the child with a thrill of aching remembrance at its feather weight. It passed from hand to hand among the young matrons, while the mother's eyes followed the mite hungrily, as if she begrudged the moments spent out of her arms, though they were numb with the strain of carrying it for hours.

"It is better with me," she said pleadingly, and the women understood, and when she let it go again for a little while to the woman from the Minnietta, they understood that also. Every one knew of the little grave at the foot of Las Vegas.

Women for whom, until then, the Castro family had not existed, went aside from their pursuits to praise and pet the Castro baby, and the mothers of the previously favored candidates, who had been on the point of heartburning, met each other carrying ice-cream to the Señora Castro, and smiled. By the middle of the afternoon it was apparent that she would have her photograph. Before the time appointed the balloting was closed, because it was time for the Castro baby to go home, and Mary Carmen Mercedes was declared the winner.

The man who would be sheriff covered himself with glory by the speech he made at the announcement, and Mary Carmen made a royal progress to the photographer's in the carriage that belonged to the station agent's twins.

The fancy bazar in the Spread Eagle saloon was carried out to its least arrangement, and the proceeds were such as to lead the Reverend Frear to add an especial clause of thankfulness to his Sunday morning petition. It had been an unqualified success, and the relaxation which followed was not too overwhelming to prevent all Maverick from turning out in carriages and wagons three days later along the dusty, shadeless road to the Six-Mile house.

The event which called them was its own justification. It was the burial of the Castro baby.

❖ ❖ ❖

Frustrate

Throughout her life Austin complained that male editors attempted "to determine what should and should not be written" about "the experiences of women, as women":

> *I wrote a story for "The Century" in which a woman tells what she suffered in finding that she was not attractive-looking. The paragraph in which she described herself was deleted. "I couldn't bear," said the editor, "to have a woman with such beautiful thoughts, looking like that"* (Earth Horizon, *320*).

The story was probably "Frustrate," which Austin published in Century Magazine *in January 1912.*

Austin never reprinted "Frustrate" in any of her collections. She may well have felt the story was too autobiographical, revealing too much about her own disappointments in her marriage. Yet Austin described herself in Earth Horizon *as never having "surrendered" to "resignation," as seeing life as "essentially remediable, undefeatable" (268). These qualities saved her from the frustration of her narrator and helped her play "her own game." Like her friend Charlotte Perkins Gilman's story, "The Yellow Wallpaper," Austin's "Frustrate" is about the woman the author might have become, yet Austin suggests a path of escape in the character of the woman writer.*

I know that I am a disappointed woman and that nobody cares at all about it, not even Henry; and if anybody thought of it, it would only be to think it ridiculous. It is ridiculous, too, with my waist, and not knowing how to do my hair or anything. I look at Henry sometimes of evenings, when he has his feet on the fender, and wonder if he has the least idea how disappointed I am. I even have days of wondering if Henry isn't disappointed, too. He might be disappointed in himself, which would be even more dreadful; but I don't suppose we shall ever find out about each other. It is part of my disappointment that Henry has never seemed to want to find out.

There are people who think it is somehow discreditable to be disappointed; and whatever comes, you must pretend to like it, and just keep on pretending. I don't know why. It must be that some things are right in life and some others are not, and unless somebody has the courage to speak up about it, I don't know how we are ever to find it out. I don't see, if nobody else is hurt by it, why we shouldn't have what we like out of life; and if there's a way of getting or not getting it, people have a right to know. Sometimes I think if I'd known a little more, just a very little . . . !

It all began, I suppose, in the kind of people I was brought up among. They'd none of them had the kind of things I wanted, so of course they couldn't tell me anything about the way to get them. There was my mother. She had to work hard, and had never been anywhere but to a Methodist conference and once to the capital when father was a delegate or something, and her black silk had been turned twice; but she didn't seem the least disappointed. I think it must have been the way things were between her and my father. Father died when I was sixteen, so I couldn't tell much about it, but I know mother never so much as thought of marrying again. She was like a person who has had a full meal, but I—I am just kind of hungry . . . *always*. My mother never talked to me about her relations to my father. Mothers didn't; it wasn't thought suitable. I think sometimes, if she had, it might have made a difference about my marrying Henry.

The trouble was in the beginning, that though I knew the world was all full of exciting, interesting things, I thought they came to you just by living. I had no idea there was a particular way you had to go to work to get them. I think my people weren't the kind to make very nice discriminations about experiences or anything. They wouldn't have thought one way of being in love, for instance, was much better or different from another. They had everything sort of ticketed off and done with: such as that all church-members were happier than unbelievers, and all men naturally more competent and intelligent than their women. They must have known, some of them, that things didn't always work out that way; but they never let on about it—anyway, not to us young people. And if married couples weren't happy together, it wasn't considered decent to speak of it.

I suppose that was what got me to thinking about all the deep and high and shining things that I had a kind of instinct went with being married, belonged to it naturally, and, when you had found a suitable man, came along in their proper place without much thinking. And that was about all I knew when Henry proposed to me at the Odd Fellows' Festival. We were both on the decoration committee, and drove out to the old Lawson place that afternoon for roses. I remember the feel of them against my cheek, hot and sweet, and the smell of the syringa, and a great gold-and-black butterfly that fled and flitted down the green country road, mottled black and gold with shadows. Things like that gave me a strange kind of excitement, and yet a kind of lonesomeness, too, so I didn't mind Henry holding my hand between us in the buggy. I thought he must be feeling something of the same sort, and it didn't seem friendly to take my hand away. But I did take it away a moment later when he proposed. It turned me kind of cold. Of course I meant to accept him after a while. I liked him, and he was what my folks called suitable; but I seemed to want a little time to think about it.

Henry didn't want me to think. He kept hinting, and that evening under the grape-arbor at the minister's, where we had gone to get the sewing society's ice-cream freezer, he kissed me. I'd heard about engaged kisses, but this wasn't anything but just a kiss—like when you have been playing drop the handkerchief. I'd always had a feeling that when you had an engaged kiss something beautiful happened. There were times afterward when it almost seemed about to, and I would want to be kissed again to see if the next time . . . Henry said he was glad I had turned out to have an affectionate disposition.

My family thought I was doing well to marry Henry. He had no bad habits, and his people were well-to-do; and then I wasn't particularly pretty or rich or anything. I had never been very popular with young men; I was too eager. Not for them, you understand; but just living and doing things seemed to me such a good game. I suppose it is difficult for some folks to understand how you can be excited by the way a shadow falls, or a bird singing on a wet bough; and somehow young men seemed to get the idea that the excitement had something to do with them. It made them feel as if something was expected of them; and you know how it is with young men: they sort of pull back from the thing that is expected of them just because it is expected. I always thought it rather small, but I suppose they can't help it. There was a woman I met at Fairshore who explained how that was; but I didn't know it then, and I was rather sensitive about it. Anyway, it came about that I hadn't many beaux, and my mother was a good deal relieved when I settled down to Henry. And we hadn't any more than got the furniture as he wanted it when I discovered that there hadn't anything happened at all! Instead of living with my mother, I was just living with Henry; I've never done anything else.

There are things nobody ever tells young girls about marriage. Sometimes I think it is because, if they knew how to estimate their experience in the beginning, there is such a lot they wouldn't go on with; and when I was married, nobody ever thought of anything but that you had to go on with it. There were times when it seemed as if all it needed was just going on: there was a dizzying point just about to be reached from which Henry and I should really set out for somewhere.

It took me fifteen years to realize that we hadn't set out for anything, and would never get anywhere in particular.

I know I tried. Times I would explain to Henry what I wanted until he seemed to want it as much as I did; and then we would begin whatever we had to do,—at least I would begin,—and then I would find out that Henry had forgotten what we were doing it for—like the time we saved to set out the south lot in apricots, and Henry bought water-shares with the money. He said it would be cheaper to own the water for the apricots; but then we hadn't anything left to pay for the planting, and the man who had sold Henry the shares turned out not to own them. After a while I gave up saving.

The trouble was, Henry said, I was too kind of simple. It always seemed to me, if you wanted things, you picked out the one nearest to you, and made a mark so you could keep tab on whether you were getting it or not; and then you picked out the next nearest, and went for that, and after a while you had all of them. But Henry said when it came to business it was a good deal more complicated, and you had to look on all sides of a thing. Henry was strong on looking on all sides; anybody that had any kind of reasonableness could always get over him, like that man with the water-shares. That was when I was trying to make myself believe that if we could get a little money together, we might be in things. I had been reading the magazines, and I knew that there were big, live things with feelers out all over creation, and if I could just get the least little tip of one. . . . But I knew it wasn't money. When I wasn't too sick and overworked and worn out trying to keep track of Henry's reasons, I knew that the thing I was aching for was close beside me . . . when I heard the wind walk on the roof at night, . . . or heard music playing . . . and I would be irritated with Henry because he couldn't help me lay hold of it. It is ridiculous, I know, but there were times when it seemed to me if Henry had been fatter, it would have helped some. I don't mean to say that I had wanted to marry a fat man, but Henry hadn't filled out any, not like it seems men ought to: he just got dry and thinner. It used to make me kind of exasperated. Henry was always patient with me; he thought it was because I hadn't any children. He would have liked children. So would I when I thought I was to have one, but I was doing my own housework, and I was never strong. I cried about it a good deal at the time; but I don't suppose I really wanted it very much or I would have adopted one. I will tell you—there are women that want children just for the sake of having them, but the most of them want them because there is a man— And the man they want gets to hear of it, and whenever a woman is is any way unhappy, they think all she needs is a baby. But there's something else ought to happen first, and I never gave up thinking it was going to happen; all the time I kept looking out, like Sister Anne in the fairy-tale, and it seemed to me a great many times I saw dust moving. I never understood why we couldn't do things right here at home—big things. There were those people I'd read about in Germany— just plain carpenters and butchers and their wives—giving passion-plays. They didn't know anything about plays; they just felt grateful, and they did something like they felt. I spoke to the minister's wife about it once—not about a passion-play, of course, that wouldn't have done; but about our just taking hold of something as if we thought we were as good as those Germans,—but she didn't seem to think we could. She kind of pursed up her mouth and said, "Well, we must remember that they had the advantage of having lived abroad." It was always like that. You had to have lived somewhere or been taught or had things different; you couldn't just start right off from where you were. It was all of a piece with Henry's notion of business; there was always some kind of queer mixed-up-ness about it that I couldn't understand. But still I didn't give up thinking that somehow I was going to pull the right string at last, and then things would begin to happen. Not knowing what it was I wanted to happen, I couldn't be expected to realize that it couldn't happen now on account of my being married to Henry. It was at Fairshore that I found out.

It was when we had been married eighteen years that Aunt Lucy died and left me all her property. It wasn't very much, but it was more than Henry would ever have, and I just made up my mind that I was going to have the good of it. Henry didn't make any objection, and the first thing I did was to go down to Fairshore for the summer. I chose Fairshore because I had heard about all the authors and painters being there. You see, when you never have any real life except what you get from reading, you have a kind of feeling that writers are the only real *own* folks you've got. You even get to thinking sometimes that maybe, if you had known how to go about it, you could have written yourself, though perhaps you'd feel that way about bridge-building or soldiering, if it was the only real kind of work you saw much of. Not that I ever thought I could write; but I had so many ideas that were exactly like what I'd read that I thought if I could only just get somebody to write them for me— But you can't; they've all got things of their own. Still, you would think the way they get inside the people they write about that they would be able to see what is going on inside of you, and be a little kind.

You see, it had come over me that away deep inside of me there was a really beautiful kind of life, singing, and burning blue and red and gold as it sang, and there were days when I couldn't bear to think of it wasting there and nobody to know.

Not that Henry didn't take an interest in me,—his kind of interest,—if I was sick or hurt, or seeing that I had a comfortable chair. But if I should say to Henry to lean upon my heart and listen to the singing there, he would have sent for the doctor. Nobody talks like that here in Castroville: only in books I thought I had heard the people calling to one another quietly and apart over all the world, like birds waking in a wood. I've wondered since I came back from Fairshore if people put things in books because they would like to have them that way.

It is difficult to tell what happened to me at Fairshore. It didn't really happen—just the truth of things coming over me in a slow, acrid dribble. Sometimes in the night I can feel the recollection of it all awash at the bottom of my heart, cold and stale. But nothing happened. Nobody took any notice of me but one woman. She was about my age, plain-looking and rather sad. I'd be proud to mention her name; but I've talked about her a great deal, and, with all my being so disappointed, it isn't so bad but it might be worse if everybody got to find out about it. She was really a much greater writer than the rest of them; but, I am ashamed to say it, just at first, perhaps because she was so little different from me on the outside, and perhaps just because she was a woman, I didn't seem to care much about her. I don't know why I shouldn't say it, but I did want to have something to do with interesting men. People seem to think that when a woman is married she has got all that's coming to her; but we're not very different from men, and *they* have to have things. There are days sometimes when it seems to me that never to have known any kind of men but Henry and the minister and old man Truett, who does our milking, would be more than I could bear. I thought if I could get to know a man who was big enough so I couldn't walk all around him, so to speak,—somebody that I could reach and reach and not find the end of,—I shouldn't feel so— so frustrated. There was a man there who wrote things that made you feel like that,—as if you could take hands with him and go out and rescue shipwrecked men and head rebellions. And when I tried to talk to him, I found him looking at me the way young men used to before I married Henry—as if he thought I wanted something, and it was rather clever of him not to give it to me. It was after that that I took to sitting with the writer woman. I'd noticed that though the men seemed to respect her, and you saw them in corners sometimes reading manuscripts to her, they never took her to walk, or to see the moon rise, or the boats come in. They spent all that on the pretty women, young and kind of empty-headed. I'd heard them talk when they thought I wasn't listening. And the writer woman sat about with the other women, and didn't seem to mind it.

I hoped when people saw me with her, they'd think it was because she was so famous, and not guess how terrible it was to find yourself all at once a middle-aged woman sitting on a bench, and all the world going by as if it was just what they expected. It came over me that here were all the things I had dreamed about,—the great sea roaring landward, music, quick and gay; looks, little incidents,—and I wasn't in it; I wasn't in it at all.

I suppose the writer woman must have seen how it was with me, but I thought at first she was talking of herself.

"It's all very wonderful out there, isn't it?" she said, looking toward the blue water and the beach shining like a shell, with the other writers and painters walking up and down and making it into world stuff. "Very wonderful—when you have the price to pay for it!"

"It *is* expensive." I was thinking of the hotel, but I saw in a minute she meant something else.

"The price you pay," she said, "it isn't being fit to be in the Great World or being able to appreciate it when you're in; it is what you contribute to keep other people in, I suppose."

I must have said something about not being able to see what the kind of women who were in contributed—just girls and flirty kind of married women.

"It's a kind of game, keeping other people in," said the writer woman. "They don't know much else, but they know the game. We are, most of us," she said, "like those matches that will not light unless they are struck upon the box: there is a particular sort of person that sets us off. It's a business, being that sort of person."

"If anybody could only learn it—" I tried to seem only polite.

"It is the whole art," she said, "of putting yourself into your appearance." She laughed. "I have too much waist for that sort of thing. I have my own game."

I seemed suddenly to want to get away to my room and think about it. I know it is absurd at my age, but I lay on the bed and cried as I hadn't since they told me my baby hadn't lived. For I knew now that all that beautiful life inside me couldn't be born either, for I was one who had to have help to be worth anything to myself, and I didn't know the game. I had never known it.

All the time I had been thinking that all I needed was to find the right person; and now I understood that, so far as anybody could guess, I wasn't the right person myself. I hadn't the art of putting myself into my appearance. I'm shy about talk, and my arms are too fat, and my skirts have a way of hanging short in front.

I've thought about it a great deal since. It doesn't seem fair. Nobody told me about it when I was a girl; I think nobody tells girls. They just have to sort of find it out; and if they don't, nobody cares. All they did tell me was about being good, and you will be happy; but it isn't so. There is a great deal more to it than that, and it seems as if people ought to know. I think we are mostly like that in Castroville: we've got powers and capacities 'way down in us, but we don't know anything about getting them out. We think it is living when we have got upholstered furniture and a top buggy. I know people who think it is worth while never to have lived in a house without a cupola. But all the time we are not in the game. We do not even know there is a game.

Sometimes I think, if it would do me any good, I could turn in and learn it now. I watched them at Fairshore, and it seemed to me it could be learned. I have wild thoughts sometimes,—such thoughts as men have when they go out and snatch things,—but it wouldn't do me any good. Henry's folks were always long-lived, and there are days when I am so down that I am glad to have even Henry. As long as people see us going about together they can't know— I'm rather looking forward to getting old now. I think perhaps I sha'n't ache so. But I *should* like to know how much Henry understands.

❖ ❖ ❖

The Divorcing of Sina

Austin wrote often about the effect of violence against woman. In Earth Horizon, she described slapping a man who was brutalizing his pregnant wife and seeing friends of her mother with bruises from being beaten. In "The Divorcing of Sina," she shows how the abuse of women is an accepted part of family behavior. Even women urge Bill Bodry to beat his wife.

Austin's exposure of wife abuse in her own culture seems foresighted to modern readers, but her treatment of the subject in "The Divorcing of Sina" is marred by racial stereotypes. First published in Sunset in January 1918, the story attempts to present an ironic analysis of marriage among the Paiutes, but the comic tone seems to mock the characters and the culture. Austin may have realized the problems with the story's tone and with the use of type characters; when she included it in One-Smoke Stories as "The Way of a Woman," she retold it from Sina's father's point of view.

Despite its problems, I think the earlier story is the more interesting version. The father in "The Way of a Woman" is too obtuse to understand his daughter's feeling, as Austin shows. In "The Divorcing of Sina," Sina's feelings are made clear, and the father's assumptions about how he can control his daughter's behavior are revealed. It is unfortunate that Austin allows her reader to draw the conclusion that Bill Bodry's behavior is influenced by his white schooling, but the contrast between his refusal to use "coercive methods" and Wind-in-the-face's use of his daughter is significant. Bill is a sympathetic character who does not see his wife as property.

Anyone who read only this Austin story might believe she was suggesting that "savage" people use "savage" customs. However, Sina's outrage at being "bought" implies that such behavior was not common practice among the Paiutes.

Ordinarily when a Piute gentleman comes home to supper to find his wife sitting beside the hut completely wrapped in her blanket, he goes away quietly and pretends to be thinking about something else. But there were several reasons why Bill Bodry felt obliged to depart from this excellent custom. For one thing he was hungry, in the next place he was very fond of his wife, and last of all there was his mother, peering out from her own wickiup with eyes keen and bright as a gopher's, ready to cry fool to him who could not manage his own household. Bill's mother had been all for his marrying Black Rock Maggie, who though she had followed the glint of a white man's eye to an extent which prejudiced her in the opinion of the young and romantic, had acquired merit in the eyes of Bill's mother by her superior powers of wheedling tinned salmon and potato culls out of the white housewives. And because there was always Maggie in the back of his mother's mind as a standard of comparison, it was not possible for Bill to admit the complete overthrow of all his domestic authority as implied in the circumstance that he had come home three successive evenings to find the hearth cold and Sina sitting with her head wrapped in her blanket. Not that some allowance must not be made for young wives, even in a campody; but even in a campody, for a man to go three nights supperless to bed points to something more serious than bridal vapors.

He was aware that it was already beginning to be whispered about the camp that Sina, his wife, had put a spell on her husband. He was aware of it while he raked up the sticks between the cold stones and when he brought up the wicker water bottle from the creek to make the coffee—and how indeed does a Piute gentleman come to be boiling his own coffee unless somebody has put a spell on him? To make matters worse, here was Black Rock Maggie coming up the trail to visit his mother. Completely at an end of his devices for having it appear that the household arrangements were going on as usual, Bill came and stood over the slender huddled figure. He stood with his back to his mother so that she could not see his face working. It was time when any husband would have been justified in coercive methods, but Bill was still very much in love with his wife. What he could see of her, the little moccasined foot sticking out, and the slim shape of her under the blanket, moved him strongly.

"Look, Sina, what I got for you." He spoke in English, for his mother did not understand English very well, and the use of the foreign tongue created the effect, at least, of an excluding bond between him and Sina. He opened his shirt now to show his young wife the present he had brought for her, a bead necklace of blue and amber that had cost him the half of his week's wages as bronco buster. It clicked as it dropped from his hand to her lap, and in spite of herself the girl peeked curiously out of her blanket, her little hand moving instinctively, but stopped when she saw Black Rock Maggie.

Maggie was the sort distrusted by young wives immemorially. She was believed to have gone with a white man as far as Pharump valley, she wore corsets, and could read writing, and little moving yellow lights swam just under the surface of her beady eyes. Moreover, she had a way of making Bill's marriage appear a mere ripple on the surface of her own superior intimacy with him. Oh, no, these things are not the product of sophistication! They are as old as men and women, or perhaps older, and it was with a sense of utter inescapability that Bill, as he heard Maggie's voice greeting his mother behind him, begged desperately.

"Won't you tell me what it is you want, Sina?"

Sina was perfectly explicit. "I want to go home to my mother!"

    Ordinarily there is no reason why, when a Piute lady finds marriage impossible, she cannot gather up her dowry in a perfectly amicable arrangement and go back to her father's house, supposing that he will have her. But the reasons why that could not be done in Sina's case are a considerable part of this story. Once before she had run away from her young bridegroom, and been brought back by Wind-in-the-face, her father, promptly and honorably. That this was exactly what would happen to her again Sina knew as well as anybody, and the unreasonableness of her request would have moved Bill to do what any Piute husband would have done much earlier, but at that moment he heard Maggie's voice purring behind him.

"Don't you want me to get you some supper, Bill?" and in the moment when he looked up at her and back at his young wife again he noted that the blue and amber necklace had disappeared.

"I guess I don't want any supper," he denied, manfully. "I guess I'll take Sina to her mother, she's sick."

"A good dose of the stick will cure her complaint," jeered the mother of Bill Bodry; but Maggie's cue was sympathy.

"I guess Bill don't want to beat her if she's sick." This brought Sina out of her blanket like a slim little snake.

"I guess Bill's got a right to beat me if he wants to," she flashed a cold, withering scorn on her lord and master. "You got a right to beat me just like a horse, Bill Bodry, you bought me!" Bill shifted miserably from foot to foot in the dust of the mesa.

"Aw, Sina—I—" not for worlds would he have laid the stick on those round young shoulders, not so round by half as when he had married her.

"You goin' to beat me, Bill Bodry?"

"I—I'm goin' to take you to visit your mother, Sina."

She couldn't have known with what desperation he clutched at this last remnant of his husbandly prerogative as he moved in the trail before her, thus to present to the scoffing eyes of his mother the spectacle of a wife following at her man's back in the ancient Piute custom. It might have answered if, at the moment behind him, Black Rock Maggie had not suddenly and shortly laughed. He heard that and then he heard the hurrying steps of Sina breaking past him. He put out his arm, he knew in his heart it was merely to prevent her stumbling, for the girl was really sick with misery, but she must have mistaken the supporting clutch of his arm for violence, for with a cry she turned and struck him full in the face with something that rattled and stung as she tore free and fled from him; something that as he stooped to gather up and stuff into his bosom before he turned aside in the twilight to hide his discomfiture, the peering eyes of old Ebia recognized as a blue and amber necklace.

I I

The reasons why Sina could not be divorced from Bill Bodry in the infrequent but traditional way, had to do with her father's appetite for fresh-water clams in excess of his discretion. He had spent too much time kicking them out of the soft mud of the river bottom with his toes, but he thought he was being persecuted by the ghost of an enemy reincarnated in the form of a coyote. Either that, or else he had been going about on some inauspicious occasion with his mouth open, and a *Winuputs*—one of the million little devils who are responsible for the inside pains of Piutes—had jumped down his throat and worked from that to his knees. Catameneda, his wife, was inclined to the latter opinion, but by the time Jim had lost the fall rodeo and the piñon harvest on account of the swelling in his legs, she was ready to believe anything.

It was just at this juncture, while she was tending Jim's pains with relays of hot stones as he lay in his rabbit-skin blanket on the sunny side of the wickiup that Bill Bodry came by on the trail with a swing in his walk like the smooth play of the flanks of a cougar. The light cotton shirt parted carelessly over the arch of his chest, his thighs were knit with power, about his head thick locks of blackness lay like sculpture work banded by the shining crease where the sombrero rested. Besides being good to look at, Bill Bodry spoke Government School English as befitted a man with a whole white name who owned a dollar watch and could tell time by it.

He had come over the barranca to talk with Yavi, grandson and sole prop of the Basket Maker, about the next rabbit drive, and had stopped neighborly to inquire as to the progress of Jim's pains. "Hurt-like-Hell," had been Jim's rejoiner, in compliment to the English in which as a member of the younger generation, Bill had addressed him. And that might have been all there was of it if at that moment Bill Bodry had not had sight of Sina.

Sina was slim and brown with budding breasts, and her eyes were as brown as the brown shadow of the creek under the birches. She was painting her face by a fragment of mirror propped in the rabbit brush, cheeks and chin a plain vermilion, as a sign that her affections were disengaged. When she saw Bill Bodry watching her she laughed, and Sina's laugh was like the sound of running water in a rainless land. Therefore Bill Bodry lingered to bargain with Sina's father for the making of a rabbit-skin blanket. Wind-in-the-face was the best blanket maker at Sagharawite. He cut the skins in thin strips around and around, and strung them on the wattles to dry. Evenings, when he sat with hot stones between his shins, he would take up the strips with his thumb and finger, twisting them between his palm and knee, ready for weaving. On one of these occasions he confided to the Basket Maker that Bill's blanket was to have a hundred skins.

"That's a large blanket for a man not married," said the Basket Maker.

"But he will not say what he means to do with it," Jim concluded his information.

"Ah," said the grandmother, "Bill Bodry was not fed on meadow larks' tongues," which is Piute for saying that Bill talked no more than necessary.

"And Black Rock Maggie talks enough for two," suggested a neighbor who had observed Maggie making eyes in Bill's direction, and she began to tell the story of Maggie and the white man, but Catameneda of the Round Arm nudged her. It was not the kind of story to be told before Sina, for there is no place in the world really where a nice young girl is kept more thoroughly nice than in a campody.

But as a matter of fact, Bill had not thought so far ahead of his blanket as that. He had said a hundred skins because it was a large number, and as he brought them as he found them, it afforded so many more occasions on which he could recommend himself to Sina by taking an interest in her father's rheumatism. But it was the whisper about Black Rock Maggie which kept Sina's mother from suggesting what he was thinking. Sometimes Bill would see the girl behind the slight screen of rabbit brush, busy about her toilet with the considered, slow movements of Indian women, unobtrusive as the preenings of quail. Other times she would be walking in the twilight with young girls of the campody. They would walk with their arms about one another, their cheeks bright with vermilion and their breasts bore up the folds of their red and purple calico gowns like apples. It was on such occasions that Bill would lend a neighborly ear to the complaint of Wind-in-the-face that there needed nothing to his recovery but the professional attendance of the Medicine Man from Fish Lake valley. When it was learned later that that distinguished practitioner had been brought over to cure Jim's legs at Bill Bodry's expense, there was probably no one in the campody besides Catameneda and her daughter who did not know what was in Bill's mind.

The therapeutic of the Medicine Man from Fish Lake valley belongs to that strip of country between the desert and the tolerable outposts of the Sierras, known as Lost Borders. It depends for its efficacy on being able to cross the border between sense and spirit by a method which ought to prove immensely popular in more sophisticated circles, since it consists largely of singing, and dancing. The point in the case of Sina's father was that it succeeded; it drove the *Winuputs* out of his legs and set him back a matter of seventeen dollars or so with Bill Bodry.

It was about this time that Bill began to build him a house with a door like a white man's and Catameneda of the Round Arm began to be uneasily aware of the frequency of his visits to her wickiup. She egged on her husband to discharge his obligation.

"I gonna pay you, Bill, soon as I get workin' for Watterson," Jim assured him, speaking English as a way of putting himself quite on an equality with his creditor. "How in hell I gonna pay you when I got no money, thass what?"

"You don't never need to pay me," Bill earnestly reassured him. "What I needin' with money when I got me a new house, I got plenty blankets, I got a sack of pine nuts, I got a house, I got blankets—" avoiding the dangers of repetition, he dug the toe of his boot into the earth floor of the wickiup. "I guess I gonna get me a wife," he concluded.

"Who you gonna get?" Windy inquired sociably. Bill smoothed out the mark of his boot carefully. Said he at last:

"I gonna get Sina."

"Huh!" remarked Sina's father. He had moments of thinking, however, when he came to break it to Sina and her mother, that it would have been better to put up with the rheumatism. For Sina of the budding breasts did not in the least wish to get married. The burden of primitive housewifery lies heavy on maiden dreams in Sagharawite, and Sina had been thinking of Bill Bodry as a friend of her father's. Sina was a spoiled and only child, and even a maiden of the Stone Age may be forgiven for insisting on being courted for herself alone rather than being handed over from one man to another in discharge of an obligation. That was the mistake Bill made, and Ebia, his mother, who should have instructed him in the proper way to win a wife, was touting for Black Rock Maggie. If a man must marry, why not have a wife who can bring something in, rather than a half-grown girl who would waste his substance in the measures of inexperience? But Bill stuck to it that Sina he would have and no other, and once the subject of the debt had been broached what was Wind-in-the-face to do, as an honorable Piute gentleman, but hand his daughter over? If a girl is to be allowed to exercise her own choice in the face of her parents' necessities, what is to become of the institution of the family? It is one of the ways, indeed, in which the family becomes an institution, by the exercise of vicarious obligation. To do them justice, Sina and her mother never thought of resisting; the most they could do they did, which was to render their men folk thoroughly uncomfortable. No doubt Catameneda could have reconciled herself in time to a match so eminently desirable. For the House with the Door had worked the accustomed effect of prohibition and mystery. Probably there was nothing more behind it than the usual Piute furnishing, but an inch of pine planking, in place of the ordinary rag of blanket or buckskin, by preventing prying eyes, magnified the bridal setting forth of Bill Bodry to magnificence. What, demanded the interested and gossipy campody, did the girl want anyway? Sina wept and surrendered, but between the girl and her mother there was the secret, unendurable pang of violation. People who have forgotten that a favorite goddess of the ancients was a fleeing virgin, must needs be reminded that the age of chipped flint was before the complaisance of women had been forced by social exigencies. Sina's time for loving had not come, and even in a house with a door her uncaptive heart pined like a wild thing in captivity. She hated Black Rock Maggie always hanging about with her proffers of superior competency, and if she could have spared any energy from hating Bill, she would have hated that whining old fox, Bill's mother. All of which would have led in due time to a proper divorce except for the distinction at which I have hinted.

Piute society is, unlike our own, when you understand it, perfectly simple. Anything that is an Indian's can always be taken back, no matter how many times he gives it, since it remains always in some respect peculiarly his own. But what he receives is never his at all except upon sufferance. If Sina had given her heart away, she could have taken it back on any justifiable occasion. But Sina had given nothing; she had been taken on demand in payment of money given by Bill Bodry, and not even Bill could release her.

That was why, when Sina, after three weeks of married life had run away to her mother, Wind-in-the-face had girded up his affections as a father, and notwithstanding his wife, who called him offal, ditchwater and many other names fit to cause him the greatest possible embarrassment, had carried Sina back to her husband. It was after this that Sina took to sitting with her head in her blanket and Black Rock Maggie's visits to Ebia had been of almost daily occurrence. And now that Sina had run away again after publicly shaming all his tenderness, the young husband, simple savage that he was, whose hurts are sore and immediate, lay alone in his blanket of a hundred skins beside the House with a Door and nearly died of it.

I I I

Tribal laws are to the highest degree exigent. That they present themselves as inexorable to our unaccustomed eye, is only because the human circumstances with which they deal have the quality of inexorable sameness. Sina couldn't divorce herself and Bill couldn't give her back, but on the other hand the tribe of Sagharawite couldn't afford to let a healthy young woman fret herself into a wasting fever. That's where they have the advantage of us, for with all our precaution against hookworm and typhus we suffer the social waste of heartache and humiliation with indifference, and permit our young to wound one another to the death with impunity.

In the case of Bill and Sina nothing was neglected which could have helped. Everybody took sides with the greatest heartiness. Bill's mother and Sina's outdid each other in the—sage hen, and flea-bitten whelp of a coyote—epithets heaped respectively on the other's offspring. Wind-in-the-face remonstrated with his child as he was duly bound, but she turned her back on him; then he beat her and she lay on the ground at his feet and whimpered like a hurt animal. Being thus at the end of his resources he painted his face, draped himself in his best blanket and asked for an Order in Council.

Infrequently as it occurs, there is no particular condemnation implied in a Piute taking his domestic affairs to the Council instead of settling them in the privacy of his wickiup, which is about as private as a bird cage. But it was unfortunate from Bill Bodry's point of view that Wind-in-the-face should have summoned the Council to sit on the case of his daughter Sina at the time of the spring shearing. That was when the shallow tide of prosperity ran at its highest in the campody. Sweet sap dripped from the canes, the earth was full of foodful roots, the clink of the shearing wage in every pocket. It was the moon of tender leaves and not far from the time of the dance of Marriageable Maidens. Those who remembered Sina as she had appeared in it for the first time the last season, saw in her drooping frame and bitten lip the figure of young pitiableness. The girl was plainly ill, ate nothing, slept little and moaned as she slept. There was not a woman in the camp who had not had the whole story from Catameneda, who was wild with fear lest her daughter should eat wild parsnip. In the open life of the campody, where there are no distractions and few conceal- ments, death as a surcease from disaster is more often than we imagine resorted to. And though no woman may speak in Council, there was not an elder among them who did not know that he would have to answer at home for whatever was done to Sina; and it was against all considerations of tribal profit that the hearts of women should be fretted. For one thing, who was to do the work if the women were discontented? "A grudging heart makes cold the hearth," says the proverb.

The Council met at the moth hour in a hollow under Togobah. New shorn sheep were white across the slope, shepherd fires winked out along the foot-hills, musk-scented gilias bloomed, burrowing owls whoo-whoed at their mating. The whole earth was full of comfortable twitterings; Sagharawite looked at Bill Bodry, handsome as he was but with the alien touch of a year of white-schooling, looked at Sina, wan and violated by a hateful marriage and decided against him. Bill, quite as sensitive as any- body to the intimidation of the mating season, whose every fibre ached with desire of her, ached indeed to the point of dumbness, made the mis- take of saying nothing of his love and staking all on the ancient ruling. The girl had come to him on a debt, who could take her from him? Of course if the debt were paid—the seventeen dollars and a half! Yavi, grandson and sole support of the Basket Maker had an inspiration. They would take a leaf out of the white-man's book and take up a collection. Yavi was thought to have an eye for Sina herself before Bill Bodry came by, and there were none too many marriageable girls that year in the campody. The sugges- tion had the smack of romance to which in the spring even a Piute is susceptible. Dimes and dollars came out of the shearing wage and clinked in the ceremonial basket. Thus the divorcing of Sina was accomplished without any violation of the tribal custom. Sina went home to Wind-in-the-face, Bill Bodry boarded with his mother, the House with the Door was shut up, and Black Rock Maggie veiled the yellow lights in her eyes and waited.

I V

Nothing much can happen in the campody in the summertime when the snakes are about to run and tattle of it to the gods. Later, when the long grass is eaten short, when the heat haze has gone up from the bare bones of the mountain, and the qualities of the earth and sky are interchangeable, about the end of the piñon harvest when the old sit with their toes in the ashes, many summer-hidden things come to the surface.

So it was about the first of November that it began to be whispered around Sagharawite that Bill Bodry had put a spell on Sina who had been his wife. How else could it be when divorce didn't help her? To lose appetite and sleep and waste with no fever; that was the way when Bad Medicine had been made against you. That was what happened to the children of Red Morning when Poco Bill had a quarrel with him; four of them one after another thinned like fat on the fire, and died in spite of all that could be done for them. And then there was a man in Fish Lake valley—instance multiplied instance to show that Sina had been coyoted.

Ebia, who knew perfectly what would happen to her son if the story gained credence, laid Sina's wasting to her general incompetence, as witnessed by her failure to rise to the honor which had been thrust upon her in becoming the wife of the one man in Sagharawite who had a house with a door like a white man's. In this she was seconded to her face by Black Rock Maggie, who had of late left off corsets and taken to wearing her blanket folded over her breast as becomes a Piute maiden who has not married nor walked in the trail of a white man. But away from the mother of Bill Bodry, Maggie was observed to listen to the tale of the man from Fish Lake valley with marked conviction. If she had doubts she used them to draw the talk in that direction.

It would have suited her very well to have Bill driven from the camp as a Coyote Doctor.

She managed her game so well that by the time the winter constellations had wheeled to their station midway over the narrow, knife-cut valley, there was open talk of bringing Bill Bodry to book for evil practices. Weevil had got into the pine nuts that year and there were many cases of pneumonia, evidence enough that Bad Medicine was working somewhere. And always there was Sina. For a month or so after the divorce she had brightened, but now she sat leaning her young head against the wickiup, her hands falling listlessly still over her basket plaiting, and nothing would induce her to paint her cheeks vermilion and put on the purple calico. It was plain enough what was the matter with her, but whenever anybody ventured to suggest it to Catameneda, she moved her closed fingers before her face, extending them suddenly outward in a gesture which is one of the oldest resources of nature against the evil suggestion, so old that it is no longer polite to explain its origin. In the privacy of their blanket, which is the only privacy possible in a wickiup, she confided to Wind-in-the-face that she had looked the girl all over for signs of ordinary sickness and found none. What she had been really looking for was the blue and amber necklace. Ebia had told of it as evidence of her son's unappreciated munificence, but not even Ebia knew what had become of it. All of Sina's dowry had come home with her, but the necklace as a present had surely been hers in some degree, and if the smallest thing of hers, say a string of beads or a ribbon, remained in the custody of Bill Bodry, might it not serve to make a spell upon Sina's undoing? So Catameneda of the Round Arm brooded over the business of the necklace, but dared not question her daughter lest by mentioning the evil thing she bring it to pass. Thus matters stood until within a week of the annual Council when, if there were any such thing as coyote doctoring going on in the camp, it would surely be looked into.

That all this could go on without Sina's knowing anything about it, was due as much to the girl's sick indifference to life as to the inviolable rule of the campody that one does not speak to another of that other's private business without invitation. It was a woman from Black Rock, visiting the Basket Maker the week before the Council, who inadvertently brought it to her attention.

Sina had moved to the further side of the wickiup to be free from her mother's solicitations, which brought her in range of Seyavi's hut and the voices of the two old crones as they sat gossiping on the kitchen-midden. As she lay there inert in her blanket, if they saw her at all, and sight goes early in the smoky huts, they must have thought her sleeping, and voices carry far in the clear afternoons of November. The woman from Black

Rock was numbering the affairs of importance which should come before the Council, and along toward the end came this business of the coyote doctoring and Bill Bodry. Did Seyavi think there was anything in that story? Since Bill had got his money back, why should he put a spell on Sina, especially as he had so pointedly recovered from his brief infatuation for her. Or, certainly, hadn't Seyavi heard? The Black Rock woman had it from a friend of hers, who had it from the wife of Red Morning, who had seen for herself, going up the creek to leash acorns of an early morning, Maggie and Bill folding up Bill's blankets—pity Bill was such a fool about women. First Sina and then this hot-eyed draggle-tail—he had only to come to Black Rock—*they* could tell him what Maggie was—

Slowly and unobtrusively as a snake changes its place in the sun, Sina crept out of sight behind the wickiup. She moved at first with the hurt creature's instinct for concealment, and as she moved two entirely distinct and contradictory impulses woke within her. She wanted to stand for Bill before the Council, to defend him from stones and obliquy, and she wanted quite as much to get him off to herself where she could kill him quietly. She remembered the affront Bill had put upon her in his House with the Door, when the moon was up and the door was shut, she remembered Black Rock Maggie and something alive and terrible stirred and turned in her. There ran a screen of black sage from the hut to the creek, and up along that were the thick, fringing willows. Past these Sina stole with a strange sick thing inside her; so at last to a close copse of willows and brown birches, within which she had often hid herself from the detested sight of Bill and the sharp tongue of Bill's mother. From here she could see the House with the Door, and a thin trail of smoke going up beside it. There was no one about, and she could not tell from this distance whether it were Bill's smoke or Ebia's. But she could not have seen very well in any case, for the sight of the smoke brought sudden tears and the strange, sick something that tore in her and strove to rend itself forth by bitter sobbing. Oh, there was no doubt about it at last, that somebody had put a spell on Sina!

She must have lain there a long time before her vision cleared, and quite empty of crying she looked back toward the House with the Door and saw Bill moving about with the awkward fumbling of a man whose hearth is deserted, and the divine instinct to mother her man awoke in Sina—but go to him? She who was bought with money? Let him get Black Rock Maggie. She saw Bill coming with the water bottle to the creek, and sure enough there over the barranca as though to an appointment came Maggie. All this was part of Maggie's game, which she played cleverly—to appear always just when a man feels himself most in need of a wife, and to answer the need in her person. That was how she had been seen by the wife of Red Morning, folding up Bill's blankets for him on the morning after Bill, to ease his desperate ache, had set the door of his house ajar and lay in it all night calling his young wife from her father's hut and calling vainly. On this particular evening Ebia was gone with two other of the campody to dig tule roots where the water of Salt Creek comes down to the river. Maggie meant to pretend she had forgotten all this—and a man likes to have a warm meal of an evening no matter who cooks it for him. Besides she had heard that at Black Rock which warned her to move quickly. If it came to Council that Bill was a Coyote Doctor, bringing evil on the camp by reason of the evil thoughts that brewed in him, he would be stoned and driven out for it. She could follow him, of course—what man could refuse comfort in banishment? They could go out Panamint way and winter in Coso, and when summer had restored the equanimity of the camp they could come again—but Maggie was a sociable soul; what she wanted more than anything else was to pose proudly before the other women as mistress of the House with the Door. If she could persuade Bill to take her before the Council convened, who could accuse him, the happy bridegroom, of putting spells on other women? So as she came over the barranca to meet him at the creek, Maggie unloosed the yellow flame in her eyes, and her hot heart shook her. It might have been that, or the unwhispered protest of Sina watching from the willows that caused her to begin badly. She slipped the bottle from him as it sagged in the water.

"Are there no women left in Sagharawite that you wait on yourself like a white man?" she laughed.

To the man sore with the want of the only woman who mattered, it sounded like a taunt to be answered. "Loss of women like white men more better than Piutey."

Bill made a practice of sticking to English with Maggie, possibly because it was so much less explicit than the speech of his fathers. Maggie met it with a flash of her fine eyes.

"And if I have followed the white man's trail and heard what he thinks in his heart, I have come back, Bill Bodry—does any one ask why I came back—" The language of the Piute is ample and lends itself to passion as easily as mountain stream to the spring freshet. "I came back," she said, "because my heart was as dry under his hand as the earth in summer.

Because the blood of the white man is pale like his face, Bill Bodry—" She swung herself across the stream to him, challenging, magnificent. "But I didn't expect to find that the men of my race had turned white also—you, Bill Bodry—wasting yourself on a girl whose breasts are scarcely grown—who weeps in the night—who shudders—"

She saw by the lift of his shoulders how the thrust had gone home to him. She swung the water bottle dripping from the creek to her shapely shoulder. "White man"—her eyes danced with veiled provocation—"come up to your house and I will cook a meal for you—" She should have gone then; past question he would have followed her, but the eternal feminine desire to be taken at more than her worth overcame her. She leaned the wicker bottle on a rock and came slowly back to him, all fire and softness. "I shall cook you a meal," she said, "and you shall teach me—all that you could not teach Sina."

You are to understand that there is nothing in Piute etiquette which prohibits love-making of this explicit character. Maggie came close and laid her hands on Bill's breast, which had tightened under her challenge, and as her hands came to rest there, they touched something hard and sound under the cotton shirt, like a woman's necklace. At the touch Bill stepped back and quivered as he would have done if the little horned snake of the desert had struck him.

"I guess you pretty fine cook, Maggie," he stuck obstinately to English, "but I ain't carin' much about anybody's cooking but Sina's."

Maggie for her part turned venomous. "Care!" she cried, "*you* care when it is known as far as Black Rock and Fish Lake valley that you have put a spell on Sina. You that bought a wife for money and couldn't keep her!" She pushed him from her. "You that turned Coyote Doctor so that she should eat parsnip root and you will be done with her. You that will be stoned in the Council—" Right here there was a sound of breaking branches and a sudden slim form flashed upon them from the opposite bank of willows. The dusk was falling and the girl with her wasted face and her once white doe skins looked unearthly.

"You snake of two tongues—" she addressed herself to Black Rock Maggie. "What right have you to say that I have a spell put on me, making trouble for Bill Bodry? For what should I eat wild parsnip when I am married to a good man and have a house with a door and plenty of blankets." She panted white with weakness, but with all the dignity of the proper matron. "You go to the Council with a story like that," said Sina, "and you'll see what you get, you—white man's leavings!" It was not for nothing that Sina had been daughter-in-law for three months to the sharpest tongued woman in the campody.

Maggie's game was up, but Maggie herself was undaunted. She struck her foot sidewise along the ground causing a little spurt of dust to fly up, an immemorial gesture of belittlement. "Prutt," she laughed, "seventeen dollars and a half's worth!" She gathered the ends of her blanket over her breast and as she ran up the trail they heard her laughing. The two young things stood still on opposite sides of the stream and looked at one another. Sudden inspiration unsealed the lips of Bill Bodry.

"Sina," he said, "I ain't never cared at all about that money. All the time I comin' to your father's house, it ain't the money I thinkin' about, Sina, it's you—Sina." He came across to her, all his young heart was in his eyes, but Sina had no word for him. She was staring at something that showed on Bill's breast where the shirt had parted under Maggie's vehement fingers, something that hung against his heart and rose and fell with its quick panting, a blue and amber necklace.

V

Bitter anxiety came and camped that night by the wickiup of Wind-in-the-face and Catameneda. Dusk fell with the owl's calling, but no Sina. A hurried round of the neighboring huts yielded no trace of her. One by one the little fires winked out. Catameneda sat in the hut and moaned on the Basket Maker's shoulder while Wind-in-the-face and Yavi went down along the river marsh where the wild parsnip grows, groping and fearing. The campody slept and searched by turns and whispered apart things best not spoken openly among the covert dangers of the night. Opinion grew as the dark thinned to blueness; by dawn it was concentrated in one word: Bill Bodry. Who else had any interest in the girl's disappearance? Just about break of day Catameneda, wild of heart, had run out across the mesa crying and calling. Close by the wild olive tree she had come upon a night-hawk squatting under the bushes; it had not stirred nor flown, but looked up at her, its eyes bright and beady—she could have taken it in her hand—it looked as if it would have come to her hand. How if that had been her daughter? Well, look at all the things that had happened of late in the campody—three deaths since the new moon! weevil! And Red Morning's mare gone lame in the night without visible occasion!

And now Sina—but for all that they waited until the light was well advanced before they called him up to answer for such evil practices.

The sun was not up from behind the desert ranges, but the vast arc of heaven was filled with the light of it and the earth with pulsating blueness as the little knot of neighbors went up the trail toward Bill Bodry's. Sticks and stones they gathered by the way, but they put Wind-in-the-face foremost; after all it was *his* daughter.

Bill was out building the fire as they crossed the creek, and had turned facing the sound of voices when the first stone struck him. "Coyote whelp! Sorcerer! Spell binder!" the cries assailed him. He stood rooted with astonishment; another stone sailed by and struck plump on the door of the wickiup, the door like a white man's; prompt as a hornet out came Sina. She was looking very well and very much the mistress of the house. Catameneda of the Round Arm wept distractedly.

"Sina, Sina, my girl, come away from him—come away home with me—" When one has expected to find one's only child turned into a night-hawk or a wood rat, one may be forgiven for a touch of hysteria. "Sina, Sina, daughter of my heart, come away from the Worker of Evil!" Sina looked at her husband's cut lip which was beginning to bleed, and then at her parents, and the look took on a touch of severity.

"I don't know what you mean," she said, though she did perfectly, for she remembered what the woman of Black Rock had said about bringing Bill to Council. "But I know one thing," said Sina in the lisping English which was the hall-mark of the younger generation, "I don't thank you for comin' here makin' trouble for me and my man so early in the morning."

❖ ❖ ❖

Unpublished Stories

❖   ❖   ❖

The Portrait

The style of "The Portrait," with its density of texture and its effort to recreate the ambiguous doubling back of consciousness and of memory, is more characteristic of Austin's late novels, which show the influence of Henry James, than of her short stories. One of the few stories to be set in the urban East, "The Portrait" shows how she experimented with style and subject matter to tell a story she had presented in many other forms. Here she retells in a more complex but perhaps less successful way "The Coyote-Spirit and the Weaving Woman," where an insightful woman artist shows a man his worth as a human being by refusing to accept the stereotypical view he has of himself.

The draft of "The Portrait" in the Huntington Library's Austin Collection (box 41) contains a number of handwritten revisions, which have been included in this text. It is not clear when Austin wrote the story, but she was obsessed with its theme throughout her life. In this sense, "The Portrait" is a self-portrait.

It was always so that the dream came, with the earliest soft light, as though, like the incidents it stood for in Saranne's life, it struggled to escape into the full day of reality. Sometimes, if only she could have stayed asleep another instant, it seemed about to issue into form and substance. Oftener, as it fled down the receding corridor of sleep before the clatter of milk cans that rose daily from the transformed mews under her studio window, it left no trace beyond the warmer pulse with which she woke, the trailing fragrance of half-remembered delight. But always Saranne knew what dream had just visited her, as one knows on entering a shut room what flower has last bloomed there. This particular dream came oftenest at the turn of the two seasons, when there was the scent of lilacs in the wind or the first blaze of autumn in the florists' windows. Or, as now, it would come of summer dawns when there were great fleeces of white clouds to be glimpsed from the top of her studio window, and a delicate waft of blossoming meadows would come stealing up the city streets freshened by the river wind. But however it came, and whether it left a picture—a huge flowering magnolia tree, a white pillared portico tapestried with climbing roses—or only a vanishing sense of presence, the dream was always the same dream and the figure in it the same figure.

There were times when, for the sake of its warmth and sweetness, Saranne hugged the dream to her, when she allowed that warmth to color her painting, and that sweetness to penetrate all her day with its inestimable values. Other times, because of the dream's renewal of an aching sense of loss, she would push it from her with sharp resoluteness of mind, with a cold shower and a busy intentness of breakfast getting. But on this particular morning, not only had the background of the dream renewed itself with a sense of being the only reality—made so by its continued power over her—but the figure had come forth with lifelike distinctness; the salient lines of the face and head, the eyes blue and alight with a vigor that the slightest hint of opposition transformed to resistance. Lying half-awake in her bed, with the dream still warm about her, Saranne felt her heart leap with a certain pride in her power of being faithful to a dream so slightly fed with reality.

"It lasts," she said. "It is the only thing that lasts!" And in that assurance she turned to the day's occupations.

Before going to bed, Saranne had drawn back the curtains of her balcony bedroom, as she often did, so that her first waking glance and freshest judgment might fall on the portrait in hand, waiting the final touch of inspiration. As the light broadened from above on the all but completed canvas, she felt the staying power of her dream to be the very source and substance of all that the portrait and the appointments of the room in which she had painted it implied. It implied first of all success, of a substantial, steady-going kind, revealing to the practiced eye the intelligent grasp, the singleness of purpose, the large capacity for loyalty to an ideal, the fruit of the faithful dream. Still under its influence she rose, flung a dressing gown about her, and as her custom was, went directly to her palette and brushes. She was busy thus for more than an hour, walking around and around her work, putting in those strong, sure strokes that, after the sitter had gone, gave to the faithful record its final touch of livingness; which, Saranne always insisted, only emerged from her when the likeness was otherwise completed, as the fragrance only comes forth when the flower is completely opened. By the time she had accomplished this for the portrait of Helmuth, the Copper magnate—it was a half-humorous, half-malicious joke among her rivals, the way Saranne specialized in the portraits of men—the warmth of her dream had receded.

As she wiped her brushes and pushed the finished canvas to the wall,

Saranne suffered a sharp reversion to indignity, because of a dream that never, *never* manifested even in so slight a sign as a picture postcard or a marked newspaper. To have justified such a personal and vivid vision, such a rise of power in the mere recollection, such an ache of realizing loss, the subject of her dream should simply have appeared there before her, should have renewed the troubling but utterly sweet and satisfying fact of his existence. And as Saranne faced again the certainty that though she could bring up recollection of the man she loved into such reality that he served as an incentive to the highest mark of creative achievement, she was still unable to bring him into any sort of substantial contact, she broke, as never before, into a tearing outburst of sobbing.

"Oh Denny, Denny!" she cried, "Come to me, come to me!" until, sobered by the realization that not only did he not come, but that she did not know even where he might be expected to come from, did not even know if coming in the flesh were still possible for him, she took herself by the shoulders with a sharp shake. "The trouble with me," she told herself, "is that it is ten o'clock and I haven't had any breakfast, and I am a silly old maid trying to make a grand passion out of a sentimental memory."

She bestirred herself then to make toast and coffee, and on the excuse that now that one portrait was finished and before another should be begun, a thorough housecleaning would be in order, managed to keep up a semblance of pressing activity for the better part of the day. Not, however, with entire success, for in the process of setting a closet to rights, she uncovered an old album full of snapshots of the garden, the lilac walk, the linden tree, the grandiose stone lions at the carriage entrance, and through them all glimpses of the white house with the paint scaling off in patches from the Corinthian columns. How it all came back: the asparagus bower that Saranne and the Clancy boy had made between the kitchen garden and the hollyhocks; the gap in the lilac hedge that Denny had stolen through!

Saranne seemed to have been somehow born to the knowledge that the sessions of secret happy play with the Clancy boy must be, if not actually fibbed about, at least protected from the criticism of the elders. And how well Denny had understood, and compensated himself for it by domineering over the timid and utterly forgiving little Sarah Anne Ravenscroft of the "Big House." Sarah herself understood that it was because she was a Ravenscroft and Denny merely a Clancy that he must never be invited beyond the great magnolia at the bend of the walk. When one was asked what kept one so busy all morning one said "Oh, just playing," without specifying what or with whom one played. And when one had climbed under Denny's tuition to the top of the magnolia tree, or learned to "skin the cat" on its lower branches, one must not mention this proud achievement under penalty of embarrassing and unaccountable laughter of the elders, with ensuing dark hints that it was all very well so long as the child *was* a child but mustn't be allowed to develop too far. Always, it had seemed to the little, dark, shy Sarah Anne that the things she most wished for and enjoyed doing were in the category of things that "mustn't be allowed to develop" beyond the point which, as it turned out, everybody was too indolent or too preoccupied to mention when it arrived.

Sarah Anne had come along inopportunely as the fruit of a second marriage after the children of the first had grown quite out of reach of her solitary—and after the first four years, motherless—growing up. As a consequence she had had a great deal of humorously indulgent petting, a great many and puzzlingly contradictory directions, plenty of affectionate fussing over in the event of a sore throat or an overburdened stomach, and more real loneliness than is good for an imaginative child. In addition to the things that weren't allowed to develop, nothing that Sarah Anne had was hers in the sense of having been originally intended for her, from her clothes to her name, which had been cut down to Saranne so early that she couldn't say when. It was then, with all the interest and charm of his being exclusively hers, that she had appropriated the Clancy boy, and she could no more have helped the various small seductions by which she drew him to her side, than the Clancy boy could have helped being redheaded. Saranne understood that Denny was interdicted because his father was in a small way a building contractor, and she herself a Ravenscroft of Ravenscroft, one of the showplaces of the town, *and* mortgaged. It was not until it closed in upon them, snapping shut the doors of the Big House forever, that Saranne realized that the mortgage was not itself a distinction, as inseparable from the Ravenscroft credit as the silver candelabra that had come down to them from a signer of the Declaration of Independence.

She had grown up accepting these things as sufficient reason for not inviting the Clancy boy beyond the gravelly place between the magnolia and the paulownia tree, and not being supposed to recognize him when they met elsewhere, save by secret glances between the swaggers of indifference with which Denny signalized their occasion as public encounters. She would even offer herself in her small way when his sense of social slight was sorest, to be trampled on, mothering him in her heart as a woman will with a man she has marked for her own. Now, as all this came back to her under the compulsion of the dream and the suggestion of Southern heat in

the long June afternoon, Saranne told herself that she was merely home-
sick for the South, and as she banged the album shut, and poked it far back
on the closet shelf, she decided that the best thing for her to do would be
to go to the Albemarle for dinner and comfort herself on chicken fricasse,
rice creole, and a thick slice of Lady Baltimore.

As Miss Ravenscroft, the successful portrait painter, she was sufficiently
well known at the cafe, when she entered the wide, dim room, to find
herself being piloted to her favorite seat by a stove-polished waiter who
was letter perfect in the role for which he had been cast of old family
retainer welcoming her home. The table was discreetly screened and comfortably removed from the palm-embowered orchestra. Beyond it the
ample, old-fashioned space was beginning to fill with its usual complement
of exiled Southerners, who, Saranne told herself with an ironic shake,
wouldn't have been persuaded to live South and were probably, like herself, nourished on dreams. Had their dreams suddenly been realized, they
wouldn't have liked it at all. And then, when she had given her order and
the orchestra from behind its back of artificial greens had burst into "The
River of Years," the dream had its way with her again.

The gray space between the tables widened to the strip of gravelly walk
under the paulownia tree, the light of the crystal chandelier softened to a
Southern moon, and there was she teaching the Clancy boy to dance. She
recalled sharply how it had all happened at some festivity of the elders, the
first which Saranne, in a cut-over organdy, had been allowed to attend.
Finding herself neglected, she had slipped away to the bottom of the garden to discover Denny curled in the notch of the magnolia tree, listening
to the music. Beyond the wide-opened windows of the Big House, the
orchestra had played "The River of Years." Saranne had asked him to dance
and the Clancy boy had said he couldn't, so Saranne had spread out her
organdy frills, whirling softly until by magic their hands met and his step
melted into hers.

That had been the summer of Saranne's growing up, and yet not so
grown up that she was missed from the social evenings which, in spite of
the menace of the mortgage, never failed from the Big House. There was
always lavish refreshment and music good enough to screen those innocent
secret sessions of dance, and the fragrance of the crushed paulownia petals
underfoot, and a renewal of the shy intimacy which had failed a little during the awkward years between twelve and sixteen. How many of them had
there been between the first and that glorious drowning moment, when
the music swung them together in a long meeting of young lips which

ended in Denny's hurried stammer, "Oh, Saranne, Saranne, I didn't mean—" and the step on the walk? Somebody else had found the garden fair . . . and there was "that child" holding hands with "that Clancy boy," and a terrible moment of half-scolding laughter, and "well really's" and "I declare's" and something about uninvited guests, struck silent by Saranne's tense untrembling voice.

"Denny is my guest, Beulah! I was just telling him good-bye. I'll walk to the gate with you, Denny."

"Well, really—" and then, after hot ploughshares, Denny, who had come in through the gap in the hedge as usual, striking angrily with his fist the iron gate. "And I'll never come in this place again until I can come by the same gate I go out of!" And Saranne, proud and firm, "That'll be soon, if I have anything to say about it, Denny."

But she hadn't had much to say about it, for Saranne, by a counsel of prudence on the part of her half-sisters, was pushed "out" and taken about to "affairs" at which she saw Denny only occasionally and never alone. The Clancy boy was what was known at the Big House as "dreadfully pushing," and Denny, who was amusing and a "perfect dream of a dancer," was occasionally invited along the fringe of the Ravenscroft circle. Only once after that had Saranne and the Clancy boy had any private and personal talk together. He had called, actually called at the Big House, to tell her that he wasn't coming to her eighteenth-birthday party, which, because Saranne had never truly had a coming-out party, was to be a transcendent occasion. "I'm not coming, Saranne, because I know I'm not really wanted. You just pried this invitation out of them, and they gave in because it could be excused on the ground of being what a Ravenscroft would do for a poor neighbor." This was so near the truth that Saranne quailed, but not so that Denny could notice it.

"That's why they're hoping," she said loftily, "that you'll feel your unsuitability to the extent of staying away."

"I'll be darned if I do, if that's the way they feel!" Denny's eyes glittered. "But if I do come, it'll be only to say good-bye."

"Oh—Denny!"

"I've heard of a school where I can work my way—learning to be an engineer. And I'm coming back here and *show* these people."

"You won't have to show me, Denny." But Denny was too full of his sense of injury and his plans to notice. He came to Saranne's party, danced with her once and went away. It was Saranne herself who dragged him, for that dance, out under the paulownia tree and insisted that the orchestra play for it "The River of Years." She couldn't, she simply couldn't let Denny go without . . . something . . . something that didn't happen.

"We've had some good times here, Denny."

"Sure; great! You were always a good little sport, Saranne."

"And your good friend, Denny." She was sure, yes, thinking it over, she has always come back to the point of being sure that his arms had tightened, that he would have perhaps kissed her. A gay group of dancers had suddenly burst on them from the house. In the end, Denny had shaken hands and gone away. And as the gate banged, the orchestra had been playing "The Blue Danube" . . . Suddenly, Saranne buried her face in her hands against the dagger-drawn sweetness of recollection, only to be recalled, by the arrival of her soup, to the realization that the orchestra behind its paper palms was playing "The Blue Danube," and she herself was the object of the puzzled attention of a man just seated at a single table not far away. It was not until she saw him rise under a growing conviction, to make his hesitating way toward her, that she realized who that man must be.

I I

D enny had come back. He had come back, exactly as he had said he would, to *show* people. He had not been with her a quarter of an hour before Saranne was sure of that, sure that though he had not come to find her, his finding her thus within forty-eight hours of his own arrival in the city sharpened the impulse that had driven him away from the Southern town where they had known one another, to prove that he was as "good," as fit for the finer uses of life, as any man. And within an hour she knew that if his coming had not been timed nor directed to her, he had come back to her, to his old use of her as the background against which he was to prove that he was what he in the old domineering way insisted on having Saranne assure him that he was, "as good as anybody."

Saranne made this out through Denny's own indifference to all that had happened to her since he had last seen her, his casual and easily satisfied inquiry as to how she came to be where she was, out of his almost impatient brushing aside of all that her studio in its spaciousness—considering what rents were in New York—its few and choice furnishings, could have told him of what she had become. He had, on that very first evening, after Saranne had taken him home with her, plunged into the saga of his own career. He had succeeded at railroad construction. He was, he gave her to understand, with a simplicity far beyond bragging, on his way to become one of the kingpins of railroading. He was there in New York on an errand that proved so securely what he was in the way of becoming, that he had arranged to linger on for a week or two in order that he might discover how to be something bigger—more expressive at least—than the "big guy" in railroading that he was sure of being in any case. The name of the man he had come to see was a great name indeed, and the name of the man who had sent him out of the mysterious "West," was one that even in New York was not unnoticed. But neither was great enough to daunt Denny's sense of being able, as railroad man to railroad man, to deal with them. What he wanted was to be able to meet them as equal to equal in the environment of wealth and power which he so convincingly assured would eventually be his.

Just how much of this Denny had frankly said and how much she had inferred at their first meeting, Saranne couldn't have told. Hadn't she always known exactly what was in Denny's mind about everything, except herself? It had always been a source of affectionate annoyance to her half-sisters that Saranne had turned out clever about everything but men. And if a girl wasn't clever about men she simply had to be about something else. Otherwise she didn't have any life; and what you would *call* life. And it wasn't as if Saranne had to marry. There was a small but saving income from her mother, placed carefully beyond Saranne's own generous disposition to spend it all on the Ravenscrofts. But for Saranne suddenly, at twenty, to make up her mind to go off alone to Paris and spend it in learning to paint! Well, after that the family gave Saranne up. Later they accepted her success thankfully as being the best thing that could have happened to a girl who had no sort of feeling for her own effect upon men.

As she dressed to go to dinner again with Denny the second evening of his return, Saranne considered that perhaps she had always known too much; she knew so acutely what was in their minds that the very knowledge inhibited her from the power to make men think anything else than what they happened to be thinking. She knew how to dress for the place Denny was taking her. He had left the choice to Saranne, she knew exactly the place Denny would like, but she wasn't at all sure that she could make Denny feel her knowledge as evidence of her own particular value to him. She saw, after they had sat down at the table reserved for them, that he appreciated at once that they were in exactly the place he would have wished to be. He was himself perfectly dressed for it; and as his eye, after a general survey of the quietly fashionable restaurant, came back to her, she realized happily that he saw in her the perfect expression in dress and manner of what he would have wanted a dinner companion to be. Studying him, Saranne discovered that he had all the ways proper to a rising railroad man, of getting the best service and of making himself felt without ostentation. But as regarding the inner meaning of the things he had set his mind on obtaining, there was still a chip on his shoulder. He was particularly noticing of the people who spoke to Saranne. Who was that elderly party with the face like a hickory nut, bowing to her? Saranne kept him waiting while she smiled and bowed in return.

"That's Nugent; the one they call the Biscuit King, T. S. Nugent. He sat for me once."

"Sat for you?"

"For his portrait, one of the most interesting commissions I ever had."

"Ah," Denny almost reproached her, "you never told me you were as good as that!" Saranne laughed with delight.

"Oh Denny, never fear, you *will* get on if you can turn them off so easily."

"I mean," he insisted soberly, "that Nugent is the sort of man to insist on having the best of everything, so if he chose you—"

"I'm not sure that he did. It was for the Nugent Foundation, my commission was from the Trustees."

"That's what I've been talking about," Denny eagerly explained. "*They* wouldn't have had anything but the best, and if Nugent didn't know himself how good you were, he would have paid somebody to tell him. There are a lot of them like that, these millionaires, they get what's good, but half the time they don't know except as they are told. But I want to *know*, on my own."

"Well, you have to begin by being told—a few things at least. I remember when I first went to Paris—" She let him know something of the path she had traveled. As she talked, she saw his attention had at last moved over from himself and fixed upon her. He was taking her in as a woman, a person at least, and not just a loose thread out of his past. Or perhaps only as a portrait painter; he might be thinking about his own portrait for the Clancy Foundation. After all, she never did know, as Beulah always said, about the effect she might be producing on a man. All that Saranne really knew was that if she let Denny go again, he would take not only her dream away with him, but every right of hers to dream again. And all the time her old instinct to mother Denny, to do for him what he couldn't do for himself, worked in her. Since that was what he wanted so much, she would help Denny as far toward being socially acceptable to the "Big House" of railroading as he would go. "If you've nothing on hand tomorrow afternoon," she said toward the dessert, "there's a Frenchwoman giving some perfectly marvelous imitations. I'm taking a girl from home, Clarissa Haden, one of the Thorndyke Hadens. She's up here trying to make her living as an Entertainer. I like to go with her to such things, her reactions are always fresh and interesting. Saranne did not think it necessary to add, "and her purse so thin she can't manage these things for herself."

Denny had heard of the Frenchwoman. "All right," he said, "I'll get the tickets." Saranne didn't tell him that she had two. "Still going in by the front gate, Denny?"

"You bet!" Clancy assured her, and never knew that the gate he went through was Saranne's generous wish to make up for him for that old slight when he hadn't dared to come into her garden except through the hedge. She explained a little however to Clarissa, who was too young and too much a Thorndyke Haden to have heard of the Clancys at home. "He wants," she said, "to be on the very inside, and I'm trying to give him a clue. You must play up to me."

"As if I ever could play up to you," Clarissa cried, "except by showing that I admire and wonder at everything you do and are. But I think your Mr. Clancy has come a long way already, if he knows he isn't inside. It was the worst surprise of *my* young life, when I first began to talk of devoting it to Art, to find that the men I had grown up with hadn't, most of them, even looked through the gate. And I had grown up with the idea that just to be a Thorndyke Haden was to be in the innermost inside of everything that was fine and desirable. And now I am not sure that we are in on *anything*. Except, of course, a kind of standard; things a Haden will or won't do."

"Oh," said Saranne, "if it's a question of standards you'll find that Denny's are the best."

"Of course, Miss Ravenscroft, if he's your friend," Clarissa fervently declared, "I'd know he'd be *that!*"

They were standing before the portrait of the Copper magnate when Denny arrived, Saranne having uncovered it for her young friend, to whom she left it to name the sitter for him. Clarissa played up. "Oh, Mr. Clancy, I wonder if you'd mind . . . It's so hard to get a genuine personal reaction nowadays . . . would you mind saying right out, what impression it makes on you? It would be too refreshing, wouldn't it Miss Ravenscroft?" Denny, by a glance having gathered that Saranne would find it refreshing, said after a moment, "I think he's a man who has worked his way up from the bottom. And that it's made him a little hard—and soft, because he's afraid of being hard. And that he calls his wife Mother." He was rewarded with a swift clapping of hands.

"But of course," Clarissa concluded, "you'd know that is just Miss Ravenscroft's lovely way of getting at the fundamentals of a sitter, and not only getting them, but presenting them exactly as the people who love them would like to see them."

"Ah," said Denny, "that's it, is it?" and looked hard at the portrait while Saranne went to get her hat.

He showed something of the same attentive detachment toward the entertainment of the afternoon, and their comment on it, which lasted on through the sumptuous tea which Denny insisted upon, in lieu of not being able to take them to dinner, which he was having with some of the men with whom he did business. He was interested in a discussion which arose between the two women, as to the extent to which the Comedienne of the afternoon was justified in "going after" her audience as she so publicly had, in a manner Clarissa thought the perfection of technique, and Saranne decided was unnecessary. The actress, Saranne insisted, should concern herself primarily with "getting" the character she meant to portray, and that, if she were successful, would of itself get the audience. If the actress went outside her part, or the portrait painter outside her sitter, and used something of herself to capture her audience, it was a sign, said Saranne, that she hadn't done her job as she ought. Clarissa for her part thought that the audience liked to be gone after, it was part of the game to them, their way of being also in the play. "Like a man," she protested, "liking to have a woman take an interest, show skill, in capturing him," and then quickly, as if she might have gone too far, turned it off to Denny. "Isn't it so, Mr. Clancy, that when you have a business proposition to put to a man, he wants to have it put skillfully?"

"It is and it isn't," Denny considered. "If it's a sound proposition, it is. But if the proposition's phony, then he remembers it against you. That's the point," he argued, "with a business proposition you soon find out whether you've been fooled or not. But with plays and pictures—or with women—how are you going to find out if it's the real thing or hokum?"

Clarissa thought if you got real pleasure out of the picture or play, it didn't matter much, and then apologized for venturing an opinion before Miss Ravenscroft. She so genuinely suffered a sense of shortcoming before the older woman that Denny covered it with a suggestion that sometime soon they should take him to see some pictures. Pictures, he reminded them, stayed where they were, not like a play or music, you could put your finger on them. He thought he might "get" pictures for the very reason that he never cared much for them. So it was arranged.

In the course of the next few days the two women hunted out and discussed before him the best that was available for the time, offering themselves as anvils on which Denny's art appreciations were to be beaten out. They made out between them, the older and the younger woman, that in addition to not wishing to be tutored too openly, the railroad man was growing a little suspicious of them. Clarissa it was who put her finger on the difficulty. "It's our point of view," she said. "We're too professional, too—well, too railroady. What he really wants is the point of view of people who play with art, not those who work at it."

"If they really play," said Saranne, "they've had to work at it first, the same as railroads."

"Ah, but that," Clarissa was positive, "is what he doesn't want to think it. He wants to think that art is mysterious and—romantic. It's the way men want a woman to make them feel about her. He doesn't really want to know how a portrait painter feels about her work, he wants to *feel* how it feels to be one of those who get their portraits painted. He can't take it straight from us that it is very much like all other work."

"But I don't want him to 'take' anything from anybody," Saranne protested. "What I'd like to help him to know is what I've always known about him, that he's got already the thing he wants in himself. Only he just doesn't know it."

"Well, you can't do much with a man," the girl put it airily, "when you've shown him that you really do know more about him than he knows himself."

Saranne reflected that she didn't want to do anything *with* Denny. She wanted to do something for him. If feeling himself on the inside was a help to his getting there, it was up to her to prove by any method in her power that that was where, for her, he had always been. And because she knew Denny so well—as nobody had ever known him—she thought all-at-once, in a moment Denny provided her, of the perfect way of doing it. He had come late to her studio, hardly hoping to find her up and in the frame to see him, to tell her that the business that had brought him East was now successfully concluded, the papers signed and delivered. But it wasn't that altogether that he came—as he said—"homing" to tell her. It was that, with the business now behind him, he could give himself with a free hand

and a cleared perception to what he had told her in the beginning he wished to do for himself.

"You don't know, Saranne," he said, settling into the ingenious absorption in his own situation which was characteristic of him, "what a grouch I've always carried about those old days when I was good enough to play in the backyard with you, and not good enough to come into the parlor. I was sore as the dickens about it because I couldn't help feel that there was something to it. Not that I thought that the Ravenscrofts were better than I, or richer. But I thought that they had some kind of life that I wasn't good enough for, wasn't up to. There was something that I was missing, and I couldn't seem to lay hands on it. Not even after the money began to come in, and I could have pretty much anything that money would have paid for. I was Dennis Clancy, the coming railroad man, and yet I wasn't *in* on things . . . things like you and Clar—Miss Haden have been showing me—Art, you know, and . . . and *Things*." Movements of his square chin indicated the room glowing with candlelight behind him, its gracious space and choice appointments. "And now I sort of see, thanks to you, Saranne. These things are just a kind of language, a way of saying something you've got to *be*. Like that portrait you showed me, your way of saying old Helmuth's just what everybody knows he is. Well, the only thing about this inside business is what I am inside, and there's no one keeping me out but myself."

"Your notion of yourself, Denny."

He considered that for a while. "Well, that's an idea. My notion of myself has been that I wasn't up to it. But I sort of see. Next winter when I come back—" he broke off. "I owe you a lot, Saranne, I hope I can do as much for you sometime."

"Well," her voice flared out, "you might let me paint your portrait."

"Why—" This took him unawares. "I hadn't thought. I suppose Mother would like it."

"Oh, I don't mean as an order. For myself, an exhibition piece. Everything I do is owned before I begin. It's private and personal." Saranne hurried on, "I haven't anything I can send around to exhibitions. And your head interests me. I'll make my everlasting reputation by it."

"Why, if you put it that way—"

III

Saranne hadn't meant to put it that way. She had meant to put it slowly, revealingly, just as the conviction had come to her that this was the way she could put it to Denny, with his awakened sense of the values of true portraiture, that the source of that good life he coveted was in himself. She could do that. She had spent fourteen years of her own life learning to give just that inestimable service of self-revelation. Wasn't it, after all, the service that women, simply as Woman, owed to man? And when she had shown him to himself as he had always been, must always be to her, he couldn't fail to understand. The idea had been growing in her mind— Wasn't this the reason why she had learned to paint, that she might be ready for his need to know what she and she alone could show, the seed and source of the good life in himself.

She hadn't meant to blurt it out like this; she had a notion of leading him on to ask it of her. It was that suggestion of coming back "next winter," with its certainty of his first going, that had brought the proposal forth from her like a shot in the dark. For she couldn't, she knew now that she couldn't possibly bear to have Denny go away. She had borne her life thus far without him because she had always somehow known that he would come back. She couldn't just ask him to marry her, as somehow also she felt if she did then and there, he would do; but she could show him with her brush that the profound unshakable revelation of the best in each by the other, which is the reality of marriage, had always been there, a live pulsing bond.

Having committed him to the adventure of the portrait, as undertaken wholly in her interest, Saranne realized that she could have practically her own way with him. Denny wouldn't know what she was about or what was expected of him; he would do exactly what he was told. She planned to make several quick sketches of him in different poses that would not tire, that might even interest him as successive revelations of what he already knew himself. Then the final portrait, which, with the aid of the sketches, could be finished without taxing him too much, under the rule that she enforced with all her sitters, of not looking until she gave them leave.

Denny was shy at first, fearful, easily teased by the first sketch in which Saranne put aside her former knowledge of him and tried to see him simply as a study for a head, the round engineering head with the jutting chin and the width between the eyes. But by the next sketch, which declared his will to succeed, he was captivated. He had come in midmorning after a meeting with his directors, chewing the obstinate end of an argument, going on with it in his mind while Saranne roughed the sketch in with swift strokes. "Oh, but the boys will know me by that!" he chuckled, and Saranne understood that he meant his own personal construction staff somewhere in the West. Then Clarissa had come in, and Denny found himself half-flattered, half-embarrassed by their ensuing discussion of his tones, his values, and how amazingly good he was for Saranne's purpose. "You'll making a killing with it," Miss Haden declared with her head on one side. "It's positively luscious." After which Denny was unconditionally delivered into their hands.

There were ten days of his stay left when the final canvas was begun. Ten days of June with the lights pure and high, and the city at its best, all the idlers gone, and the workers not yet dragged down by the summer's heat. From the very first day, Saranne knew by the feel of the brush between her fingers, by the power that sang in her like the taut string of a violin, that the portrait was going to be good, that it would make, as she had promised Denny, her everlasting reputation. She set her studio for it, cleared it of everything but the piano, the model throne, and the heavy easel pushed this way and that to the cool light. As often as possible Clarissa came in by arrangement, as she was being paid for doing, to keep Saranne's sitter interested, for Saranne at her best worked in a daze of absorption, of an intensity that Clarissa declared kept her in mortal suspense for fear the sitter might have starved to death under it.

The girl had all the natural aptitudes which, without great talent, qualified her as an entertainer, an easy trick of catching the note of the moment, and a positive genius for raising or lowering insidiously the social key. She would slip in after the sitting had begun, and going to the piano, croon old ballads sprightly or tender, or touching the keys lightly, stray away into persuasive melodies that subdued attention without once arousing an emotion at variance with the painter's need. She knew when to set Denny to talking, and, instructed by Saranne, to talk revealingly about himself. She knew, too, by signs that seldom had to be translated into words, when to slip away and prepare tea, for Saranne, when she came out of her trance of work, was never more than half-awake. She would sit sipping her cup, taking little sips of Denny at the same time, and while the others talked, would often flit back to her easel for a touch that had just come to her. And Clarissa would say, Denny being half-flattered, half-fearful, "Oh, but you'll not have a rag left to hide your soul in, Mr. Clancy, by the time she gets done with you."

In the beginning of the sittings, Clarissa had contrived to let Denny know that there were times when it was best for both of them to get quietly away. And Saranne was vaguely aware that they sometimes prolonged these hours together by excursions of which they lightly gossiped while she painted, with comment and argument to which she lent a half-attentive ear. Toward the end of the sittings they would all fall rather silent, and on a day when Saranne had signaled to the girl that she was to go and leave Denny behind her, Denny himself happy to be left and waiting without curiosity the event, suddenly she showed him what she had done. She swung the great easel about for just the correct light, and turning away for long enough to say to herself that she simply couldn't bear it unless Denny . . . and then discovering that she needn't finish what she couldn't bear, for Denny was standing rapt before the canvas, and his face had gone white.

Presently she moved over and touched his sleeve. "Well, Denny?"

"So that's me, Saranne?" He gasped a little. Oh, there was no doubt it was Denny! Denny of the keen mind and high spirit and uncomplicated male temperament. Denny who knew men as they love to be known and would never know any woman wholly. Suddenly he took her fingers in a cold hand. "Look here, Saranne, you haven't tried to . . . fool me?"

"Oh, Denny, I wouldn't do that!"

"Oh, no, I see . . . it's too good for that. Too good as a painting, I mean. But I didn't realize . . . I wasn't prepared." Color was coming back to his face. "Look here, Saranne, I must see this again. By myself, I mean. I . . . I can't take it in."

"You can come in any time, Denny." Of course Denny would be slow and deadly honest, and intelligent. She could absolutely count on Denny's intelligence. For a long time after he was gone she looked at the portrait, knowing that she would never do anything better and content with what she had done. Next morning she left orders that Mr. Clancy was to be left with the picture if he called; after which she walked and walked until she lost the feel of her feet under her, and saw the city moving around her like a city on the silver screen without captions or continuity. On her return she learned that he had been in the house for about an hour. After that she lived in suspended consciousness until the afternoon of the second day, when he called her on the phone. "I'm coming over. Right away if I may. I want to talk—" His voice seemed full of light. His face, too, when he came hastily in at the door and took her two hands, looking down at her with an attention more personal, more considering than she could recall, "You're tired, Saranne," he insisted. "You've put too much of yourself into that portrait." He put his arm about her shoulders and led her to her chair and rang for tea. Whatever other people might be, Denny was not tired, he brimmed over with vigor like a cup; he could not even sit still, he pulled the easel out and paced around the picture from point to point, blushing a little like a boy who had been caught looking at himself in the glass. "Clarissa was crazy to come," he said, "but I told her I must have an hour of you to myself."

"You've been out with Clarissa?" She knew of course that they went out together; hadn't she sent them? But out with Clarissa, *today*.

"All morning," he said. "She'll be around later. You're going out to dinner with us. Oh, Saranne, I don't know where to begin!" But it wasn't until the tea arrived that he said anything important, and that in reference to the portrait. "I don't quite believe it yet," he said. "I was here an hour, day before yesterday. I had to be *sure*. By every time I look I thank God I'm man enough to know what I see and take it from you."

"Ah, if you do take it, Denny?"

"As I would from the very Mother of Heaven herself," he breathed, and it sounded somehow not extravagant. "It's your heavenly goodness, Saranne, which I've always loved you for, even when I have hated you for knowing that I needed goodness done to me. But this—" he made a large gesture toward the portrait, "I'd be meaner than mud if I didn't see that you've opened your heart to let me see myself in its goodness, as I needed to see myself if I was ever to have what I've wanted worse than the souls in Purgatory want Heaven. And I thank you for it and take the heaven that's held out to me."

"'Tis a fact, Saranne," he declared boyishly, drawing his chair toward her, dropping into a touch of Irish as he often did in his high moments. "When I first saw what I wanted in this room and knew that I wanted it, it was like a knife in my ribs to think that I mightn't be worthy of it."

"That you should ever have thought such a thing, Denny!" Her voice was soft and choked, her hands trembled.

"I did that though, and when you said you would paint my portrait, 'twas sweating I was with cold fright. 'For,' I said, 'Saranne is one that knows, and what her brush tells me, that I'll have to put up with.' 'Twas Judge and Jury and Kingdom Come with me, Saranne, especially when Clarissa would come and look over your shoulder, and when she stopped giving me the josh about it. Said I, 'The women have given you the gate, Denny, stand up now and take it, like a man.'" He paused, wiping his brow with his handkerchief, breathing heavily.

Saranne just quavered, "But you saw, Denny, you saw?"

"I saw, and my heart was in my mouth with hoping and in my boots with fearing to believe. That was why I was wishful to see it myself. For I knew you too kind in your heart, Saranne, to trust you. And after I had been here I went straight to Clarissa, and said I, 'Is that picture true as you see me, Clarissa?' Said she, 'As true as paint can show you.' Then said I, 'Such as it shows me, will you have me?' And she did, Glory be, she did!" He pushed back his chair and began to walk about in the room beginning to be barred with late light and warm shadows. "She did," he cried again, "and it's you we are owing it to. And never think that either of us will be forgetting it." He walked over to Saranne and taking her face between his hands kissed it heartily.

"You mean—" Saranne's words came whisperingly, "you and Clarissa—"

"Engaged, and more. We're to be married in a week's time. For now that I've got her, how can I bear to let her go again? She'll be here telling you in a moment, but before she comes, there's an arrangement I want to make with you. When you're done toting my picture around for your exhibitions, will you tell me the top price you're offered and I'll double it. It's for a wedding present I want it, for I'm thinking," his voice dropped here to the utmost grave simplicity, "there'll be times when maybe she won't see me the same and she'll be thinking I was presumptuous to take her, and she so much younger. And I'll be wanting the picture to remind her—" He went and stood before it for a time, so absorbed that it escaped him that Saranne had made no sound until he came and stood beside her. "Can I have it? Is it a bargain, Saranne?"

"Oh yes, Denny," she accepted blindly that hand he held out to her, pulling herself up from the chair as the bell rang. "But as a present, Denny, my present to you both." She moved stiffly and stood where he had just been standing, "But I wish you'd ask Clarissa to excuse me . . . I . . . there are a few touches I want to give to the portrait, something that's just come to me. It's often that way. Clarissa will understand. Don't keep her waiting."

He was far too much the lover to do that, and Saranne, without waiting to see him go, turned to the canvas. Denny and Clarissa! And the things that Denny would never know; never be able to grow into knowing! But then Clarissa would never let him discover that there was anything missing; even if she knew herself, she would keep him from knowing. She would make him happy, she would make him *think* he was happy. And turning as the dying turn their faces to the wall, Saranne turned and painted that into the portrait.

Kate Bixby's Queerness

When I found the manuscript of "Kate Bixby's Queerness" in the Huntington Library's Austin Collection (box 41), it had paperclipped to it a note written in Austin's handwriting. The note read: "Written about 1905 and rejected by many editors as too 'radical.'"

As was often the case, Austin's "radical" message had to do with women's work. "Kate Bixby's Queerness" is her fictional challenge to the policy of denying employment to married teachers. As a married woman, Austin had worked as a schoolteacher to support herself and Ruth because Wallace would not provide support; she knew that many women needed to work, to earn salaries. Others, like Mrs.

Wills, find that they can support their families better than can their husbands. Some men, like Mr. Whitacre, need to be taken care of. Austin's "reversal of the order of things" is radical indeed.

But Kate's "queerness" is linked to more than her job. Many people infringe on her need to have "a little space in which to live my own life in my own way," most particularly her mother. Like A Woman of Genius, "Kate Bixby's Queerness" examines the ways mothers try to control their daughters' behavior. The portrayal of Mrs. Bixby, a club woman run amok, is one of Austin's best satiric treatments of the woman devoted to "true womanliness."

For some time Mrs. Bixby had been troubled by a misgiving, and it was so new to her complacency that she did not know quite what to do about it.

The misgiving took the form of a suspicion that her eldest daughter might be doing something queer. Everything not directly within the pale of Mrs. Bixby's activities that was not absolutely immoral was "queer"; but she was not prepared for the evidence of it in Kate, on whose account she had supposed herself done with anxiety these dozen years, ever since the girl had fitted herself for the teachers' examination and settled down in the Santa Lucia Schools.

When Mrs. Bixby herself had been a young lady in Bloombury, Connecticut, school teaching had been the only possible employment for a woman too well connected to become a seamstress or a domestic; so when

Kate and Roxanne began to look about for means of amending the family income, their mother turned them naturally toward a calling which, raised to the dignity of a profession by the salaries paid in Santa Lucia, California, had other advantages in Mrs. Bixby's estimation.

To begin with it was essentially womanly—a quality somewhat hazily connected in Mrs. Bixby's mind with the care of children, not crossing your knees in company, not being too sure of your dates in history. It was a calling which allowed, for all its drudgeries, the pleasing consciousness of dispensing sweetness and light. It was, if you were able to look at it in that way, a means of exercising the missionary spirit and being paid for it at a rate fairly commensurable with other employments that afforded no such spiritual occasion.

So, though Mrs. Bixby had taken a natural satisfaction in Emma's marriage to a raisin-grower in the South, it was with actual complacency that she had accepted the necessity of teaching for Kate.

Mr. Bixby had just died of the lung complaint that had been the reason for his removal west, leaving an income a little less, so little that only the family themselves knew it, but a little less than their actual necessities. If the occasion pressed more hardly on Kate than was just to a girl of eighteen, nobody, least of all Mrs. Bixby, was aware of it. The girl was then in her last year at the high school, and if she got up an hour earlier, or sat up an hour later to compass the extra studies required by the teachers' examination, and acquiesced in her mother's suggestion that since she hoped for a position of so much responsibility she should not mix too much in the gaieties proper to eighteen, it was not supposed, for a girl of so serious a turn of mind, to be particularly a deprivation. This, with the year of quiet enforced by her father's last illness and death, just about covered the period in which Kate Bixby might have learned that to be young and alive is a joyous affair; and no one thought of attributing it to any sense of loss or insufficiency that Roxanne had an easier time of it when it came her turn at the wheel. Roxanne had pretty clothes and three years at the normal school. She justified the clothes by looking very well in them, and the extra term of schooling enabled her to be elected to exactly the same salary Kate had worked up to in five years.

Mrs. Bixby, having taken Kate's calling in the manner of a devotion, experienced a jolt to her virtuous attitude in Roxanne's interests and enthusiasm. Roxanne touched life at so many points: she studied French one winter and did hammered brass work in the long vacation and had innumerable love affairs, which never came to anything chiefly through Roxanne's unwillingness to accept conditions which would preclude there being any more of them.

However, as time went on and Mrs. Bixby found the responsibility of the family income adequately carried by her two daughters (and her hands freed by her husband's death), she came to accept Roxanne's flirtations as her contribution to Advanced Womanhood, and felt free to devote herself to her favorite occupation of Helping the World Onward. She gave herself to Causes, nominated in the initials of many societies, dubbed collectively by Roxanne The Alphabeticals, and thanked God for the successful issue of her life.

Then, when the school board congratulated themselves on securing in Kate Bixby a teacher little likely to dissipate in social pleasures those out-of-school hours which it is understood are covered by the teacher's obligation if not by her salary, when Mrs. Bixby, as President of the W.F.M.S. and the Equal Suffragists, Secretary to the W.C.T.U., and a member of the Pastor's Relief Committee, was particularly placed to be the target of invidious remark which might arise from any irregularity in her own family, Kate began to give evidence of insuperable queerness.

I I

It began in a talk Kate had with her mother just when her cousin Serena Haven was taking it hardest that the only way to realize on an expensive college education was to accept the district school at San Marco, when, though everybody was certain Evan Lindley meant to propose, nobody could take any account of it, so long as he had not done so. Mrs. Bixby had been so well pleased with the performances of her own girls that when the care of her niece fell to her for a few years, she would certainly have inducted the girl into the same calling had not Serena fortunately escaped into marriage; and in her hearty support of the situation, Kate had let fall something that awoke in Mrs. Bixby a late perception that her eldest daughter would have preferred to be married herself, and that she somehow laid it to the career her mother had accepted for her that she was not. Mrs. Bixby had married at nineteen, and at fifty-four all that went with mating and romance lay so far behind her that she suffered in this discovery not so much the pangs of her daughter's legitimate disappointment as an uneasiness lest other people should find it out. If at times she had experienced a motherly wish to see her girls well settled, she had consoled herself with the reflection that Roxanne would marry when the right man came along and Kate would probably never be married in any case. But it was disconcerting when you had labored to turn out a noble woman Helping the World Onward, to have her thrown back on your hands, a man-desiring old maid. Mrs. Bixby talked it over with Roxanne at the first opportunity.

"I am sure," she said with a sense of injury, "Kate never gave the slightest evidence of being interested in men."

"Oh, she isn't," protested Roxanne, "that is just the trouble. She is only capable of being very much interested in one man, and you don't get the opportunity to be that unless you know something of the creatures in general."

This was a sort of wisdom which Mrs. Bixby always felt went a little too far beyond the pale of true womanliness to admit of discussion, besides she was never very sure of her ground with Roxanne. She returned to another point of her grievance.

"I don't know why Kate should turn against school teaching now," said Kate's mother, "when she has always been so fond of little children."

"Ah," Roxanne admitted, "perhaps that's the reason,"—and Mrs. Bixby found nothing whatever to say to that.

Roxanne was a good sister: she had paid back all that her schooling had cost Kate, and made her the confidant of all her love affairs. It occurred to her now that she had taken her sister's exclusion from the purely feminine art of pleasing men too much for granted. Looking at her attentively by lamplight that night, she discovered that Kate had clear, steady eyes and a beautiful line from the upper lip to the chin, and it seemed suddenly of amazing pitiableness that no one should ever tell her so.

"I've been rather a pig about my good times," said Roxanne to herself, and sat up evenings making a rose-colored silk waist which she insisted on Kate's wearing to the Social Saturday Night and the Camera Club. Kate enjoyed the Camera Club, and the rose-colored waist served to freshen the tints of a too sallow complexion. She modeled herself as much as possible on Roxanne, and Roxanne loyally undertook not to see wherein the man-alluring purpose of her own charms, laid bare by Kate's downright handling, offended her. And at this juncture occurred the episode of Mr. Francis Whitacre.

Mr. Whitacre had a chronic bronchitis and an income that hardly served to support him in the intervals when the bronchitis interfered with more strenuous employments. He was a mild, pale brown man, who got invited about chiefly because he could always be counted on in the room of men more consistently occupied; and perhaps because nobody had told him that she was habitually outside the pale of social attention, perhaps for quite different reasons, the first time he came to the Camera Club, he walked home with Kate Bixby. Whatever he may have meant by it, it was perfectly clear, when this had occurred a few times, what it would mean to Kate; and her family flinched, for by the standards that Emma and Roxanne had set, and by all reasonableness as well, Mr. Whitacre was impossible.

"Mother had a very bad quarter of an hour when it was brought home to her that Kate was going to be an old maid." Roxanne confided to Serena Lindley, "but it was nothing to what she has now that she thinks she isn't." By this time it was perfectly evident that if Mr. Whitacre committed the indiscretion of asking Kate to marry him she was equal to the indiscretion of doing it.

"But why shouldn't she if she loves him?" Serena, who was very fond of her cousin, wished to know. "I'm sure Kate's salary . . ."

" . . . would be stopped immediately," said Roxanne. "You aren't supposed to be fit to instruct other people's children if you put yourself in a position to have any of your own."

"Is is true, Evan," Mrs. Lindley put the case to her husband that evening, "if a teacher in the Santa Lucia Schools—like Kate, for instance—should marry, she would lose her position?"

"Well, marriage isn't a misdemeanor; she couldn't be discharged for it, but she wouldn't be reelected another year. A married woman," explained the young attorney, "isn't supposed to need a salary."

"Oh, if it is a matter of needing it . . ." His wife could have told him of at least one married woman who, if she was not actually in need of a salary, would have known very well what to do with it, though there was small comfort in that for Kate. It seemed probable that Mr. Whitacre was entirely aware of the disability of his bronchitis, for his attentions to Miss Bixby apparently never got beyond being a great deal in her company and following her wistfully with his eyes. And if he entertained any laxer views on his obligation to posterity, Mrs. Bixby would have seen to it that nothing transpired likely to affect her standing as President of the Society for the Promotion of Eugenics; and though she might have turned back the pages of her own married life and the ten years of her husband's illness to find ground for it, she preferred to express her sense of the situation by plying Mr. Whitacre with pamphlets dealing with heredity and such matters as, rid of the shibboleths of her society, Mrs. Bixby would have blushed to name. Whether Kate suspected the pamphlets her mother never knew, but Mr. Whitacre evidently grasped the point of them, for he took himself off to Santa Barbara without having said anything of sufficient definiteness to come to Kate's family.

"If we could only be sure," sighed Mrs. Lindley, "if only it had come to something one could talk over, it wouldn't seem such a skimpy little experience." But in the main, Kate's family devoted themselves to hoping that if anybody had noticed how obviously Kate wanted Mr. Whitacre, they would stop talking about it now that he was gone. Mrs. Bixby, observing that Kate's salary was no longer threatened and that there was nothing in her own family to contradict either her theory of Eugenics or her favorite moral attitude on the position of married women in the home, gave thanks accordingly. She had one daughter rich in possibilities of loving, dying at her work, and another keeping herself alive at it by relations which were prudently checked when they threatened the proprieties or approached the point from which the critical functions of life proceed. But to Mrs. Bixby, whose perceptions did not go much beyond the bulk of things, they were nobly occupied with the world's work under circumstances that abated no whit of traditional womanliness, and she thanked God. As for Kate, she put back her hair, already a little gray, more tightly from her forehead, and began to behave queerly.

I I I

The first of those extraordinary performances that afterward got Kate Bixby so much talked about took insidiously the form of improving her condition. Without taking her family any more into her confidence than the mere announcement of the fact implied, she resigned her place in the Santa Lucia Schools, and secured another in San Francisco.

Her manner of going about it admitted of so little question that Mrs. Bixby was forced to conclude that though she was a little sore perhaps on the subject of Mr. Whitacre, her daughter had recovered from her brief aberration and meant to advance herself in her profession.

San Francisco being a scant three hours from Santa Lucia, it was understood that Kate was to come home for the weekends; but as the days shortened and the mist of rain hung forever about the Santa Lucia hills, and the bay whipped white and stinging under the winter winds, it was so good an excuse for remaining snug in one's own place, that by midseason it was accepted by Kate's family that she was not coming home at all.

More slowly they adjusted themselves to her evident intention not to be visited. That was all very well when the weather was so disagreeable that nobody thought of visiting; but when the hills began to emerge from winter grayness, green with the presage of spring, Roxanne, whose energies suffered an eclipse in the rains, proposed that she should come up to the city regularly on Saturdays so that she and Kate might "take a course of study in something"—and was incontinently denied.

"You've been taking courses in something or other all your life," Kate told her, "but that is no reason why you should impose it on me."

"Well, of course," admitted Roxanne, "you needn't if you don't want to; but I should like to know what I am to tell mother."

"That if I do not have a little space in which to live my own life in my own way, I shall die," put in Kate fiercely. Roxanne looked at her with commiseration.

"You can't expect mother to understand that," she said.

"No, but I expect you to." And later, about the time of prune blossoming and lengthening afternoons, Roxanne thought she did understand when Julia Stairs, who was spending a great deal of time in San Francisco that spring, told her that she had seen Kate sitting in the sand dunes at Black Point with a strange man, one Sunday afternoon.

"Of course, if that is it," Roxanne confided to Serena, "I don't blame her for not wanting us to know. Mother was really nasty about Mr. Whitacre. Let us hope this one hasn't bronchitis."

But to Mrs. Bixby they agreed to say only that Kate was overtired and had best be left alone for a complete rest.

Evidently Kate meant to have it, for she carried her exclusion of her family to the point of not telling them where she spent her long vacation.

"I am going into the mountains to a perfectly safe and comfortable place. If it is any satisfaction to you I will wear a card of identification around my neck, and I shall send you a picture postcard once in a while, but I will not be written to and I shall not write."

She came back from that venture so much improved as quite to justify its unusualness. Some subtle change in her suggested the renewal of bloom. She dressed her hair in a different way, had filled out more, wore better clothes. But by the beginning of the fall term her avoidance of her family began to be remarked upon; and since it included the townspeople as well, there were not wanting insinuations that Kate was beginning to feel above her situation. Too many Santa Lucians went to and from the city for her to have the entire freedom from observation that she coveted, and there were rumors filtering through the general talk to Serena and Roxanne, and in a modified form to Mrs. Bixby herself, to the effect that whatever Kate might be up to, there in San Francisco, it was certainly queer.

Not one of the women of Mrs. Bixby's connection had ever been talked about, and the mere hint that she should suffer such an indignity in the person of her eldest daughter was sufficient to disturb Mrs. Bixby even beyond the barrier of Causes in which she had entrenched her mind. This might have happened much earlier if she had heard what Evan Lindley told Serena when he came back from San Francisco at the end of the midwinter holidays. Knowing, as all Santa Lucians did, a little about every other Santa Lucian, and especially aware through Serena of some anxiety of Kate's account, Evan had had an incident of uneasy conjecture thrust upon him.

He had gone to call upon Dr. Jasper, once the old doctor's nurse and assistant, now handsomely installed with Furniss, the great surgeon, but held forever by his temperament tense and quick to respond to the old claims. Evan had waited, after sending up his name, in one of those ill-lit tunnels like the borings of mighty insects between the intercommunicating cells in which expensive and much demanded physicians hive themselves, and far at the end of the passage had seen Jasper come out of a doorway, approaching him under the pale diffusion of the skylight, talking to a woman who was seen to wring her hands and to bear herself with the emotions of despair. He remained looking at her as she came on, without any thought of curiosity or intrusion, himself obscured by the gloom of the hallway, and more intent upon the improvement he observed in Jasper and the serious kindliness he bent upon the woman's distress, when all at once the couple stopped before the elevator, and he discovered as the woman raised her veil to wipe away the tears that it was Kate Bixby. But before he had so much as named the fact to himself, Dr. Jasper joined him and put it for the moment out of mind.

Evan had related the incident to Serena on his return home, but the chief reason why Mrs. Bixby did not hear of it was that at that time she was on no better terms with her niece's husband than a member of seven societies for advancing the social standard of the world could be expected to be with a member of the city council who had declined to enforce the suppression of pink plaster models used in the window displays of ladies' hosiery. And by the time Aunt Luella had overlooked Evan's dereliction, the incident of the corridor was a month old. Serena had reasoned that since Kate was still at her place in the Haight Street School, she could not be suffering seriously in health; moreover, her choice of Dr. Jasper, which would seem to indicate a preference for the old friend rather than the established practitioner, implied that Kate's trouble, if it amounted to that, was more of the mind than of the body. But though she refrained from mentioning it, the incident colored her mind toward the nature of Kate's queerness when it came up in family talk, and early in April vague uneasiness gave way to downright anxiety.

IV

It happened on Saturday that Roxanne had gone up to the city quite unexpectedly. She had spent the morning shopping and at the end of the afternoon had taken the car to Kate's boarding place, meaning to have a cup of tea with her, and if possible to come a little nearer to a sisterly confidence. There was no one at home but the serving maid, who answered her inquiry with some surprise and the statement that Kate "wasn't living there no more."

"She ain't never lived here a Saturday and a Sunday," the maid insisted, "an' now she ain't livin' 'ere at all." Being asked since how long, she made answer, "more'n a mont," and as to where Miss Bixby might be living at this precise time she could give no information.

"She didn't go for to give us no address; she come for her letters herself," said the maid, and volunteered the information that Miss Bixby had not been there for several days and that there were two letters awaiting her.

If it had been a teaching day, Roxanne would have gone straight to the school, but as she did not know the address of Kate's principal nor of any of her fellow teachers, and as her train was due in an hour, she took it and went straight to lay the matter before Evan Lindley, and at last, since Evan could make nothing of it, before Mrs. Bixby herself. It appeared that if this was only another queerness of Kate's, at any rate it was a sort of queerness that justified her family's looking into. Since Roxanne could hardly get away from her own school on such short notice, it was decided that Mrs. Bixby was to go up Monday morning, and in the event of not finding Kate at her work, or of finding her in serious trouble, she was to wire Lindley.

Serena, mindful of the incident in the corridor, but reluctant to mention it now, contented herself with forcing Jasper's office address on Aunt Luella, and insisting that he be called upon if nothing could be learned from Kate directly.

In the three hours that intervened between Santa Lucia and the Third and Townsend Depot, Mrs. Bixby's apprehension had increased to such a point that she directed herself at once toward the Haight Street School without so much as waiting for her luncheon. She found the yard full of high-voiced children collecting for the afternoon session, very ready on her asking to point to Miss Bixby's room. "Only," they told her, "she ain't there now since four days. It's Miss Price's room now."

Mrs. Bixby felt herself grow faint; she sat down on the front steps of the schoolhouse and loosened her bonnet strings. She sat there so long that the principal noticed her and came out inquiringly. He did not know Miss Bixby's address. He called Miss Price, and Miss Hyde and Miss Leonard, who had the rooms on each side of hers, but none of them knew more than the old address of the boardinghouse where Roxanne had already ascertained she was not. Miss Bixby was not supposed to be ill, she had appeared in her usual health when she asked for leave, which had been regularly granted on the ground of illness in her family. With the bugaboo of being talked about uppermost in spite of her anxiety, Mrs. Bixby had not given her own name, and as every member of the family was in perfect health, this evidence of Kate's duplicity confirmed her in the suspicion that it was something more than queerness. Her next move was to find Dr. Jasper. Between her and the address Serena had given her lay a wilderness of roaring streets and crosstown trolleys, all going at once in every direction except the one she wished.

It was full three o'clock when, after having taken the wrong car twice, being carried past her destination and having to walk back to it, Mrs. Bixby found Dr. Furniss's office. It was one of those gusty San Francisco days when every street corner maintains a private little whirlwind of its own with the express purpose of proving its superior dustiness over every other street corner. The dust lay in the creases of Mrs. Bixby's face deepened by fatigue; her bonnet was awry and her hair loosened wispily about her neck. She had forgotten by this time that she had had no luncheon and thought that the trembling of her limbs was due to her anxiety. It was her forlorn appearance as she sat in Dr. Furniss's anterooms, of which the polished furniture and the row of patient sitters presented the cheerful aspect of waiting for the corpse to be carried out, that got her the consideration of the smart attendant long out of her turn. She was told that Dr. Jasper was out. When would he be in? This attendant disappeared behind a succession of softly sliding doors and after a long interval extracted the statement that, as the case which called Dr. Jasper out was a critical one, he was not expected back that day. This was so much of a disappointment that the attendant had time to disappear again, and several individuals had been quietly detached from the solemn row and folded away behind the noiseless doors before Mrs. Bixby bethought herself to ask if she might know where Dr. Jasper had gone. It appeared there was an unusualness about this request that gave the attendant pause, and Mrs. Bixby had time for urging that the matter was very serious, and that she was from out of town, from Dr. Jasper's old home, and had special claims upon his attention.

After another interval in which the folding doors were several times brought into requisition, the attendant came back with the desired street and number neatly written on a slip of paper like a prescription, and Mrs. Bixby treasured it as if it had really been such to heal the wracking torment of her mind.

The prescription involved another long trip across the shabbier sort of streets that, in the slack of the afternoon, seemed to Mrs. Bixby full of mysterious and terrifying suggestions; dark alleys led to mantraps; shut doors seemed to be bursting with unnameable news; groups of children running together on the street corners appeared to whisper of murderous happenings in the houses from which they ran. Torn scraps of Sunday Supplements blown about the corners inducted Mrs. Bixby into the conviction that the proper place to have looked for Kate would have been a morgue. There was, however, nothing suspicious looking in the neighborhood to which she came at last, except that the houses here, in a city all built of wood, had a surpassing woodiness, and though they were not very large, betrayed in the multiplications of contrivances to the end, that no man was expected to have a whole one of them to himself. The half of the house where Dr. Jasper was supposed to be was reached by an outside stairway going up directly over the front entrance of the lower half, with steps so narrow and slight it suggested the cleated incline by which heavy furniture is gotten into a moving van. When Mrs. Bixby had elevated herself by this means, and knocked, there was as yet no surmise in her mind of all the dark surmises the day's anxiety had bred there which prepared her to have Kate open the door to her.

The first thing Mrs. Bixby noticed was that Kate was wearing a loose wrapper and was evidently at home there, and next was that though she moved hastily to close the door that opened into a room beyond, it was not so soon done but that Mrs. Bixby had time to observe the figure of a man standing between it and a window in the wall behind. As soon as she had done this, Kate turned and faced her.

"Mother," she said, "how did you come here?"

"Daughter," said Mrs. Bixby, "how do you come here?"

Neither of them volunteering any answer to this, they remained looking steadily at each other until Mrs. Bixby spoke again.

"Kate," she demanded, "who is in that room?"

"Mother," said Kate, "what is that to you?"

Vague intimations of turpitude and shame urged upon Mrs. Bixby's mind.

"Everything in the world," she declared. "Tell me who is in that room or I shall go in and see for myself." Suddenly the door opened from behind and Dr. Jasper came out of it.

"There is a very sick man in that room," he said quietly, "and I must ask you not to speak so loud, Mrs. Bixby, lest you disturb him."

The impersonal quality of his voice, together with the white lock that stood out conspicuously above his thin forehead, made for a distinction that added greatly to his professional assumption. In spite of knowing that he was only Jap, the Doctor's man, Mrs. Bixby lowered her voice, but insisted.

"Tell me who is in that room. I must know who he is."

"My husband." Kate turned abruptly and went in, closing the door behind her. Jap looked at Mrs. Bixby in his quiet way and Mrs. Bixby looked at him. Her lips trembled, her cheeks hung flaccid, as if the habitual expression of moral complacency had slid down them and away.

"Is it true?" she said at last.

Dr. Jasper bowed. His attention was bent on any sound that might come from the room behind.

"How long?" Mrs. Bixby could not say any more than that, she felt her knees give under her.

"Mr. and Mrs. Whitacre," said Jasper, "have been married almost a year now."

Mrs. Bixby opened her mouth once to speak, and shut it again. She began to walk unsteadily across the room. She opened the door Kate had shut and went in. She made out presently, for the room was darkened, that Mr. Whitacre lay in the bed and that Kate knelt beside him holding his thin hands in hers and fondling them. She held them against her cheeks, which were wet, and she whispered, "My husband, oh my poor husband!"

"Kate," said Mrs. Bixby. Kate raised her head and looked at her across the bed.

"Stop," she said. "Stop where you are until I have had my say to you, for I mean that you shall hear it and I do not know if by this time tomorrow I shall still have the heart to speak. This man is my husband. I love him as much as you loved my father when he lay dying in your arms, as I remember him. I am a strong, well woman and able to work as hard for him as ever you worked for your husband and your four young children, able to earn more money than for many years my father earned for the support of his family. All I asked was to be able to spend my money in the care of those I loved. But I was unfortunate in this, that the only way I knew how to make money would have been closed to me if I had married. It is to you and to those like you that I owe it that this is so."

"To you . . ." she insisted, to the warding gesture, for Mrs. Bixby was past all speech, "to you and those like you who talk much of woman's work and yet would make the fundamental fact of marriage subservient to your little laws and regulations, and make the work I do for my husband discreditable to me and to him because it is done openly for a salary instead of secretly in a kitchen. If I had married in Santa Lucia, I might, by bringing all the family friends to bear, and by making capital of my husband's weakness, have been able to retain my position a while on the ground that I needed it. If I had married openly in San Francisco I should not have been able to keep it on any grounds." She had risen now, and, still holding by her husband's hands, thrust her words forward as if she meant them to have gone over him, but the man was too far sunk in sickness to have heeded if he had heard. He turned now and then wistfully toward the sound of her voice and lay still. There was a curious likeness in Mrs. Bixby's face to the face on the pillow, in the way her jaw dropped and the astounded dullness that swam up to her eyes at this arraignment.

"I . . . meant it for your best . . . Kate."

"Yes, for my best that I should deny my heart and cheat myself of all the care and sacrifice and tenderness that you had not done without . . . that you would have reproached me as an unnatural child and an unwomanly woman if I had suggested it was for your best to have done without."

"We had meant," went on Mrs. Whitacre, "to have done without marriage and be satisfied with loving, but a year ago when it seemed as if . . . as if . . ." She left the supposition unfulfilled and hurried on—"when he was no longer able to do without my care, and I was no more able to desert him than you to abandon Father when he lay like this, I married him. And now," she sank upon her knees again and held his poor hands to her face and fondled them to her breast, "and now go back to your own work and set the world in order, but leave me to mine."

"Kate," said Mrs. Bixby, faltering and at sea, "Kate!"

"Go," said her daughter. "Oh, go, and leave him to die in peace."

The thin dark form of Dr. Jasper came out of the shadow of the room and his professional, firm hands came down on Kate's and gently loosened their hold.

"I have already told you, Mrs. Whitacre, that I do not mean to let your husband die, but you must save yourself to take care of him." He led her gently to the door and held it open for Mrs. Bixby to go out after her. The two women looked at one another drearily and without comment for an interval, and the habit of a lifetime reasserted itself.

"Sit down," said Kate with cold compunction, "you look tired. I will make you a cup of tea."

"Kate," said her mother pleadingly—she held out her arms, tears ran over in the dusty furrows of her cheeks; "Kate, daughter . . . honey . . . I know . . . I know!"

With a cry Kate turned and with the old, instinctive gesture put her face to the cherished bosom.

"Oh, Mother," she sobbed, "I cannot bear it, I cannot bear it!" And there was no other sound in the room for a long time while the widowed mother sat and rocked her daughter in her arms.

V

Dr. Jasper was as good as his word about not letting Kate's husband die, at least not at that juncture. He would never be any good as men are accounted good, he would always have a weak heart and a chronic bronchitis, and the pittance that was his would just keep him in pills and plasters. His wife must always be a wage earner and himself a potterer about the house, which is manifestly a reversal of the order of things, with no economic excuse for it, nor any other excuse except that Kate wanted it so. He was inefficient as a citizen and, according to the postulates of Mrs. Bixby's societies, totally unfit for parenthood.

But if it was a mortification to Mrs. Bixby to have all her theories of living, which she had thought so exemplified in her own family, go down before the common clinging of the heart, the pang of it was not so deep that motherliness did not go deeper, nor prevent her from letting lapse two secretaryships and a presidency to help Kate nurse her husband back to his little space of life. And the very advanced nature of her views, so much in advance of her way of life that they were able to proceed independently of it, permitted of so much reshaping around the fact of Kate's marriage that by the time Mr. Whitacre was able to be moved to Santa Lucia, Mrs. Bixby had provided herself with a whole set of new phrases on the economic independence of women.

If there had wanted anything to temper Mrs. Bixby's attitude toward queerness in general it would have been found in the disposition Kate made of her affairs as soon as she was sufficiently relieved of care for her husband's life to look about her. Her mother had thought she might regain her old position in the Santa Lucia Schools, since she could make out so good a case of needing it; but Kate would not hear of an application being made. She consulted much with the Lindleys, and showed a wounding disposition to exclude her mother from those councils, which Mrs. Bixby, mindful of the last assault upon her cherished convictions, dared not openly resent. It ended in as much of Kate's saving as could be spared being invested in a small plot of ground, and the rest in a very small house, and the establishment of the Whitacres in a modest business of cut flowers and bulbs for market. If you kept your mind steadily on the cutting and tying (which was mostly done by Mr. Whitacre) and away from the weeding and manuring (which fell chiefly to Kate), it assumed an aspect not inconsistent with true womanliness such as even Mrs. Bixby could admit. There were times, though, when she looked at Kate's thin figure in church, beginning to stoop with unaccustomed labors, and at the toil-marked hands poorly concealed by mended gloves, and the hat, which, though it had been trimmed over twice, made a very poor showing against Roxanne's smartness, she suffered a sensible check in her motions to set the world in order by the mortification of having a daughter of her own who had not turned out well. Such times she would go so far as to pray that since the good Lord evidently meant to take her son-in-law by the way of bronchitis, that it would please Him to do so before it was too late for Kate to return to the safe and creditable way of life. And indeed it was observed by all Kate's family, when in the fourth year of marriage her husband began to fail rapidly, that there was an elevation of spirit upon her as of the hope of deliverance. From unknowable sources she drew a force and sustenance that precluded the ordinary phrases of condolence and led even the casual observer to remark that it was really wonderful the way she kept up.

It would not have been surprising in the estimate of the Santa Lucians if Kate had looked forward with something like relief to the end of her long period of drudging. If the Whitacres realized a living on the cut-flower trade, it was a very poor one, and Mr. Whitacre could never in his best days have been called an interesting man. He was slight and stooping, with almost nothing to say for himself, and had pale brown eyes that turned every way about the house where his wife went, like a faithful dog's.

In the presence of Kate's family he bore himself as if he could never get Mrs. Bixby's pamphlets on Eugenics out of his mind. But when the lamp was lit in the little house and the door was shut, when his wife sat by his bed and took his thin hands in her worn ones, the eyes lighted at hers deep points of fire and melting tenderness; they looked each upon the other and entered into the joy of quiet souls.

"Are you sure," he would ask, very feebly at the last, "that you have never regretted it?"

"Oh regret? regret!" his wife would say, and fall to kissing his poor hands, and then, "Say that I have never made you feel that I have, even for one poor moment. Say it to me." And he would protest so long as his staggering breath allowed; then, when the fit of coughing was past, lying back in the relief of feebleness, he said: "There was a time when I knew my life must be short, that I was bitter at having to go before I knew what life was, but now we have had it all, the rapture and the wonder . . . All!" he insisted; and his wife kissed him, whispering, "All!"

They were sitting so one evening in March, the wind rasping the budding branches of the prunes against the roof, the faint odor of hyacinths falling with the wind; and he said after a long silence: "I wish I might have lived until September"; but at the change in his wife's face, adding hastily, "No, no, it would only make it harder for you. But say that you are glad."

"I am glad for everything," she said; and wished him to sleep. But he insisted: "You won't forget what you promised about having a man to do the weeding and reset the hyacinths. I am sorry there isn't more to leave you, but it is enough to pay for a man; and you'll be very careful, dear?"

She promised again, but he whispered feebly, with his head upon her breast, "You will not let them blame me . . . when . . . when they know."

"No one shall blame you," she reassured him, and would have put him back upon the pillow that he might rest, but the coughing seized him and Lindley, whose turn it was to watch, came in from the other room.

Turning toward him, the sick man raised upon his elbow—"You bear witness . . ." he gasped, "you bear witness . . . that she said . . . that . . . she was glad . . ." And so saying, died.

It was really wonderful, as everybody said, the way Kate Whitacre kept up through the first days of her widowhood, but with a quality in her courage that made it seem not so much a relief from great strain as a part of the unusualness from which her situation sprung. She could not, for example, be induced to leave the poor little house and the budding hyacinths, even for a proper and consolatory stay with her family, nor appreciate particularly the company that a pervasive neighborly sympathy thrust upon her. She pleaded the care of her garden, emerging in its third year from the experimental stage. But of course, as Mrs. Bixby was careful to explain, it was merely by way of keeping poor Kate's mind occupied until another school year afforded her the opportunity of resuming her profession, for, having so long rendered her daughter's situation tolerable to herself by looking upon it as a heroic expedient, it did not occur to Mrs. Bixby that it could have any charm in itself.

The sense of the community was so much with Mrs. Bixby that presently it began to swell with its own magnanimity, and to anticipate the moment of renewal.

The Santa Lucians took it so well in themselves that they should make nothing of Kate's four-year lapse, now that it was practically done with, that as time went by and Mrs. Whitacre made no move in that direction, the neighborly impulse developed a genuine unease, lest lingering still in some maze of grief, she should miss the point of their relenting. The city superintendent of schools himself called upon Evan Lindley to assure him that if Mrs. Whitacre wished her old place again, her widowed estate should be no bar, and Lindley sent his wife to sound Kate upon it.

"It is rather rubbing it in that she had to look out for herself, when poor Whitacre is hardly cold in his grave," he advised; "but if she lets it go this time, the chance may not come again."

Serena found her cousin tying up narcissus on a bench behind the plain little house that was built of up and down battens and had the scantiest possible doorway. She had on an old straw hat of her husband's and a dress with some red in it, which might have been excused on the ground that Mrs. Whitacre could hardly have afforded a complete and proper mourning.

She made room on the bench beside her, and made neither more nor less of the errand which Mrs. Lindley bungled over. She had no notion, said

Mrs. Whitacre, of teaching again, for though there was not so much money in the cut-flower trade, there might be more, and a greater independence; but her manner of saying it was plainly rather to provide Serena an excuse than from any need of being excused.

Serena looked at Kate's hands, which, though the spring was well advanced, were rough and red from cold, and at her dress, cut off well above ankles never meant for displaying, and yet draggled at the edges, and she sighed.

"It would be ever so much easier," she suggested.

"That," Kate answered her, "is a matter of preference."

"And not so lonely."

"Ah!" said Mrs. Whitacre. "That is just it. I am not lonely . . . I miss my husband . . . terribly," a quiver passed in her face and was quieted by an effort; "but I shall never be lonely any more . . . I haven't told anyone yet, not even Mother. Francis was afraid you would all blame him . . ."

Serena had both the cold hands now in her soft gloved ones, and tears fell upon them, "Oh my dear, my dear!" she said for all comment.

"In September," whispered Kate—"say you are glad for me." And "I am glad, I am glad!" sobbed Serena, seeing at last, and perceiving herself forever shamed in seeing so late, that with all their meticulous care for her, they had made it strange for Kate to arrive as she had at the proper function of life rather than a mere nicety and ease in the perquisites of living.

❖　❖　❖

Blue Roses

"Blue Roses" is surely one of Austin's finest stories. In it many of her trails converge. The story is about individuals and about the culture they live in, the culture that shapes them. The two women folk artists bring their community together; their art is central to cultural rituals and village relations; the village feels a sense of achievement in their art and deprived without it. Both women work within identifiable artistic traditions, but they also express indi-vidual visions. Although they are rivals, they define themselves in relation to each other. The story's ending is vintage Austin, and "Blue Roses" contains one line that characterizes all of her work: "The heart is greatly comforted by [art] —especially when one works in a medium which ties one to all the familiar, homely things."

The manuscript of "Blue Roses" is located in the Huntington Library's Austin Collection, box 41.

This is a story of the artistic temperament. It is also a story of the Americanization of Rio Andorrero, New Mexico.

The temperaments—there were two of them—belonged respectively to Doña Josefa De Vargas, proud and bereaved grandmother of Aurelio Juan y Maria, hero of San Mihiel, and to Señora Assunta Martinez. If you are versed in social distinctions in New Mexico, you will see at once how the two ladies stand toward one another and the rest of the community. Doña Josefa had been Doña in her own right, *and* a De Vargas, before she married the cousin twice removed of her husband's uncle, distinctions which Señora Martinez balanced in her own mind by the certainty of having descended from Sun-priests and Caciques in the days when Rio Andorrero had been a Tewa Pueblo, before it had been absorbed by a small detachment of half-Spanish, half-Thalascan colonists.

It is necessary, in order to account for the temperaments, to be explicit on points like this. Every Indian is artistic and every Spaniard temperamental. When the two have been mixed and mellowed for three hundred years únder a New Mexican sun, the combination is bound to exhibit occasional surprises.

Assunta Martinez made artificial flowers. Doña Josefa also made them—

wreaths and clusters and symbolic pieces to adorn the altars of the Saints or to hang on the little blue crosses of the Campo Santo on All Saints' Day. But with a difference!

The flowers that grew up under Assunta's hand were rooted deep in the Thalascan strain, feather roses that were as white as the wings of angels, from which Assunta would undoubtedly have tweaked a plume now and then had the opportunity occurred, feather roses that were a deep heart red, dyed according to a recipe which she had from her mother's mother, who had it from hers, straight down the Thalascan line, a thousand years deep in feather craft. She also made roses that deepened like wine to rich purples, and, occasionally—this was when Doña Josefa vexed her—Assunta made blue roses, blue as the stripes in old Chimayo blankets, of which the secret had been long lost. She made thick, well-rounded wreaths, and flat sprays, and, by request, though she regarded it as a *tour de force* unworthy of her art, pyramidal bouquets, twining red and white to the tips of nicely whittled and painted sticks.

Doña Josefa also made roses—but alas for the decay of the Arts!—she made them of tissue paper which she bought from the mail-order catalog which her grandson spelled out to her. But she scorned to make any which were not true to the known colors of roses as it had pleased God to make them.

Public taste was greatly divided between the roses of Doña Josefa and Assunta. There were those who maintained that it came to the same thing in the end, since if tissue paper was brighter, feathers were more lasting. Such detachment was only possible to newcomers, those who had married into the village within a generation or two. The permanent population was actively of one school or another. Toward San Isidro Day, feeling ran so high that Padre Simon, who came from San Juan to celebrate mass on the fiesta of the *Patrón,* was at last obliged to take notice of it.

It was the custom on these occasions for each of the artists to present the Padre with a specimen of her handiwork for the parish church at San Juan. For weeks previous there would be little else talked of, talk being the one thing of which there was always more than enough at Rio Andorrero. Although they each affected, up to the last day or two, to be ignorant of what the other was doing, there was a race between them as to which should surpass the other in her offering.

For this first lap, Assunta had rather the advantage. In the matter of material, she would make the whole village, and even the housewives of Rio Frio, three flocks' journeys to the north, partners in her enterprise.

Who so poor as not to be able to afford a feather toward the Padre's wreath? Sheepherders on their rounds kept an eye out for dropped plumes of the waterfowl blown up the Rio Grande by the Gulf winds, and wood-cutters brought her eagle feathers from the mountains.

Three or four weeks before San Isidro Day, the *parlatorio* of Señora Martinez's house would be closed to casual visitors. Assunta would be seen coming out of it, rapt, aloof. The great work had begun. During the last week one was permitted to inquire circumspectly, as one asks after the health of royalty, how it progressed; but just at first one hesitated to sully the fresh radiance of inspiration. What if one should turn out to have something of the evil eye? *Verdaderamente!* No one in Rio Andorrero was so unneighborly as to risk thwarting a new enterprise by asking about it until its success was well assured. Assunta was, however, so sure of herself that, during the last week, privileged members of her faction would be taken into the *parlatorio* to inspect the masterpiece where it reposed on the table covered with a white cloth, or to stand admiringly by while she warmed and stroked and trimmed a feather into place.

In the meantime, Doña Josefa had not been idle. She could be seen in deep consultation with her grandson, Aurelio Juan y Maria, over the mail-order catalog. That she herself could read only Spanish, and Spanish of the Prayer Book, made it none the less important for her to scan the printed words which otherwise might not come true to their promises, which, after the manner of all mail-order catalogs, were magnificent. On the day that she sent off her order she was accompanied to the Post Office by two or three friends, who, as they met other friends on the way home, affected the detachment of great affairs.

"I have just been to the Post Office with Doña Josefa. She has sent off her order for materials for Padre Simon's wreath."

"Ah, ah! I'll warrant, a fine one!"

"Fine, *Amigo?* No doubt, her finest!"

The mail order to Chicago required usually eight days for fulfillment, as everybody in Rio Andorrero knew, but it was always proper after the fifth day to venture a casual inquiry of the postmaster. "Doña Josefa's package will not have come yet, *Amigo?*" And the postmaster, after consulting his calendar with the air of having possibly overlooked the matter in the press of other affairs, would admit that it had not yet arrived. You would know, of course, when it had, because the postmaster, who was also the store-keeper, and knew what made trade and good feeling between neighbors, never failed to call out to his son, Pedro, to run down to Doña Josefa's and tell her there was a package for her. Between such announcement and the arrival of Doña Josefa, there was always time for several of her friends to be on the spot for the dramatic moment of its delivery, which was always according to ritual.

"You have a package for me Señor Postmaster?" Great was the dignity of Doña Josefa.

"From some fine friend of yours in Chicago, Doña Josefa." Great show of searching for it, and flourish in the official records.

"It is only the material for the Padre's wreath, Postmaster."

"Ah, ah!" weighing it on his hand for all to see, "Then it will be a fine one, I'll warrant."

"It will be as it has always been, *Amigo*."

Thus was expectation built up before the event.

For the first twelve or fifteen years the two ladies made a practice of speaking diplomatically of one another's work. "Without doubt," Doña Josefa would remark, "if there were blue roses—*if!*—they would be as Assunta has made them."

And for her part, the Señora Martinez would say, scanning the pointed tags of green paper with which Doña Josefa in her search for realism would occasionally surround her plump clusters, though she made feather roses she did not attempt to enter into competition with the good God himself. Both of which statements were well within the bounds of legitimate art criticism.

That was before Assunta's husband died of a pneumonia, caught while saving his flock from one of the sudden shifts of channel which gave Rio Andorrero, the "Wanderer," its name. As for Doña Josefa, she had been a widow these many years. Her only daughter died in childbirth, leaving as sole legacy Aurelio Juan y Maria. Being left thus with Art for their comforter, as time went on, a sense of the preciousness of their craft sharpened the artists' tongues. Each year when, on the third day before the arrival of Padre Simon, they paid one another a visit of compliment on the completion of a masterpiece, there were visible reservations in the compliments.

Rio Andorrero, having no church of its own, was long accustomed to setting up a temporary place of worship in Doña Josefa's long room. Every adobe house of more than a generation's standing has one of these rooms, as long as the founder's purse and as wide as the nearest attainable cottonwood *vigas* for supporting the flat roof. Contributions were made of the village Saints, candlesticks, bright oleographs of the Blessed Personages, and, finally, San Isidro, as tall as life and gratifyingly thin, in a red dressing gown and a collar of that webby handmade lace, the secret of which may still be learned in the mountain towns of New Mexico. The two wreaths reposed in full view on either side of him, objects of general admiration and local pride.

On the third day before San Isidro's, occurred the visits of the artists, each to the house of the other. Greatly to be envied were the friends of either who had the honor to be invited. How the faces of the artists were scanned for those intimations of the private opinion which lent spice to its relation! Every year it was confidently affirmed by the adherents of Señora Martinez that Doña Josefa had been completely bowled over by the masterly execution of Assunta. And the followers of Señora De Vargas were certain that Assunta would never recover from the splendor of the paper roses in all the *natural* colors and shades of the same. Thus Rio Andorrero was stirred by artistic emulation—a sense of achievement that melted agreeably in the mouth as the two wreaths, each in its appropriate box, went away at last in the saddle bags of Padre Simon.

This was the case up to the year 1914. In that year, Assunta's version of "It's pretty, but is it Art?" as applied to the tissue-paper roses, had more than a touch of acerbity; and Doña Josefa's stricture on blue roses had reached the point of suggesting that the saints themselves might not be so pleased with roses which attempted to be other than as God had made them. To which, when it reached her by way of two-thirds of the two-score population of Rio Andorrero, Assunta had replied that it was possible that the Saints grew weary of things as they were, and sighed for variety, even in Paradise. In this she was thought to have gone rather too far. For when one considers the eternity of Paradise, it is not wise to contemplate the possibility of growing weary of anything connected with it.

While the state of tension induced by this interchange added to the mild exhilaration of San Isidro Day, there were those who shook their heads with well-founded foreboding. By the summer of 1915, factional feeling reached the point at which Padre Simon was obliged to interfere.

I have discussed this business of the Padre's wreaths with various matrons of Rio Andorrero, as well as with Assunta and Josefa themselves, and I am sure they are right in attributing the whole of that unhappy affair to the *brujería* which set the whole world by the ears in 1914. It is the nature of *brujería* not to be contained in the hearts that brewed it, but to rise and spread like a devil's steam, polluting the air of many pleasant places. That the bad feeling between Assunta Martinez and Josefa De Vargas was affected by what happened in Belgium the summer before is as certain as that the ceasing of that great conflict brought release from the bitter rivalries of art in Rio Andorrero.

But to return to the Day of San Isidro in 1915: feeling between the factions ran so high that it reached the point at which the Padre put his foot down. No more wreaths woven in rivalry and heartburning could come into the church at San Juan. And, having rated his parishioners soundly for the sins of envy and backbiting, he departed without either of the proffered works of art.

Thus is the rabbit let out of the bag, as we say in New Mexico. For it was quickly discovered that the town was thereby deprived of a great honor and much entertainment. No more happy contributions to Assunta's stock of feathers! No more trepidations as to whether Doña Josefa's mail-order package would or would not arrive within the allotted eight days! No more private views! In short, no drama!

For this state of affairs everybody blamed everybody else. San Isidro himself turned his face away, for in August, Rio Andorrero overflowed its banks and cut a new channel down the opposite side of the valley. Right out of the busiest season there was a month's work patching the breach between its waters and the *acequia madre* by which the small irrigating ditches to the ranches were fed. With such good backing for his decision, Padre Simon failed to relent on the following Saint's day, and a pall settled over the pleasant life of Rio Andorrero.

Doña Josefa gallantly did what she could to lift it by displaying a Red Cross in her window. But the gloss was taken off her achievement by Assunta, with a framed acknowledgment from the Belgian Relief at Santa Fe, where one of her rose sprays had been sold for the truly munificent sum of seven dollars. After that, time halted, and even the rise in the price of wool failed to bring back the zest of life to Rio Andorrero. Nothing whatever happened between the summer of 1915 and the twenty-first of April, 1917.

On that day, Aurelio Juan y Maria kissed his grandmother good-bye and went down to Española with the mail carrier to enlist in the Army. On that day, which was the first they had heard of the entry of the United States into the Great War, the community flag flew its wide, wavering shadow above the three-cornered plaza, not much larger than the flag itself, and the community band of three pieces stood solemnly abreast, playing the Star Spangled Banner. After that they played "Lupita," whose swinging waltz measures come closer to the heart of the Spanish-speaking than the barbaric intervals of the national anthem. It was conceded on all sides that Don Aurelio had done no less than was expected of him.

These last scions of the fighting Dons expected no less of themselves. From the *lomas* and the *prados* they came in to the recruiting stations, from lonely sheepherding hamlets and wide southern ranches, they came in leisurely, as all things are done in the sun-warmed lands—one by one—as the news trickled to them by belated posts passed from mouth to mouth of wandering herders. About that time it was noticed that the Saints in the century-old chapels of New Mexico rode or marched with diminutive three-colored banners, tucked under an arm or borne upright between the symbols of martyrdom. The little Santiago in the Penitente Chapel of Rio Andorrero rode so gallantly on his ten-inch steed that Pedro Mendoza, praying there for his youngest, who had written from Silver City that he had joined an officers' training camp, was heard to shout the ancient war cry of the Spanish-speaking—"Ha! God and the United States!"—with such an excess of fervor that it would have taken very little to persuade him that it was the Santiago himself who cried in him.

Sancho Valdez also enlisted. Miguel Salazar wished to, but that *animal* of a recruiting sergeant would not take him because of his teeth. "*Dios y Santos!* As if one fought with the teeth nowadays!"

Later the draft reached out and took Pedro Garcia and a boy from Rio Frio, which, as we say it, is Cold Creek. "Eh, but we do our part, we old American families of Va'e Andorrero!"

On the news of the arrival in France of Aurelio Juan y Maria's regiment, Doña Josefa gave a *velorio*. A *velorio* is a party to the Saints, who appreciate such attentions. Doña Josefa's long room was cleared. The table was covered with a white sheet and a cloth deeply encrusted with drawn-thread work. San Isidro was brought in, and the little Santiago, riding hard with his American flag held aloft. There was also a chipped Spanish lacquered Madonna and a smart and smiling Guadalupe of Doña Josefa's own private collection. A row of candles was stuck across the floor in front of the table, and the *velorio* was ready to begin.

At the last moment Assunta Martinez sent an offering: nothing less than one of her pyramidal bouquets of feather roses climbing up a painted stick, red, white, and blue, three of each, in their proper order. Miguel Salazar, chosen *Cantador* both on account of his beautiful tenor voice and the disappointment about his teeth, taking the pyramid in his hands before discovering what it was, hesitated. Doña Josefa was magnificent. "Who knows," she said, "but there may be blue roses in that country where my grandson is making War!" And she crammed the stick into one of Señora Valdez's silver candlesticks, loaned for the occasion. All day the red and white and blue roses bloomed at the feet of San Isidro while the unoccupied portion of Va'e Andorrero prayed and sang, and the community flag from the plaza cast its wavering shadow across the unpainted floor.

On the day of the Patrón that year, though there were no private views and no rivalry, Padre Simon took away with him in his saddlebags two wreaths for the altar of San Juan.

Thus the feud rested until Armistice Day, celebrated in Rio Andorrero as soon as they heard of it, which was not until two or three days after it had occurred, but nonetheless an occasion for rejoicing. All the ovens smoked and the pots bubbled. At night there were *luminarias*—little low fires in front of the principal doors, and the three-piece band, reinforced by a violin and two flutes from Rio Frio, played in the plaza. Then one saw how beautifully things are ordered, for if your plaza is no bigger than a pocket handkerchief, it is then possible for everyone to dance to the music in his own *parlatorio*. Dance they did, for had not Rio Andorrero played its part and come out scatheless?

A week later came the belated news that Aurelio Juan y Maria had fallen in the last ten days' fighting. Thus had they of Va'e Andorrero sealed themselves to the great world of aspiration and affairs!

In these old communities, where personal relations have mellowed through generations, the shock of death is distributed along the many fibers of kinship by which that particular life is held in the common consciousness. But they wanted the grave of Aurelio Juan y Maria as a witness to their sacrifice. They hungered for the ritual of condolence, the pomp of death, which gives to such takings away the sense of completeness that the older dramatists understood so well when they made death the climax to all their most heartfelt plays.

II

The Campo Santo of Va'e Andorrero lies on the *loma* across the river, or what had been the river before its last *errante*—a silver trickle in the wide boulder-strewn streak of sand. The road wound at an easy footpace up the front of the *loma,* lined with little crosses of the *Estancias,* where the bearers had set down their caskets to rest. Here and there the humble muse of Rio Andorrero had penciled a tender remembrance. Thus, the road to the Campo Santa was like a friendly path leading from the three-cornered plaza to the Blessed Rest. From the doorways, when the leafage was off the chaparral, one could see the tips of the grave markers and the flowers of remembrance. At all times the great cross in the center of the Field of the Saints stretched over them its extenuating arms.

To Doña Josefa, then, it was unbearable that she could not name among them the cross of Aurelio Juan y Maria. How shall we have the comfort of Paradise for our beloved when there is no settled place from which our thought of them takes flight?

The sense of a double loss, not only of Don Aurelio but of his resting place, hung over the village all that winter. It was augmented in the spring by the return of their other two soldiers, one of them with a wound stripe on his sleeve.

Doña Josefa sent no more orders to Chicago for colored paper, and Assunta gave out that at last she herself had retired from the artistic life, which had lacked for some time the zest of rivalry. Besides, who would have the heart to hang wreaths on his own graves when Doña Josefa lacked a like reminder of Aurelio Juan y Maria.

Padre Simon saw that something must be done about it. The priest who, in a parish as large as several states, would keep the minds of his people stayed on the omnipotence of God must know to a hair what they can and cannot bear. Padre Simon knew that Rio Andorrero could not bear to be deprived of the grave of its hero. He did what he could for them with an extra mass, but he also wrote letters and made a journey as far as Santa Fe on that business. At last it was reported that Rio Andorrero's martyred soldier was, through the wise providence of the Government, on his way home. He was on the sea; he was somewhere on the land; he would reach the nearest railroad station, at Maderadura, sometime in May. It began to be appreciated that there was at Washington a Government not unmindful of its remotest citizens.

All the village, including the hamlet of Rio Frio, prepared to receive the body of Aurelio Juan y Maria with high circumstances.

But there was a difficulty. Padre Simon could hardly be expected to make a special journey from San Juan for the reinterment. All Souls' Day, the immemorial holiday of the dead, was five or six months away. How could Don Aurelio repose so long, officially unhonored?

Suddenly it was discovered that those two veterans, Valdez and Garcia, had something to say. There was a day expressly set apart by the Government of the United States for the honoring of soldier dead. Nothing less! The day of the thirtieth of May! It would not only be proper, it would be little short of a scandal if Aurelio Juan y Maria went uncelebrated on that day. Here at last was something to talk about.

To bring it all to a focus, it turned out that Don Aurelio—it was so always he was spoken of, as if he were to come in the full flush of life—would arrive at Maderadura on the twenty-fifth of May.

Garcia and Valdez and the lad from Rio Frio, with Rio Andorrero's best wagon and team, would go out as escort. The community flag lay folded under the seat for his last covering; the music was to join them at Rio Frio on the way home. Doña Josefa was to await her grandson at the bridge. It was not to be said that Va'e Andorrero did not know what was due to heroes, and this one of its own blood.

But the inhabitants of Va'e Andorrero reckoned without their capricious river. They reckoned also without the Pueblos of the Rio Grande, who are, as everyone knows, potent weathermakers. About the end of May of the year 1918 the Pueblos wanted rain for the sprouting corn. All day and all night there was the roll of mimic thunder in the *kivas* and the rush of pebbled guards like the sound of summer rain. By the time the cortege set out for Maderadura, the southern spurs of the Rockies had put on their cloud-plumed bonnets. The escort had hardly climbed the barranca out of the *arroyo hondo* when the river began to rise. It rose steadily—a yellow, greasy flood. It broke back into its channel between the Campo Santo and the town. By the end of that day, the props of the straddling wooden bridge, which had not been mended since the river's last wandering, began to go. In the night the villagers heard it crash and the river swallow gulpingly.

Maderadura is a wood station on the Denver and Rio Grande. Its sole contribution to humankind is a high, roofless platform and a tiny, seldom-used section house. The pine woods and the junipers shut it close in green, waiting silences. Here the escort waited a day and a half for one of those oblong boxes such as carried to waiting towns all that was mortal of young-hearted sacrifice. Reverently, Rio Andorrero took its portion from the hurried and hardened train hands, and laid it on a bed of juniper boughs. Tenderly they spread over it the flag whose wide, wavering shadow had attended so often the little running feet of Aurelio Juan y Maria.

The boy from Rio Frio sat at the head, Garcia and Valdez at the foot, their arms folded, their campaign hats tipped over faces further shadowed by such memories as will rest for a long time on the faces of young men.

So, between the funeral pines and the crowding junipers passed the body of Aurelio Juan y Maria.

Woodcutters who marked the gleam of the red and white leaned on their axes with bowed heads as the rude hearse went by. Solitary herders crossed themselves. Vaqueros searching for strayed cattle turned back and rode beside it for a hatless mile or two. At Agua Dulce, where the cortege rested for the night, the roadhouse keeper had a room waiting and a row of candles alight. An arroyo hondo del Andorrero, where they first discovered the rise in the river, the Brothers Penitente walked singing on either side, high over them the immortal Emblem of willing sacrifice. The flute wailed piercingly; the wooden rattle woke the squalling jays. At Rio Frio, fine rain began to fall. Looking up from Rio Andorrero toward the Rio Frio, one makes out the whitewashed walls of the hamlet. Above it the barranca lifts into the pine woods, and the road, after climbing it, dips into a hollow out of sight until it reappears again on the loma, a quarter of a mile from the bridge. It was not yet raining at Rio Andorrero when the watchers at the ford saw the wagon climb the barranca. After three hours it came in sight again on the *loma*, followed by the musicians, with their instruments under their coats. Between them and Doña Josefa flowed a wide, clay-yellowed flood.

Doña Josefa had been waiting there for an hour, all the village, including San Isidro, beside her. It was hoped that the Patrón would exert a soothing influence on the flood. But San Isidro had other things at heart—nothing less than the wiping out of the ancient source of discord. The waters rose and rose, past the last fragments of the bridge, lapping the edge of Señora Martinez's artichoke patch. Assunta herself was with the watchers around Doña Josefa. With all the other women she wept when young Garcia and Valdez, just visible between the blown veils of rain, stripped back the protecting blankets and showed them for an instant the tragic oblong outline of their flag. At that the fortitude of Doña Josefa broke down. She who had sent him proudly to his death in a foreign land found it insufferable that he should lie all night in the summer rain so near his home. Resolutely she waded into the swirling yellow flood. It sucked at her aged knees. Women screamed, men struggled with her, leaning together against the push of the river.

Suddenly the voice of Assunta, quiet and decisive, bore in upon her frenzy. "From my roof you can see everything much plainer, Josefa." Doña Josefa yielded without a word.

It was true. The Martinez house was the last on the river road, and from its flat roof the last camp of Aurelio Juan y Maria showed plainly above the chaparral. Against the last campfire that was to be built for him, it showed the wagon, backed under the willows, and the three figures in resuscitated khaki uniforms standing guard. From the roof the women watched until the whole cortege melted into the darkness.

San Isidro was carried back to the *morada* where he lodged. It was thought that his influence had caused the rain to cease at nightfall, and no doubt the river would go down in the Patrón's own time. His work of pacification went on, as several persons have since confided to me, in the house of Señora Martinez.

Nothing would have torn Doña Josefa away from the house where she could catch the first morning light on her beloved. Neither would she sleep.

"Thus it turns out excellently," declared Assunta. "Otherwise I would not have finished the memorial wreath I have been making for Aurelio Juan y Maria." She threw back the sheet from the table, where reposed, unfinished, a flat wreath of roses in three colors—red, white, and blue.

Doña Josefa wept. "To think that I, his own grandmother, should have forgotten to make him a wreath!"

"That also is of the Saints," Assunta decided. "There is no one else whose fingers would have the skill to help me. Now it shall be from both of us." So they warmed the irons for curling the feathers and sat down together.

"I have not the skill I once had," admitted Josefa.

"Truly, it comes back when the heart is in the work," Assunta assured her. "These white ones now . . . they are from Maria Garcia's pullet, that the boys stole last Guadalupe Day for making *podrida* of their own . . ."

"Eh, but the only time I ever smacked my Aurelio was for that same trick . . . Never was such a lad for chicken, and never one could cook it to please him like his old grandmother."

"That I'll warrant! These are from the Valdez gander. Ai, but he was of a toughness!"

"And is he gone? *Dios y Santos,* what may not have happened in the town since my heart has been away with my Aurelio!—Am I doing these right, Assunta?"

"As if you had been born to it, Josefa *Querida.*" Thus they had addressed one another as girls before the rivalry began.

So it is when one is an artist and comes back to the work after an absence. The heart is greatly comforted by it—especially when one works in a medium which ties one to all the familiar, homely things. The night of Aurelio's last watch passed, as one might say, without so much as a striking of the clock, and by daylight, as they carried the completed wreath to Doña Josefa's house, it was noted by the two friends that the river had begun to fall.

This is how it happened that the funeral day of Rio Andorrero's soldier occurred, as was most fitting, on the very day that the Government had set for it; for, by the miracle of the automobile of one of his parishioners at Española, Padre Simon managed to get over that morning from San Juan. For all of which San Isidro was duly given credit.

Also, since it was the day of the Government, it was thought becoming to observe it after the American fashion by heaping all the little mounds with blue lupin and white borage and scarlet painted cup—truly a holiday of the dead! Thus do old American families according as their country expects of them in the Va'e Andorrero!

Assunta Martinez walked home with Doña Josefa. "For," said the latter, "it is obvious that your garden is ruined for this season, and my house is desolate. Also, you may have the long room for teaching your feather work as you have long promised to do." And immediately, such is the happy capacity of heart which God has given the Spanish-speaking, no sooner had she said this than she saw herself in her true relation to the situation, as the patroness of an ancient and honorable craft. "Perhaps," she added, "some of the more stupid ones will care to learn a little about tissue paper."

"Without doubt it will be a great comfort to them for their stupidity," agreed Assunta.

But Doña Josefa, being a De Vargas, never did anything by halves.

"You must help me to send for papers," she said. "And we will have this time some that are blue also. For it is in my mind," said Doña Josefa, turning for a last gleam of color on the new cross that was Aurelio Juan y Maria's, "—it is in my mind that from this time forth there will be red, white *and* blue roses in Paradise."

Index